Contents

Theory of Automatic Control

THEORY OF AUTOMATIC CONTROL

H. TAKAI

Translated by Scripta Technica Ltd
Edited by E. J. Feakes
Northampton College of Advanced Technology, London

LONDON ILIFFE BOOKS LTD

Originally published in Japan by The OHM-Sha, Ltd, Tokyo

First published in Great Britain in 1966
by Iliffe Books Ltd, Dorset House
Stamford Street, London, S.E.1

Translated and prepared for press by
Scripta Technica Ltd

Printed in Great Britain by
Butler & Tanner Ltd, Frome and London

Introduction

At the present time, various automatic control systems are successfully used for various purposes in nearly every industry. Moreover, further development of automatic control systems is anticipated. Accordingly, a fundamental knowledge of automatic control systems is indispensable not only for engineers who are engaged in the design, manufacturing, and supply of industrial equipment but also for those who operate and maintain such equipment. On the other hand, most engineers are greatly interested in acquiring a broad and systematic knowledge of automatic control systems, University curricula for engineering students are putting more emphasis on automatic control engineering than before, and the number of students who take courses in automatic control engineering is increasing.

In connection with these trends, the present text was written as a text-book or a reference for engineering students and for those engineers engaged in industry who desire to learn about automatic control systems. The material is a revision of lecture notes prepared for courses given to undergraduate and graduate students in the Tokyo Institute of Technology and the Tokyo Institute of Electrical Engineering by the author for the past few years. Chapters I-V are mainly based on the lecture notes for undergraduate courses given to electrical and mechanical engineering students; Chapters VI-IX are based on the lecture notes for graduate courses.

In the author's view it is more important in lectures to show how to treat the important subjects in the field rather than to exhibit a vast amount of material in a poorly organized way. Therefore, the author has attempted to illustrate thoroughly the more important subjects and their interrelationships. An important purpose of engineering is the design, manufacture, and operation of useful and serviceable equipment. Since automatic control engineering is a field of engineering, its ultimate purpose is to construct many useful automatic control systems. With this purpose in mind, the material in the present text was selected, presented, and illustrated so as to emphasize the synthesis of automatic control systems.

In order to apply theory to automatic control engineering usefully, it is also necessary to know the properties of certain instruments that are generally used as elements of automatic control systems. They are not discussed in detail in the present text, since they do not form part of the theory of automatic control. The examples and exercise problems include many practical problems.

Chapters VIII and IX contain some new material studied by Professor Kensuke Hasegawa of Tokyo Institute of Technology and the present author that has not yet been published.

The author is greatly indebted to Professor Kensuke Hasegawa for his assistance in the preparation of the lecture notes which form the basis of the present text.

November, 1961

Hiroyuki Takai

1

Outline of Automatic Control

1.1. CONTROL AND AUTOMATIC CONTROL

The various machines and equipment used in industry need to be subject to adjustment in order to meet certain requirements. This adjusting operation is called a control. Among the specific items controlled are position, angle, velocity, number of revolutions, force, tension, voltage, current, power, liquid level, rate of flow, pressure, temperature, humidity, chemical composition, concentration, and viscosity. Methods of control include: simple on-off controls, on-off controls with unequal time intervals, continuous controls, etc. A control may be regarded simply as a command to a system regarding its behaviour or state. It does not supply the energy necessary for the operation of the system. Of course, energy is consumed in the act of controlling. However, such consumption is regarded as a loss due to the imperfect efficiency of the device; it is usually not significant.

Stated in general terms, an automatic control is a control effected automatically. The various automatic control techniques constitute control engineering - also called automatic control engineering in a broad sense.

Automatic control may be roughly divided into two categories: automatic operation and feedback control. The latter is also called automatic control in a narrower sense. An automatic operation is a control that causes a device which has reached one of its sequence of states to proceed automatically to the next state. An automatic operation is sometimes also called an open-loop automatic control. In an automatic operation, the action of the system proceeds only from the element to which the commanding signal is fed toward the element to be controlled. Therefore, the behaviour of the whole system can be studied by examining the variation of the commanding signal as it passes through each element. That is, the relation between the characteristics of the elements and that of the whole system is relatively simple.

Unlike an automatic operation, feedback control is an automatic control determining (on the basis of the state or behaviour of a device at a particular instant) what commanding signal will be given to control the next state. That is, the result of the control is measured at each instant, and an appropriate correction signal based on this measurement is sent out so that the controlled object will behave in the desired way. To achieve this automatically and systematically, the control system must necessarily be a closed loop. Thus a feedback control is sometimes called a closed-loop automatic control. Often, it is simply called an automatic control. In general, the term "automatic control" is used to mean feedback control, and we shall follow this convention. In an automatic control system, the actuating signal circulates around the closed loop. It is determined by both the commanding signal and the result of the control at the previous instant. Consequently, a phenomenon occurring in one part of an automatic control system affects all other parts. Therefore, unlike automatic operation, the behaviour of a whole automatic system cannot be simply studied by successively examining the behaviour of the individual parts.

Therefore, in a closed-loop automatic control system, the relationships between the elements and the whole system are rather complicated, and special techniques have to be developed in order to study them. All feedback-control systems have the common property of being closed loops (and, in fact, there are many common points in their analyses, syntheses, and other technical aspects). A field of engineering devoted especially to feedback control has therefore been developed. The theoretical part of this engineering field is known as feedback-control theory. Feedback-control theory is, of course, only a branch of control engineering in general, though at the present time it is the most highly developed branch.

1.2. PROBLEMS IN AUTOMATIC CONTROL ENGINEERING

Automatic control engineering involves special types of problems not often encountered in ordinary engineering. Let us mention some of these.

1. Automatic control engineering is closely connected with many other engineering fields. Therefore, the study of automatic control engineering requires a knowledge of these other engineering fields. Even a fundamental knowledge of economics is sometimes necessary. Without familiarity with these fields, it may be difficult to understand automatic control engineering fully or to synthesize automatic control systems - a matter of great practical value.
2. Automatic control engineering is mainly concerned with time-dependent variations in a certain state, particularly with transient phenomena. This is not usually treated in great detail in ordinary engineering.
3. The mechanism of an automatic control system is exceedingly complicated. It is necessary therefore to disregard some of the less significant characteristics of a system or to approximate complicated characteristics suitably by simpler ones. A practical approximation requires experience and knowledge.

These three features, which are characteristic of automatic control engineering, create problems. The purpose of engineering in general is to find optimum methods for designing and constructing useful machines or equipment. The purpose of automatic control engineering is the solution of the above three problems.

1.3. STRUCTURE OF AUTOMATIC CONTROL SYSTEMS AND PERFORMANCE MECHANISMS

Automatic control is achieved by the following procedure. A variable (known as the controlled variable) is measured and compared with a certain desired value. If there is a difference between them, the system acts automatically in such a way as to bring the controlled variable to the desired value.

A desired value for a controlled variable is called a reference input, 'output' and 'input' are also standard terms for the controlled variable and the reference input respectively. The terms 'reference', 'set point', 'desired value', and 'command' are often used for the reference input. The difference between a controlled variable and the reference input is called the deviation or error. A disturbance is a signal (other than the reference input) that causes a variation in the controlled variable. An automatic control is an operation maintaining a controlled variable at a reference input in the presence of disturbances and a variation in the reference input. A system or equipment achieving such a performance is called an automatic control system. As stated above, a measured variable has to be sent back from the output side to the input side. Therefore, an automatic control system necessarily forms a closed loop. Moreover, to achieve automatic control, the measured variable has to be sent back as a signal with negative phase angle. The general structure of such automatic control systems is illustrated diagrammatically in Fig. 1.1. A controlled system like that shown in Fig. 1.1 is a part (element) of an automatic control system whose output is the controlled variable of the automatic control system. That is, a controlled system is the equipment or machine that is to be controlled. In most cases, disturbances are involved in these controlled systems. An amplifying means is a device that amplifies an error to a level required for controlling the controlled system. The output of an amplifying means is frequently called a manipulated variable. A detecting means is a device that translates a controlled variable into the same kind of quantity as the reference input when it is originally a different kind of quantity. If the controlled variable and the reference input are already the same kind of quantity, a detecting means is unnecessary. A discriminating means is a device that calculates an error by subtracting a measured variable (if necessary, translated by the detecting means)

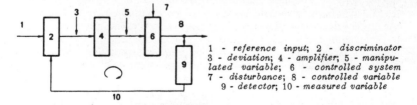

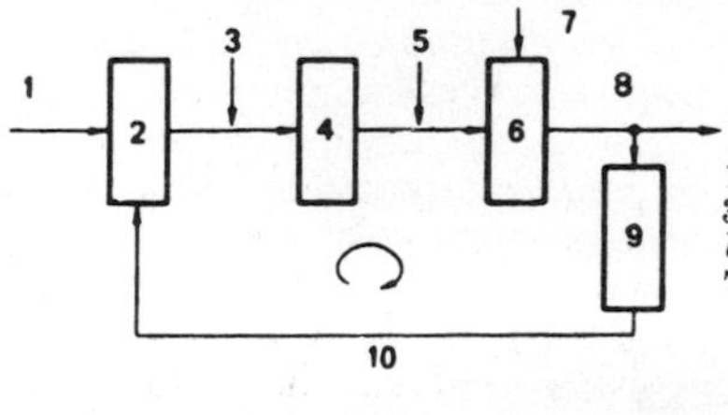

1 - *reference input*; 2 - *discriminator* 3 - *deviation*; 4 - *amplifier*; 5 - *manipulated variable*; 6 - *controlled system* 7 - *disturbance*; 8 - *controlled variable* 9 - *detector*; 10 - *measured variable*

Fig. 1.1 Structure of an automatic control system

from the reference input. Often the detecting means and the discriminating means are contained in a single element known as a detector. Furthermore, when the reference input is maintained at a constant value, the device producing the constant reference input is also often included in a single element, again known as a detector.

In order to see the purpose and the effect of automatic control, let us investigate the performance of a negative feedback amplifier like that shown in Fig. 1.2. A negative feedback amplifier is not usually considered as an automatic control system. However, its operating mechanism is the same as that of an automatic control system and negative feedback and automatic control systems have common characteristics.

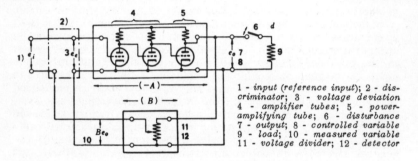

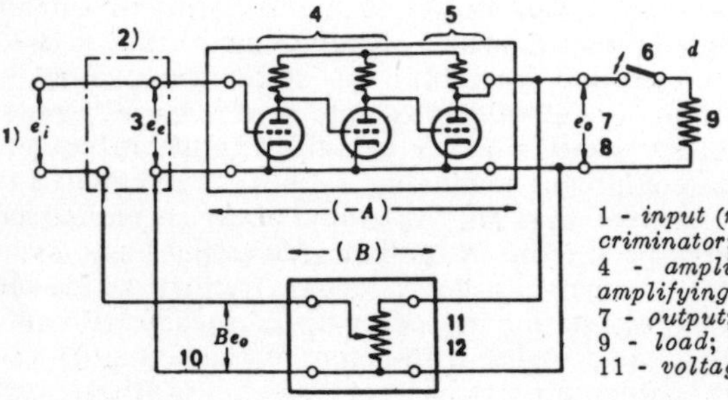

1 - *input (reference input)*; 2 - *discriminator*; 3 - *voltage deviation* 4 - *amplifier tubes*; 5 - *power-amplifying tube*; 6 - *disturbance* 7 - *output*; 8 - *controlled variable* 9 - *load*; 10 - *measured variable* 11 - *voltage divider*; 12 - *detector*

Fig. 1.2 A negative feedback amplifier

Comparing the structure of the negative feedback amplifier shown in Fig. 1.2 and the general structure of the automatic control system shown in Fig. 1.1, we see that the amplifying means and the controlled system in the negative feedback amplifier are combined in one unit. Specifically, the last tube (that is, the power tube) corresponds to the controlled system, and other tubes correspond to the amplifying means. In this system, the controlled variable and the reference input are both voltages. Therefore, there is no detecting means in a strict sense of the term. However, the system contains a voltage divider to reduce the controlled variable to a voltage of the same level as the reference input, and this voltage divider may be regarded as a detecting means. Also, there is no one device used as a discriminating means. Instead of computing the difference between the controlled variable and the reference input by using a detector, the sum of the divided output voltage and the reference input (the difference between the two voltages) is fed to the amplifying means directly as a deviation to achieve the negative feedback, since the output voltage itself has an inverse phase angle to the reference input voltage.

If the negative feedback amplifier is regarded as an automatic control system, then the input voltage e_i is the reference input and the output voltage e_o is the controlled variable. The disturbance consists of several factors. Variations in system constants due to the variation in the voltage of the electric source for the amplifying means or due to the variation in the temperature surrounding the system are examples. Any variation in the load resistance, as shown in Fig. 1.2, will exert a great influence on the output voltage e_o. That is, a load variation causes a great variation in the amplification factor. Therefore, it is the most significant factor in the disturbance in this system. Since a load variation can be measured, we shall, for simplicity, take the load variation as the only disturbance in this system and disregard the other factors.

Let us now investigate the relation between the controlled variable (output voltage) e_o, the reference input (input voltage) e_i, and the variation d in the controlled variable due to the disturbance (load variation) existing before the control is executed. In Fig. 1.2, the deviation voltage e_e, which is to be fed to the amplifying means, is $e_i + Be_o$ (where B is the coefficient of the divider). This deviation voltage e_e is intensified to $-A(e_i + Be_o)$ by the amplifying means. Then, the sum total of $-A(e_i + Be_o)$ and the variation (voltage variation) d due to the disturbance will be equal to e_o. Therefore, we have the relation

$$-A(e_i+Be_o)+d=e_o \tag{1.1}$$

Then e_o can be computed from this equation as follows:

$$e_o=\frac{-Ae_i+d}{1+AB}=\frac{-A}{1+AB}e_i+\frac{1}{1+AB}d \tag{1.2}$$

If the amplification factor A is sufficiently large (so that AB is much larger than 1), we have the approximations

$$\frac{-A}{1+AB}\doteqdot-\frac{1}{B},\qquad \frac{1}{1+AB}\doteqdot 0 \tag{1.3}$$

Substituting these approximations into equation (1.2), we obtain

$$e_o\doteqdot-\frac{1}{B}e_i \tag{1.4}$$

This last equation shows that the controlled variable (output) e_o is determined almost entirely by the reference input e_i and the coefficient B of the divider (the magnifying coefficient of the detecting means) and is almost independent of the disturbance and the amplification coefficient A.

Since the load variation was taken as the only disturbance, the fact that the controlled variable (output voltage) e_o is independent of the disturbance means that the inner impedance of the system observed from the output terminals is almost zero. That is, as long as the system is operating satisfactorily, we can obtain a large power from the system without variation of the controlled variable (the output voltage).

This is a property not just of negative feedback amplifiers; other automatic control systems with the same behaviour mechanism possess the same property. Even if a controlled system itself is unstable or can be appreciably affected by disturbances, it is possible to maintain the controlled variable at the reference input by forming an automatic system. Accordingly, by forming an automatic control system, it is possible to obtain in a relatively simple way a stability that could not be obtained from a single unit. When a system with certain characteristics is required, such a system can often be constructed by forming an automatic control system with cheap elements or components that would have quite low efficiencies if used separately. Thus, automatic control systems are often economical. It should be noted, however, that in practice we do not always have ideal situations like the above. For example, it is not always easy to get an amplification coefficient of the amplifying means sufficiently in excess of 1. To construct automatic control systems, we have to use elements with properties such as inductance, electrostatic capacitance, inertia, or elasticity. These elements accumulate energy and cause undesirable transient phenomena. Occasionally, a transient phenomenon completely invalidates the control. Furthermore, such phenomena can cause damage to a system.

These transient-phenomenon problems have to be solved before practical automatic control systems can be constructed. However, it is much more difficult to solve these problems than to find the characteristics in the steady state, just as is the case in the analysis of negative feedback control. Solution of these problems is also quite laborious. As a result, the greatest effort often goes into the solution of the transient problems. This does not mean, however, that the transient characteristics are of greater importance in the applications of automatic control than are the steady-state characteristics.

1.4. CLASSIFICATION OF AUTOMATIC CONTROL SYSTEMS

Automatic control systems are used for various purposes in different engineering fields. Accordingly, there are various types of automatic control systems and various ways of classifying them.

First, we shall classify them according to the nature of the controlled variable. From the standpoint of purpose, automatic control systems are usually referred to in terms of the nature of the controlled variable. For example, an automatic control system controlling speed is called an automatic speed controller; an automatic control system controlling temperature is called an automatic temperature controller.

We may also classify automatic controls according to the performance mechanisms. If the reference input is fixed throughout a control, the control is called an automatic regulation. If the reference input varies during a control, the control is called a follow-up controller. It is clear that a follow-up controller can be used as an automatic regulator if so desired. Often an automatic controller can also be used as a follow-up controller. However, their characteristics are different in certain respects, and their syntheses, structures, and constructions have the emphasis on different elements or parts. Occasionally, variation of the reference input is already prescribed for a follow-up control. Such a follow-up control is called a programmed control. There is another classification commonly used. Automatic control systems are classified as servomechanisms, process controllers, and automatic regulators. This classification is based not only on the differences in the performance mechanisms or structures but also on the purposes of the systems and the manufacturing processes. This is the customary classification, though it might be noted that there are no clear-cut lines dividing the three types mentioned.

A servomechanism usually means a follow-up control system whose controlled variable is a position or an angle. The reference input of a servomechanism is usually of the same kind as the controlled variable, that is, a position or an angle. However, a voltage or a pressure may occasionally be used as the reference input.

As an example, Fig. 1.3 shows a servomechanism using oil pressure. The load whose displacement is to be controlled, is connected to the piston of the oil-pressure motor. The displacement x_l of the load is the controlled variable (or the output signal) of this servomechanism, and the displacement x_s of the piston of the pilot valve is the reference input (or the input signal). The purpose is to let the output displacement x_l follow the input displacement x_s precisely. However, the direction of the output displacement x_l is opposite to that of the input displacement x_s. If the piston of the pilot valve moves upward from an equilibrium position, receiving a displacement x_s as shown in Fig. 1.3, the compressed oil in the pilot valve flows into the upper compartment of the cylinder of the oil-pressure motor, pushing down the piston. The piston then moves downward, and this movement is transmitted to the cylinder of the pilot valve through the lever linking the piston of the oil-pressure motor and the cylinder of the pilot valve. The cylinder is then pushed upward, and this movement results in equilibrium of oil pressure in the servomechanism again. This series of actions proceeds in a manner controlled by the variation in the input signal. Consequently, the displacement of the piston of the oil pressure motor (which is the output signal) exactly follows the displacement of the piston of the pilot valve (the

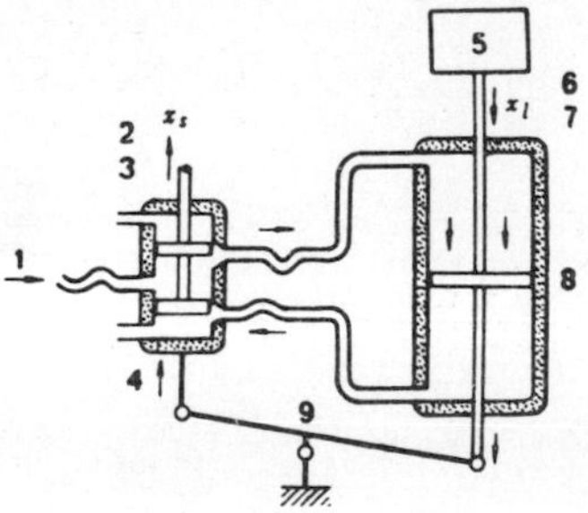

1 - *oil pressure*; 2 - *input*; 3 - *reference input*; 4 - *pilot valve*; 5 - *load*; 6 - *output* 7 - *controlled variable*; 8 - *oil-pressure motor*; 9 - *lever*

Fig. 1.3 An oil-pressure servomechanism

input signal). As can be seen from the above discussion, in a servomechanism, there is not always a clear distinction between the controlled system, the amplifying means, the detecting means, and the discriminating means.

Fig. 1.4 shows an oil-pressure type of servomechanism applied to an automatic lathe. A cutting tool is attached to the piston of the oil-pressure motor. The horizontal motion of the cutting tool is such that the tool follows the movement of the piston of the pilot valve. Thus, if we give a suitable vertical drive to the cutting tool during the operation of the lathe, we can cut out a piece with exactly the same shape as the model. Since the reacting force of the cutting tool does not affect the piston of the pilot valve, there is no danger of causing damage to the model or having the accuracy decrease because of stress involved in the cutting.

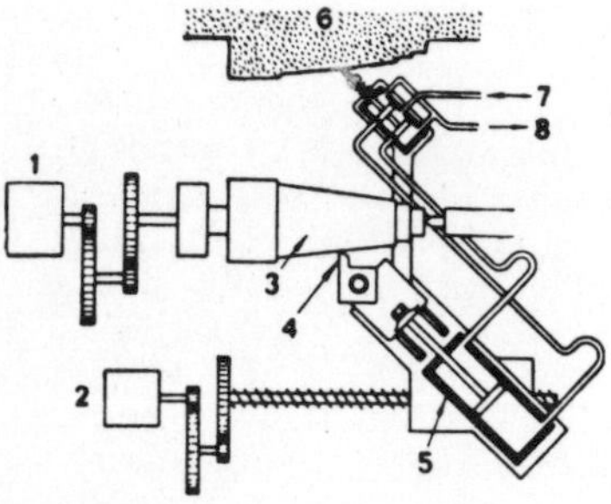

1 - *primary motor*; 2 - *cutting tool vertical drive motor*; 3 - *material*; 4 - *cutting tool* 5 - *oil-pressure motor*; 6 - *model*; 7 - *oil pressure*; 8 - *oil return*

Fig. 1.4 An automatic lathe: an example of the application of a servomechanism

A process control is a control used primarily for controlling a production process in such industries as chemical plants, petroleum refineries, paper mills, etc. The controlled variable of a process control can be temperature, pressure, flow of liquid or gas, mixing ratio, liquid level, hydrogen-ion concentration, viscosity, humidity, etc. In most cases, a process control is an automatic regulation. However, a follow-up control or a programmed control may also be used as a process control.

Fig. 1.5 shows a process control system controlling the temperature of a liquid in a continuous heating plant so that the temperature of the outflow liquid will be constant. The controlled variable is the temperature t_o of the outflow liquid, and it is detected as the difference e_m between the electromotive forces of two thermocouples. One thermocouple is inserted in a hole near the outlet pipe, and the other is inserted in a thermostat which maintains the temperature at freezing point. The reference input voltage e_s is given by a battery (whose voltage is e_B) and the divider R_D. Then the deviation voltage e_e is the difference between the reference input voltage e_s and the voltage e_m. This deviation e_e is transformed into an angle of rotation θ_0 by a simple servomechanism. Then, the cock opens or closes, depending on the angle θ_0, so that the inflow of the steam is controlled, reducing the deviation e_e to zero. This sequence of operations proceeds at each instant to achieve the desired control. The relation between the deviation e_e and the angle θ_0 of the cock rotation can be suitably arranged by an appropriate construction of the feedback circuit in the servomechanism. For example, the deviation e_e will pass through the feedback circuit if we set B = 1 in Fig. 1.5. Then, the deviation e_e is proportional to the rotation angle θ_0. On the other hand, we can get a suitable relation between e_e and θ_0 (so that the transient behaviour of the system will be satisfactory) by using a feedback circuit suitably constructed with resistors and capacitors. Thus, it is possible to let the temperature control system behave almost ideally in both the transient and the steady states. The diagram shown in Fig. 1.5 is intended only to illustrate the structure and operational mechanism of a process control system. In actual cases some part of the system may be replaced by a simpler device or, to get the desired control, some part may have to be replaced by a more complicated device.

If more power is necessary to operate the cock, the output of the motor shown in Fig. 1.5 is often amplified (by using another servomechanism or by other means) to a sufficiently large power. Such a device is frequently called a manipulating means.

As is clear from the above example, there is a rather sharp distinction between the controlled system (the liquid vessel) and the controller, that is the set of devices executing the control (the devices between the thermocouple and the motor). Such a controller can be used for other controlled systems without major alteration (the detector may be replaced by another type if necessary). A controller that has wide application (such as the above) is sometimes called an industrial controller.

For a process control system, the engineering fields applied in manufacturing the controlled system are quite different from those applied in manufacturing the controller. Accordingly, process control systems are quite different from other automatic control

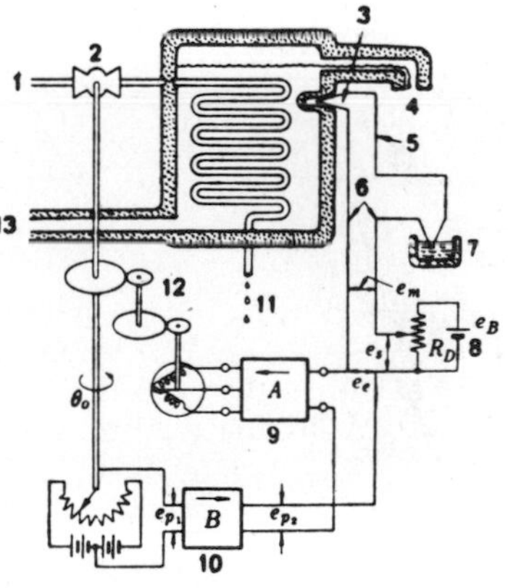

1 - *steam inlet*; 2 - *cock*; 3 - *thermocouple* 4 - *temperature* to (°C) *of outflow liquid* 5 - *constantan*; 6 - *copper wire*; 7 - *thermostat (with temperature set at freezing point)*; 8 - *standard battery*; 9 - *amplifier* 10 - *feedback circuit*; 11 - *drain*; 12 - *gear train*; 13 - *input liquid*

Fig. 1.5 An automatic temperature control system: an example of a process control system

systems with regard to manufacturing procedures and in the operation of the control system.

An automatic regulating system is an automatic control system that keeps electrical or mechanical quantities such as voltages, currents, velocities, or rotational forces at certain fixed quantities. Fig. 1.6 shows an automatic speed regulator that uses the Ward-Leonard system. The purpose of this regulator is to maintain the rotation speed n_o of the motor M at a fixed number determined by the reference input voltage e_s. The reference input voltage e_s is given by the battery voltage e_B and the divider. The controlled variable is the rotation speed n_o of the motor, and it is detected as a voltage by the tachometer generator. Then the deviation voltage e_e is obtained by taking the difference between the detected voltage and the reference input voltage e_s. This deviation voltage e_e is amplified by the amplifier, the exciter, and the primary generator, which regulates the rotational speed of the motor so that the deviation voltage becomes zero.

As shown in this example, most automatic regulating systems have certain fixed reference inputs. Accordingly, the most important duty of the control is to keep the controlled variable from being affected by the disturbances. There are disturbances of many kinds. The load variation is the one with the greatest effect, as shown in Fig. 1.6. In particular, if we are concerned with the transient performance, we treat the load variation as the only disturbance. Actually, if an automatic regulating system is designed so that the transient performance is satisfactory despite the load variation, the other disturbances are usually of no great consequence.

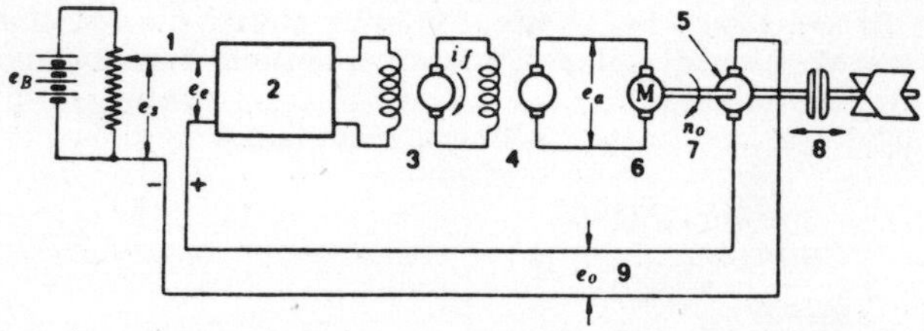

1 - *reference input*; 2 - *amplifier*; 3 - *exciter*; 4 - *primary generator*; 5 - *tachometer*; 6 - *motor*; 7 - *controlled variable* 8 - *clutch*; 9 - *measured variable*

Fig. 1.6 An automatic speed regulator: an example of an automatic regulating system

In principle, the performance of an automatic regulating system is not significantly different from that of a process control system. However, the means used are quite different in the two cases. This can be seen by comparing Figs. 1.5 and 1.6. An automatic regulating system responds more rapidly than a process control system does, and in most cases a rapid response is required for an automatic regulating system.

2

Signal Transmission and its Representation

2.1 AUTOMATIC CONTROL SYSTEMS AND SIGNAL TRANSMISSION

As mentioned earlier, an automatic control system contains at least one closed loop, and the control is achieved by passing some quantity around this closed loop in one direction. For the study of automatic control, it is immaterial whether the systems are electrical or mechanical or what the quantity is. What is important is the variation in that quantity. In fact, this variation determines the quality of the automatic control system.

An abstract concept of the quantity, the effect of variation in which it is useful to study around the loop, is called the signal. In order to examine the behaviour of an automatic control system, we need to know how the signal delivered to the sytem from the outside varies within the sytem and what path it travels along before it leaves the system. In general, transfer functions and block diagrams are used to represent the variation in the signal and the path of signal transmission respectively. The transfer functions represent the variations of the signal in the elements of the system, and the block diagram shows in what order the signal passes through the transfer functions (that is, the elements) of the system.

2.2 TRANSFER FUNCTIONS AND METHODS OF DETERMINING THEM

Suppose that the amplifier shown in Fig. 2.1 is used as an element of a closed loop in an automatic control system. Assume that the amplifier produces an output voltage e_o which is proportional to the input voltage e_i. It is clear that the signal-transmitting characteristics of this amplifier can be simply and clearly represented by its amplification coefficient.

In general, a transfer function is a generalized concept of an amplification coefficient. It represents the ratio of the output signal to the input signal. Accordingly, we may say that the transfer function of the amplifier in Fig. 2.1 is $A = e_o/e_i$, instead of saying that the amplification coefficient is $A = e_o/e_i$. This becomes clearer if we examine the diagrammatic representation shown in Fig. 2.2. The arrow symbols in the diagram represents the direction in

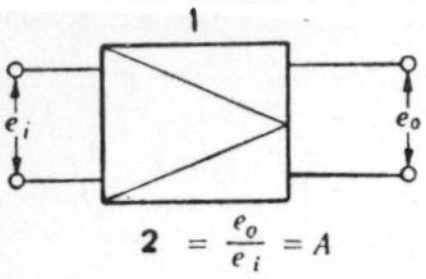

1 - *amplifier*; 2 - *amplification coefficient*
Fig. 2.1 An amplifier

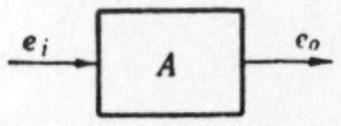

Fig. 2.2 Transfer function of an amplifier

which the signal is transmitted. The voltage-dividing circuit shown in Fig. 2.3 is an example of a transfer function that is not an amplification coefficient of an amplifier. The transfer function is

$$\frac{e_o}{e_i} = \frac{R_2}{R_1 + R_2} \tag{2.1}$$

which can be obtained by the approach used for the amplifier. It can also be represented diagrammatically, as shown in Fig. 2.4. In this case, e_o / e_i is a transfer function but not an amplification coefficient.

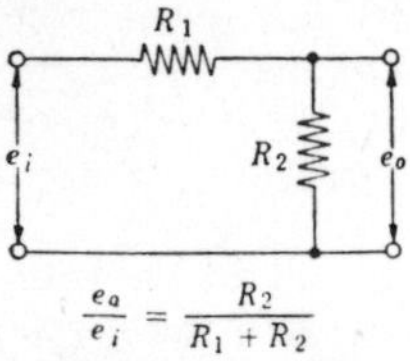

Fig. 2.3 A voltage-dividing circuit

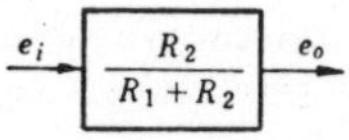

Fig. 2.4 Transfer function of the voltage-dividing circuit

Consider the oil-pressure amplifying device shown in Fig. 2.5. This was one of the examples of servomechanisms given in the previous chapter. Let us compute the transfer function. We assume that the cylinder of the pilot valve is fixed. Let the input signal be the distance x_i in which the piston of the pilot valve moves upward from an equilibrium position, and let the output be the displacement x_o, corresponding to the input signal x_i, of the position of the oil-pressure meter. We shall now find the relation between the input and the output.

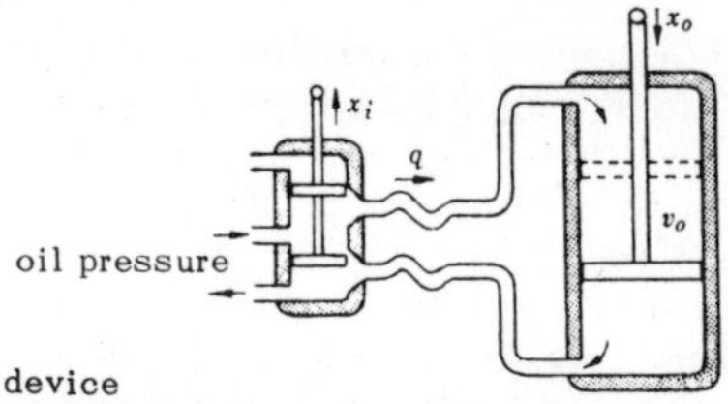

Fig. 2.5 Oil-pressure amplifying device

Let q be the quantity of compressed oil flowing into the upper compartment of the cylinder of the oil-pressure motor per unit time; hence q is also the quantity of oil flowing out from the bottom of the cylinder per unit time. Then the flow quantity q is approximately proportional to the displacement x_i of the piston of the pilot valve. That is, we have the relation

$$q = kx_i \tag{2.2}$$

If we denote by v_o the volume of oil that flows into the upper compartment of the cylinder of the oil-pressure motor during time t, then v_o is also the volume of oil flowing out from the lower compartment during time t. And we have a relation

$$v_o = \int q dt \tag{2.3}$$

between q and v_o. If A is the area of cross section of the piston, the displacement x_o of the piston can be expressed as

$$x_o = \frac{v_o}{A} \tag{2.4}$$

Eliminating v_o and q from equations (2.2), (2.3), and (2.4), we obtain the following relation between the input signal x_i and the output signal x_o:

$$x_o = \frac{k}{A}\int x_i dt = K\int x_i dt \tag{2.5}$$

where $K = k/A$. Since the input signal x_i and the output signal x_o can be considered as functions of time t, we may denote them by $x_i(t)$ and $x_o(t)$, respectively. Then, equation (2.5) may also be written as

$$x_o(t) = K\int x_i(t) dt \tag{2.6}$$

This equation is a differential equation. If the input signal $x_i(t)$ is given in the form of a specific mathematical expression, the output $x_o(t)$ can also be computed specifically. It can then be inferred that the ratio of the output signal to the input signal, which is the amplification coefficient of this oil-pressure amplifying device, is a function whose graph is a wave. This relation can also be represented diagrammatically as shown in Figs. 2.2 and 2.4. The diagrammatic representation of the relation is shown in Fig. 2.6(a).

More generally, let $e_i(t)$ and $e_o(t)$ be the input signal and the output signal, respectively. Suppose that the relation

$$e_o(t) = \frac{de_i(t)}{dt} \tag{2.7}$$

between $e_i(t)$ and $e_o(t)$ is given. It can then be represented diagrammatically as shown in Fig. 2.7(a). If the relation

$$e_o(t) = \frac{d^2}{(dt)^2} e_i(t) = \frac{d}{dt}\left(\frac{de_i(t)}{dt}\right) \tag{2.8}$$

is given, it has the diagrammatic representation shown in Fig. 2.8(a). If for simplicity we use the letter p for d/dt, we have

$$\frac{d^2}{dt^2} = p^2, \qquad \int dt = \frac{1}{p} \tag{2.9}$$

For example, equation (2.6) is then

$$x_o(t) = \frac{K}{p} x_i(t) \tag{2.10}$$

Similarly, Figs. 2.7(b) and 2.8(b) can be used instead of Figs. 2.7(a) and 2.8(a).

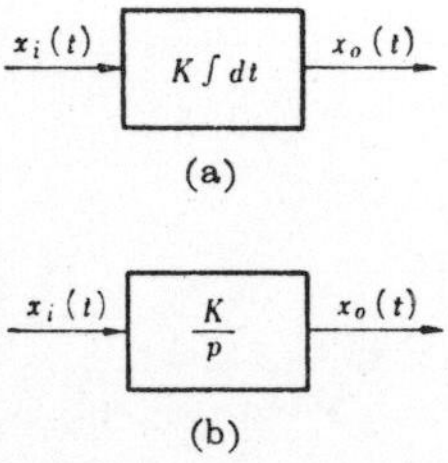

Fig. 2.6 The transfer function of the oil-pressure amplifying device (see Fig. 2.5)

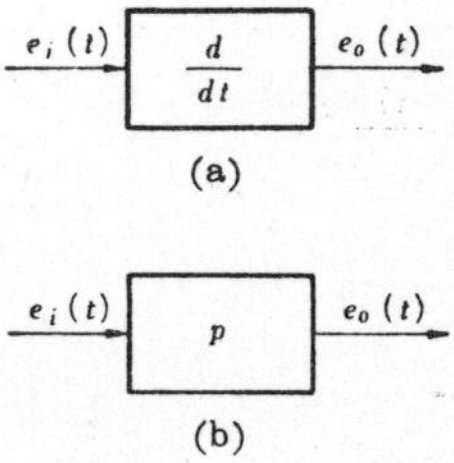

Fig. 2.7 The transfer function of a differential element

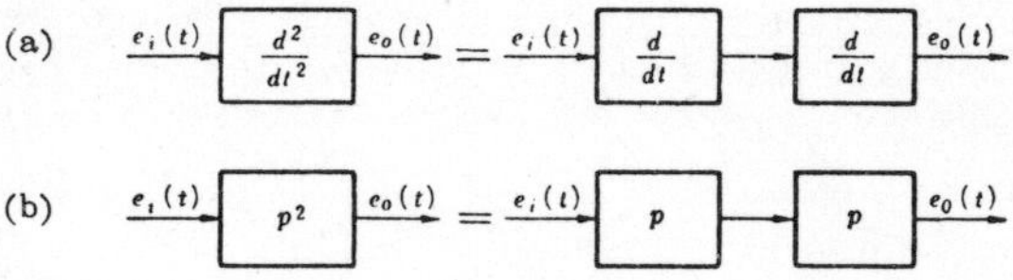

Fig. 2.8 The transfer function of a second-order differential element

In this notation, a general signal transmission can be represented in exactly the same form as an amplification coefficient of an amplifier. However, a transfer function is essentially different from an amplification coefficient since the equations expressing the relations between the input and output signals are differential equations. If differentiation or integration changes the amplitude but not the general pattern of a wave, then, with respect to this wave pattern, the symbols in the blocks shown in Figs. 2.6(b) and 2.7(b) act in exactly the same way as an amplification coefficient does.

For example, if the input signal $x_i(t)$ in equation (2.6), equation (2.7), or Fig. 2.6 is representable in the form

$$x_i(t) = A_i e^{at} \tag{2.11}$$

where a is a real constant, then the output signal $x_o(t)$ is

$$x_o(t)=K\int A_i\epsilon^{\alpha t}dt=\frac{K}{p}A_i\epsilon^{\alpha t} \tag{2.12}$$

$$=\frac{K}{\alpha}A_i\epsilon^{\alpha t}$$

$$=\frac{K}{\alpha}x_i(t) \tag{2.13}$$

This equation shows that the output signal $x_o(t)$ is K/a times the input signal $x_i(t)$. In this case, we may regard p as a numerical value a instead of a mere symbol in the above computation. That is, we may set

$$p=\alpha \tag{2.14}$$

in the computation. Since this substitution is permissible only when the input $x_i(t)$ is of the form of ϵ^{at}, we may use new notations $X_i(a)$ and $X_o(a)$ in place of $x_i(t)$ and $x_o(t)$. Then the relation between the input and output signals can be expressed as follows:

$$X_o(\alpha)=\frac{K}{\alpha}X_i(\alpha) \tag{2.15}$$

This equation has the diagrammatic representation shown in Fig. 2.9. If an input signal is given in the form

$$x_i(t)=A_i\epsilon^{j\omega t} \tag{2.16}$$

that is, if the input signal is sinusoidal (strictly speaking, the real part of the expression (2.16) is a cosine curve and the imaginary part is a sine curve), then the output signal $x_o(t)$ in Fig. 2.6 is

$$x_o(t)=\frac{K}{p}A_i\epsilon^{j\omega t}=\frac{K}{j\omega}A_i\epsilon^{j\omega t} \tag{2.17}$$

$$=\frac{K}{j\omega}x_i(t) \tag{2.18}$$

These equations show that we may simply use the substitution $p = j\omega$ to compute the output signal. We note that the amplification coefficient is also multiplied by $1/j$. However, this means simply a phase lag of 90° according to the theory of alternating currents. Since the input is sinusoidal, the relation between the input and the output will be expressed by the equation

$$X_o(j\omega)=\frac{K}{j\omega}X_i(j\omega) \tag{2.19}$$

as before. Here, $X_o(j\omega)$ is the output signal and $X_i(j\omega)$ is the input signal. The relation (2.19) has the diagrammatic representation shown in Fig. 2.10.

As a further generalization of the above discussions, consider an input signal of the form

$$x_i(t)=A_i\epsilon^{st} \tag{2.20}$$

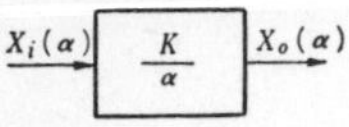

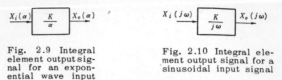

Fig. 2.9 Integral element output signal for an exponential wave input signal

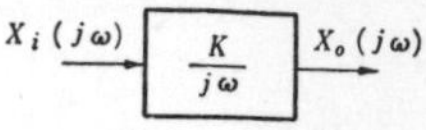

Fig. 2.10 Integral element output signal for a sinusoidal input signal

where s is a complex number $s = \alpha + j\omega$, and α, ω, A_i are invariant quantities with respect to the time t. This input signal is a sinusoidal wave whose amplitude attenuates or increases along the exponential curve e^{at}. In particular, it represents a sinusoidal input signal if $a = 0$, an exponential input signal if $\omega = 0$ and a direct current input signal of intensity A_i if $a = 0$ and $\omega = 0$. If we make the substitution

$$p = s \tag{2.21}$$

the output signal $X_o(t)$ for the general input signal is

$$x_o(t) = \frac{K}{s} x_i(t) \tag{2.22}$$

This relation can be also written

$$X_o(s) = \frac{K}{s} X_i(s) \tag{2.23}$$

and it has the diagrammatic representation shown in Fig. 2.11.

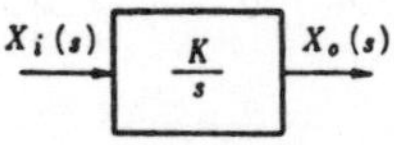

Fig. 2.11 Integral element output signal for a general input signal

As shown above, if the input signal is of the form $A\epsilon^{st}$, then the ratio of the output signal to the input signal has a specific meaning just as an amplification coefficient does even when a differential or integral operation is contained in the performance mechanism of the circuit or device. If a differential or integral operation is contained as a signal-transmitting element in the diagrammatic representation of a signal transmission, then the ratio of the output signal to the input signal of such an element is a function of $p (\equiv d/dt)$. The ratio expressed as a function of p is called a transfer function and is denoted by $F(p)$. In particular, if the input signal is of the form $A\epsilon^{st}$, then the transfer function has a specific numerical value and the value can be found by replacing p with a complex number s corresponding to the wave pattern of the input signal. Then, the transfer function is denoted by $F(s)$. In fact, this is the most useful form for a transfer function.

The usual procedure for finding a transfer function is as follows. First, we replace the symbol d/dt by p or s in the differential equation of the given system. Then, we solve the resulting equation algebraically for the ratio of the output signal to the input signal. The symbol p is called a differential operator. It is used to find a transfer function when the input signal is given in the form of a function of time such as $f_i(t)$ or $f_o(t)$. The complex number s is called the Laplace variable. It is used to find a transfer function when the input signal is given in the form of a function, such as $F_i(s)$ or $F_o(s)$, of the complex variable s, which is determined by the wave pattern of the input signal.

Now, we shall show some examples illustrating the calculation of transfer functions. For example, consider the electric network shown in Fig. 2.12. If the internal impedance of the electric source for the input is 0 and if the output current is 0, then the current flowing through the resistance R also flows through the capacitance c. If we denote this current by i, we have the following differential equations:

$$Ri + \frac{i}{pC} = e_i \tag{2.24}$$

$$e_o = \frac{i}{pC} \tag{2.25}$$

where $1/p = \int \ldots dt$. Eliminating i from these two equations, we obtain

$$e_o = \frac{e_i}{1+pCR} \tag{2.26}$$

If we denote by $F(p)$ the transfer function of the network shown in Fig. 2.12, then $F(p)$ is the ratio of the output e_o to the input e_i. Therefore, we can compute $F(p)$ as follows:

$$F(p) = \frac{e_o}{e_i} = \frac{1}{1+pCR} \tag{2.27}$$

If we express this transfer function in the form of $F(s)$, we obtain

$$F(s) = \frac{1}{1+sCR} \tag{2.28}$$

However, if the given network is that shown in Fig. 12, then the transfer function (2.28) can be obtained directly without setting up a set of simultaneous differential equations like equations (2.24) and (2.25). That is, the transfer function (2.28) can be easily obtained by merely substituting s for $j\omega$ in the a.c. theory formula for the network and by taking the ratio of the output signal to the input signal.

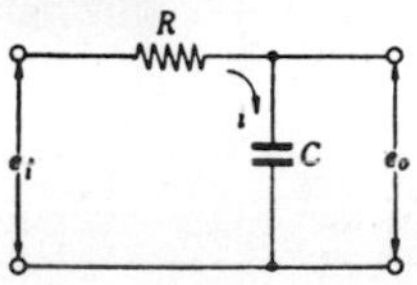

Fig. 2.12 A simple *CR* network

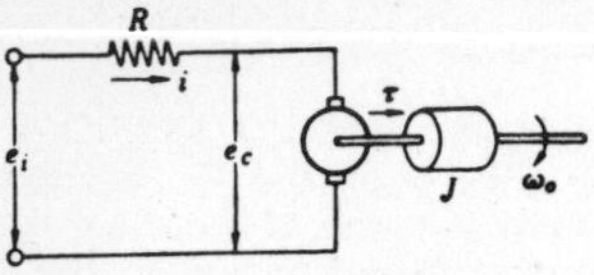

Fig. 2.13 Direct current motor

As a second example, consider the d.c. motor shown in Fig. 2.13. We assume that the magnetic flux in the magnetic field of the d.c. motor is constant. We take the voltage e_i applied to the armature of the motor as the input signal and the angular velocity ω_o of the rotation of the armature as the output signal. With these assumptions let us compute the transfer function.

Let i [amp] be the current flowing in the armature, and let τ $[N-m]$ be the driving torque of the armature. Then,

$$\tau = Ni \tag{2.29}$$

Here, N is a constant determined by the structure of the d.c. motor and the magnetic flux in the magnetic field. On the other hand, if we denote the electromotive force of the armature by e_c [volts] and the angular velocity of the armature by ω_o [rad/sec], then we have

$$e_c = N\omega_o \tag{2.30}$$

where N is the same constant as in equation (2.29). Furthermore, the relations

$$e_i = Ri + e_c \tag{2.31}$$

and

$$\tau = Jp\omega_o \tag{2.32}$$

hold in Fig. 2.13. Eliminating the quantities τ, e_c, and i from equations (2.29), (2.30), (2.31), and (2.32), we obtain a relation between ω_o and e_i:

$$\omega_o = \frac{\frac{1}{N}}{1 + p\frac{JR}{N^2}} e_i \tag{2.33}$$

Therefore, if we denote the transfer function by $F(s)$, we have

$$F(s) = \frac{\frac{1}{N}}{1 + s\frac{JR}{N^2}} \tag{2.34}$$

If we set

$$\frac{JR}{N^2} = T, \quad \frac{1}{N} = K \tag{2.35}$$

then equation (2.34) becomes

$$F(s) = \frac{K}{1 + sT} \tag{2.36}$$

Equation (2.28) is a special case of the expression (2.36) obtained by making the substitutions $T = CR$ and $K = 1$. A transfer function of the form of equation (2.36) is called a first-order phase-lag transfer function or, simply, a first-order transfer function. Transfer functions of this form are frequently encountered in automatic control engineering. Even if an automatic control system has a complicated transfer function, the transfer function can often be expressed as a product of first-order transfer functions. Moreover, a first-order transfer function is frequently regarded as a basic form of transfer function in automatic control theory. The constant T in the expression for the first-order transfer function (2.36) is called the time constant and the constant K is called the gain constant or the d.c. amplification coefficient.

It is often convenient to use the form

$$F(s)=\frac{A}{s+a} \tag{2.37}$$

for a first-order transfer function instead of the form (2.36). Then, the transfer function (2.28) is obtained by applying the substitutions $a = 1/CR$ and $A = 1/CR$ to the transfer function (2.37). The transfer function (2.34) is obtained by applying substitutions $a = 1/T = N^2/JR$ and $A = K/T = N/JR$ to the transfer function (2.37).

Figure 2.14 shows a network whose transfer function is of second order with respect to the Laplace variable s. In order to

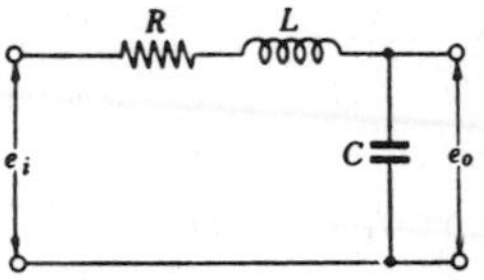

Fig. 2.14 A resonant network

find the transfer function of this network, we denote by sL the impedance of the inductor, and by $1/sC$ the impedance of the capacitor of capacitance C. Then the transfer function is the ratio e_o/e_i. Denoting the transfer function by $F(s)$, we have

$$F(s)=\frac{\frac{1}{sC}}{sL+R+\frac{1}{sC}} \tag{2.38}$$

$$=\frac{1}{1+sCR+s^2LC} \tag{2.39}$$

If a transfer function is of second order with respect to the Laplace variable s (as in the present case), then the transfer function is called a second-order transfer function. The transfer function (2.30) can also be written as a product of two first-order transfer functions:

$$F(s)=\frac{1}{(1+sT_1)(1+sT_2)} \tag{2.40}$$

In order to find the values of the constants T_1 and T_2, we compare the expressions (2.39) and (2.40). Then,

$$\left.\begin{aligned} T_1 T_2 &= LC \\ T_1 + T_2 &= RC \end{aligned}\right\} \tag{2.41}$$

from which we can compute T_1 and T_2 as follows:

$$\left.\begin{aligned} T_1 &= \frac{1}{2}\left(RC + \sqrt{(RC)^2 - 4LC}\right) \\ T_2 &= \frac{1}{2}\left(RC - \sqrt{(RC)^2 - 4LC}\right) \end{aligned}\right\} \tag{2.42}$$

To simplify these expressions, we set

$$\begin{aligned} RC &= T_c \\ \frac{1}{\sqrt{LC}} &= \omega_n \end{aligned} \tag{2.43}$$

where T_c is the time constant for the resistance R and the capacitance C and ω_n is the natural angular frequency. Then,

$$\left.\begin{aligned} T_1 &= \frac{1}{2}\left(T_c + \sqrt{T_c^2 - \left(\frac{2}{\omega_n}\right)^2}\right) \\ T_2 &= \frac{1}{2}\left(T_c - \sqrt{T_c^2 - \left(\frac{2}{\omega_n}\right)^2}\right) \end{aligned}\right\} \tag{2.44}$$

Thus, if $T_c > 2/\omega_n$ (where $T_c > 0$, $\omega_n > 0$), then T_1 and T_2 are real numbers. If $T_c < 2/\omega_n$, then T_1 and T_2 are complex numbers. This shows that the time constants are real numbers in most cases but that they can occasionally be complex.

The transfer function (2.39) can also be written as

$$F(s) = \frac{A^2}{(s+a_1)(s+a_2)} \tag{2.45}$$

These constants a_1, a_2, and A have the following values:

$$\left.\begin{aligned} a_1 &= \frac{2}{RC + \sqrt{(RC)^2 - 4LC}} = \frac{2}{T_c + \sqrt{T_c^2 - \left(\frac{2}{\omega_n}\right)^2}} \\ a_2 &= \frac{2}{RC - \sqrt{(RC)^2 - 4LC}} = \frac{2}{T_c - \sqrt{T_c^2 - \left(\frac{2}{\omega_n}\right)^2}} \\ A &= \frac{1}{\sqrt{LC}} = \omega_n \end{aligned}\right\}$$

2.3. ACTIVE AND PASSIVE ELEMENTS

There are two kinds of elements constituting an automatic control system: passive and active. These elements transmit the signals.

A passive element transmits not only signals but also electric power or some analogous quantity. Needless to say a passive element transmits signals from the input terminals to the output terminals. It can also transmit signals from the output terminals to the input terminals. That is, the direction of signal transmission is reversible in a passive element. Therefore, a reaction caused by loading on the output side also affects the input side. In contrast, an active element transmits signals only from the input terminals to the output terminals but no power. Therefore, any reaction caused by loading on the output side does not affect the input side. That is, an active element transmits signals in only one direction. The networks shown in Figs. 2.12 and 2.13 are both passive elements. It can easily be seen that signal transmissions are reversible in these networks. On the other hand, the oil-pressure amplifying device shown in Fig. 2.5 is an active element. Any variation in the input signal x_i directly affects the output signal x_o; however, any loading on the output side does not affect the input signal x_i. The principal elements of ordinary tube amplifiers or of d.c. motors used in field controls are active elements.

As mentioned above, an automatic control system consists of passive and active elements connected so as to form a closed loop. Direct computation of the transfer function of such an automatic control system by observing the system as a whole is extremely complicated. It is therefore convenient to use the following procedure in actual computations. First we decompose the closed loop of the automatic control system into a number of suitable parts. Then we compute the transfer function of each part. Finally, we combine the transfer functions of the parts to obtain the transfer function of the whole system.

In making this decomposition, we should not separate two adjacent passive elements. To see the reason for this, consider the network shown in Fig. 2.15. The transfer function of this network is

$$F(s)=\frac{1}{1+s(R_1C_1+R_1C_2+R_2C_2)+s^2C_1C_2R_1R_2} \tag{2.47}$$

Suppose that we cut the network at the points b and b' and decompose the network into two parts. If we compute the transfer function of each part, and if we combine the results, we obtain

$$F(s)=\frac{1}{(1+sC_1R_1)(1+sC_2R_2)} \tag{2.48}$$

as the transfer function of the whole network. The transfer function computed in this manner does not agree with the correct transfer function (2.47). However, if an amplifier is inserted after the terminals b and b' as shown in Fig. 2.16, the transfer function (2.48) is the correct transfer function of this network.

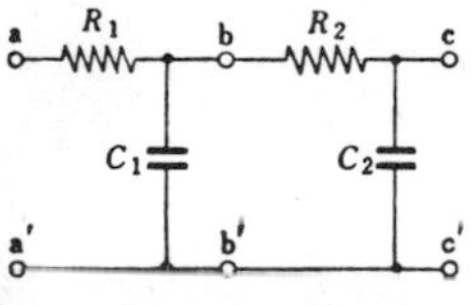

Fig. 2.15 Two adjacent passive networks; an example of incorrect network decomposition for transfer function computation

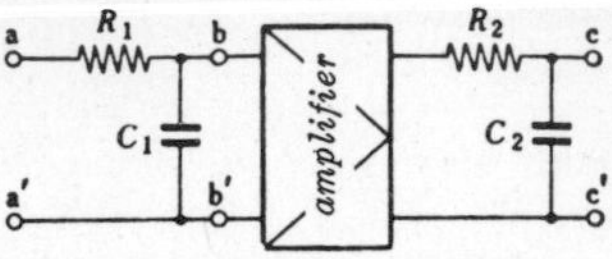

Fig. 2.16 A network in which passive and active elements are connected; network separation at points b and b' provides correct network decomposition for transfer function computation

The above example shows that for a correct decomposition, the network should be separated at points where power is not transmitted. Such a pair of points is located on the input side of an active element. Sometimes we may separate the closed loop at points on the output side of an active element in order to obtain a correct decomposition. This is permissible when the active element can be regarded as an ideal one.

For example, consider a system in which a d.c. generator and a motor are connected as shown in Fig. 2.17. If we separate the system at the points b and b' between the generator and the motor, and if we compute the transfer function of the whole system by combining the transfer functions of the parts, we do not obtain the correct transfer function of the system. To obtain the correct transfer function of the system, we proceed as follows: since the field current i_f is the input to the generator, we separate the field circuit from the generator. We then compute the transfer function of the field circuit, regarding the input voltage e_i as the input signal, and the field current i_f as the output signal. We also compute the transfer function of the remaining part of the given system, regarding the field current i_f as the input signal, and the angular velocity ω_o of the motor as the output signal. Then we combine these two transfer functions to obtain the transfer function of the entire system.

Let us go through the computation to obtain the transfer function of the given system following the above procedure. Let $F_1(s)$ be the transfer function representing the relation between the input voltage e_i and the field current i_f. Then, we obtain

$$F_1(s)=\frac{1}{R_f+sL_f} \tag{2.49}$$

If we denote by $F_2(s)$ the transfer function representing the relation between the input signal i_f and the output signal ω_o (the angular velocity of the motor), we obtain from equation (2.34)

$$F_2(s)=\frac{\frac{1}{N}R_c}{1+s\frac{J(R_1+R_2)}{N^2}} \tag{2.50}$$

In equation (2.50), we have the sum of the internal resistance R_1 of the generator and the internal resistance R_2 of the motor (instead of R as in equation (2.34)). Also, the numerator is multiplied by the amplification coefficient R_c between the field current and the electromotive force of the armature. Since the input signal is a current and the output signal is a voltage, the amplification coefficient R_c has the dimensions of resistance. Thus, the transfer function $F(s)$ of the system shown in Fig. 2.17 is

$$F(s)=\frac{\frac{1}{N}\cdot\frac{R_c}{R_f}}{\left(1+s\frac{L_f}{R_f}\right)\left(1+s\frac{J(R_1+R_2)}{N^2}\right)} \tag{2.51}$$

The transfer functions (2.48) and (2.51) are products of two transfer functions each of which is a transfer function of a part of the entire network. This fact can be represented diagrammatically as shown in Figs. 2.18 (a) and 2.18 (b). In these figures and in Figs. 2.2, 2.4, and 2.6-2.11, each transfer function is enclosed by a block, and each block has two arrow symbols attached to it. One arrow symbol indicates the direction in which the input enters and the other indicates the direction in which the output leaves. A diagram consisting of one or more such blocks with arrow symbols is called a block diagram. Each block in a block diagram represents a maximal part of an automatic control system such that the output of the part does not affect the input. Thus, the first element in the part represented by a single block (that is, the element to which the input signal to the block is applied) is an active element, and any reaction occurring within a block does not affect the preceding block. Construction of the block diagrams for complicated systems will be discussed in detail in Sections 2.9 and 2.10.

Consider again the network shown in Fig. 2.15. If the relation

$$R_1C_2 \ll R_1C_1+R_2C_2 \tag{2.52}$$

holds for this network, the transfer function (2.47) can be written in the simplified form

$$F_o(s)=\frac{1}{1+s(R_1C_1+R_2C_2)+s^2R_1C_1R_2C_2} \tag{2.53}$$

$$=\frac{1}{(1+sC_1R_1)(1+sC_2R_2)} \tag{2.54}$$

That is, the transfer function of the given network may be obtained by computing the network shown in Fig. 2.16, under the assumption that this network is a satisfactory approximation of the given network. It is not always permissible, however, to make such an assumption even if the relation (2.52) holds. This can be seen from the following numerical example.

For example, consider a network whose constants have the values shown in Fig. 2.19. Then,

$$R_1C_2=10^3\times 0.01\times 10^{-6}=0.01\times 10^{-3}\ \text{[s]} \tag{2.55}$$

$$R_1C_1+R_2C_2=10^3\times 10^{-6}+100\times 10^3\times 0.01\times 10^{-6}=2\times 10^{-3}\ \text{[s]} \tag{2.56}$$

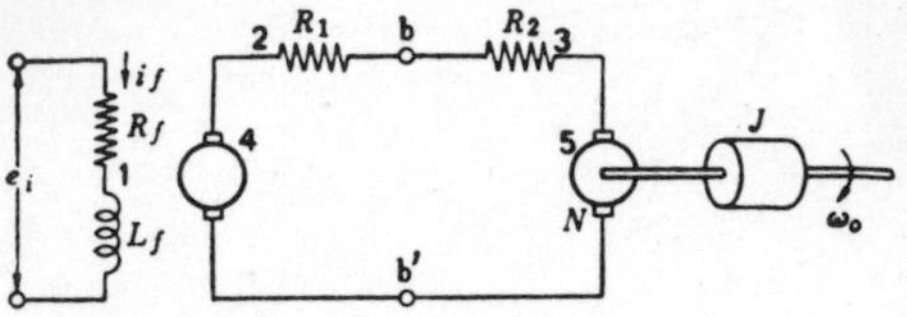

1 - *field circuit*; 2 - *armature*; 3 - *armature*
4 - *generator*; 5 - *motor*

Fig. 2.17 A d.c. motor-generator; network separation at points b and b' would be incorrect

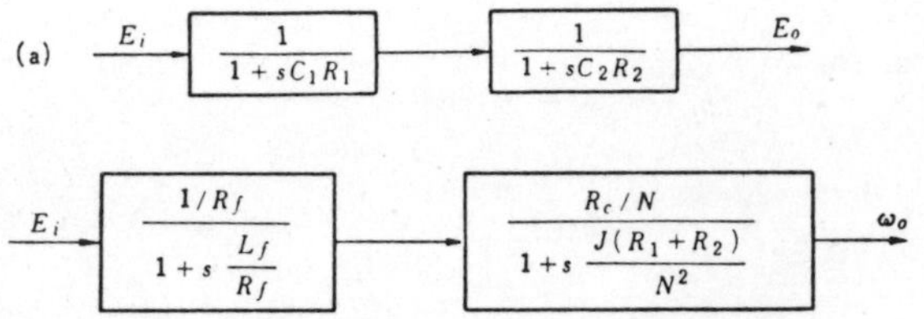

Fig. 2.18 Block diagrams: (a) Block diagram of the *CR* network (see Fig. 2.16) and (b) Block diagram of the d.c. motor-generator (see Fig. 2.17)

Therefore,

$$\frac{R_1C_1+R_2C_2}{R_1C_2}=200 \tag{2.57}$$

and hence the relation (2.52) holds for this network. If we compute the approximate transfer function $F_a(s)$ by formula (2.54), we obtain

$$F_a(s)=\frac{1}{(1+10^{-3}s)(1+10^{-3}s)}=\frac{1}{(1+10^{-3}s)^2} \tag{2.58}$$

Then,

$$T_1=T_2=1\times10^{-3}\ \text{[s]} \tag{2.59}$$

On the other hand, the exact transfer function $F(s)$ is

$$F(s)=\frac{1}{1+(10^{-3}+10^{-3}+10^3\times0.01\times10^{-6})s+10^{-6}s^2} \tag{2.60}$$

$$=\frac{1}{1+2.01\times10^{-3}s+10^{-6}s^2} \tag{2.61}$$

Factorising the denominator of this transfer function, we obtain

$$F(s)=\frac{1}{(1+1.1\times10^{-3}s)(1+0.9\times10^{-3}s)} \qquad (2.62)$$

If we denote by T_1' and T_2' the two time constants of this transfer function, we have

$$\left.\begin{array}{l} T_1'=1.1\times10^{-3}\ [\mathrm{s}] \\ T_2'=0.9\times10^{-3}\ [\mathrm{s}] \end{array}\right\} \qquad (2.63)$$

Although the value of $R_1C_1 + R_2C_2$ is 200 times the value of R_1C_2, comparison of equations (2.59) and (2.63) shows that an

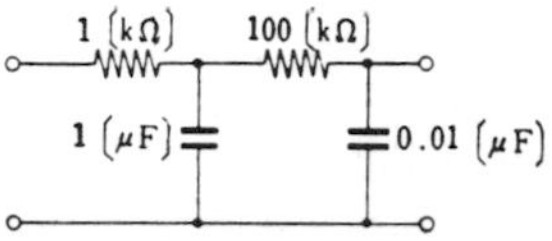

Fig. 2.19 A two adjacent passive elements network

error of approximately 10 per cent results in the values of the time constants by use of the approximation of the transfer function. This example shows that an approximation of the transfer function shown in equation (2.53) may result in a relatively large error even when equation (2.52) holds for the system.

2.4. IMPULSE RESPONSE OF A TRANSFER FUNCTION

When a unit impulse is used as an input signal for a transfer function, the output signal is called the impulse response of the transfer function. A unit impulse is an impulse such that the area under the impulse curve is 1. A more precise definition will be given later. The impulse response is a basic tool for investigating the transient characteristics of a system. We shall discuss the method of finding the impulse response.

Suppose that an impulse of extremely narrow width is applied as an input signal to the transfer function $1/(p+a)$ shown in Fig. 2.20. We are interested in investigating the shape of the curve $f(t)$ of the output signal. If we choose as our time zero the instant at which an impulse is applied to a transfer function (system), then $f(t)$ is 0 for $t<0$ but can have nonzero values for $t>0$ since $f(t)$ is the output signal. For example, it can be easily inferred that the output signal is a wave form starting at $t=0$, as shown in Fig. 2.21(b). If we compare the signal input shown in Fig. 2.21(a) with the corresponding output signal shown in Fig. 2.21(b), we note that the output signal has a certain finite nonzero value even when the input value is zero at a certain time $t>0$. As mentioned above, the transfer function $1/(p+a)$ is a number representing an amplification coefficient. Therefore, the value of the transfer function is infinitely large.

That is,

$$\frac{1}{p+a}=\infty \tag{2.64}$$

or

$$p=-a \tag{2.65}$$

If the output signal $f(t)$ is not identically 0 for $t>0$*, then $f(t)$ has a wave form such that the value of p is equal to $-a$. Since p is a differential operator, the fact that $p=-a$ means that differentiation of a signal is equivalent to multiplying the signal by the constant $-a$. Therefore, the fact that the output signal $f(t)$ is such that $p=-a$ means that $f(t)$ is a function of t such that differentiation of $f(t)$ is equivalent to multiplying $f(t)$ by $-a$. Therefore the output signal $f(t)$ must be a function of the form $f(t) = K\epsilon^{-at}$. This can be clearly seen by comparing equations (2.11) and (2.14).

However, the output signal $f(t)$ is of the form $K\epsilon^{-at}$ only for $t>0$; $f(t)=0$ for $t<0$. This can be expressed by

$$f(t)=K\epsilon^{-at}\,U(t) \tag{2.66}$$

where $U(t)$ denotes a unit step signal. A unit step signal $U(t)$ is a function whose value is 0 for $t<0$ and 1 (a unit quantity) for $t>0$, as shown in Fig. 2.22.

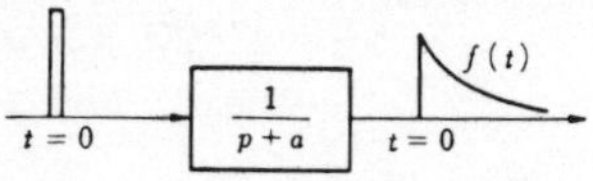

Fig. 2.20 Relation between input and output wave forms

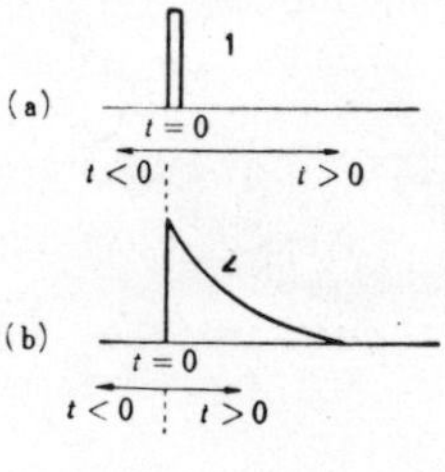

1 - *input wave form*
2 - *output wave form*

Fig. 2.21 Relation between input and output wave forms

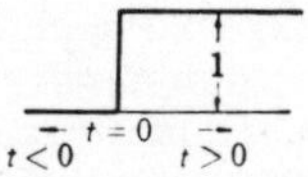

Fig. 2.22 Unit step signal

The value of K in (2.66) can be found by setting $t=0$ in the expression $K\epsilon^{-at}$. In general, the value of a signal wave at the instant $t=0$ is called the initial value of the signal wave. If the given signal has the form $f(t)=K\epsilon^{-at}U(t)$, then the initial value of $f(t)$ can also be found by setting $a=0$ instead of $t=0$ in the expression for $f(t)$. If we set $a=0$, the signal $f(t)$ has a step shape whose amplitude (height) is K. The input signal, the transfer function, the output signal, and the wave forms of both signals are shown in Fig. 2.23. Since the transfer function $1/p$ represents integration with respect to time t, the output signal K is the integral of the impulse (area under the impulse curve). If an impulse

*If the output signal $f(t)$ is identically 0 for time $t>0$, the $nf(t)$ is an impulse. The transfer function then is a constant, and hence no transient phenomena occur.

whose area is 1 is used as an input signal, the value of K in the corresponding output signal (2.66) is 1, and hence the output signal $f(t)$ is expressed by

$$f(t)=\epsilon^{-at}\,U(t) \tag{2.67}$$

An impulse whose area is 1 is called a unit impulse and is denoted by $\delta(t)$. That is, a unit impulse is defined as an impulse $\delta(t)$ satisfying the relation

$$\int_0^{\infty}\delta(t)dt=1 \tag{2.68}$$

It has an extremely small width and an extremely great amplitude (height). As is clear from Fig. 2.23, a unit impulse can be defined as the derivative of a unit step signal:

$$\delta(t)=p\;U(t) \tag{2.69}$$

Since the impulse response is defined as the output signal to a unit impulse input, the impulse response of the transfer function $1/(p+a)$ is $\epsilon^{-at}U(t)$ as given by equation (2.67). Here, the constant a is a real number. However, in the general case, it may be imaginary or complex. If we use this fact, the impulse response of a more complicated transfer function can also be computed easily.

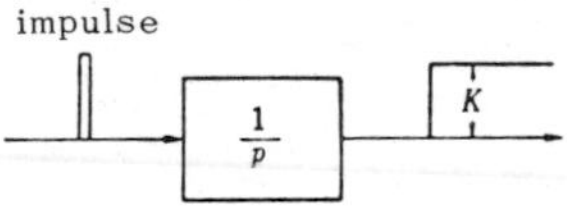

Fig. 2.23 Relation between unit impulse and unit step signal

For example, consider a system whose transfer function is

$$F(p)=\frac{K}{(p+a)(p+b)} \tag{2.70}$$

as shown in Fig. 2.24. We shall compute the impulse response of this transfer function. We first write the transfer function (2.70) in the form

$$F(p)=\frac{A}{p+a}+\frac{B}{p+b} \tag{2.71}$$

where A and B are undetermined constants. In order to find the value of the undetermined constant A, we multiply both sides of equation (2.71) by $p+a$. We then obtain

$$(p+a)F(p)=A+(p+a)\,\frac{B}{p+b} \tag{2.72}$$

If we now set $p=-a$, the second term vanishes and the value of A is

$$A=\left|(p+a)F(p)\right|_{p=-a} \tag{2.73}$$

Similarly, the value of B is

$$B=\left|(p+b)F(p)\right|_{p=-b} \tag{2.74}$$

If we substitute (2.70) into (2.73) and (2.74), we finally obtain

$$A=\left|\frac{(p+a)K}{(p+a)(p+b)}\right|_{p=-a}=\left|\frac{K}{p+b}\right|_{p=-a}=\frac{K}{b-a} \tag{2.75}$$

$$B=\left|\frac{K}{p+a}\right|_{p=-b}=\frac{K}{a-b} \tag{2.76}$$

$$F(p)=\frac{K}{b-a}\left(\frac{1}{p+a}-\frac{1}{p+b}\right) \tag{2.77}$$

Substituting these values of A and B into equation (2.71), we obtain the transfer function $F(p)$ in the desired form. This shows that a system with the block diagram shown in Fig. 2.24 can be represented by the block diagram shown in Fig. 2.25. In Fig. 2.25, the symbol ○ stands for addition or subtraction of signals, and the symbol $\overset{+}{\underset{-}{\circ}}$ represents the difference signal resulting from subtraction of the

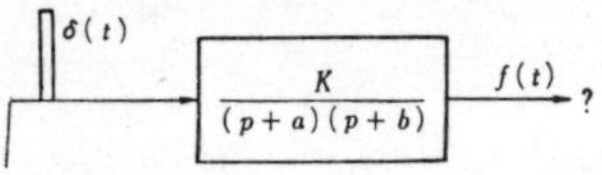

Fig. 2.24 Computation of impulse response

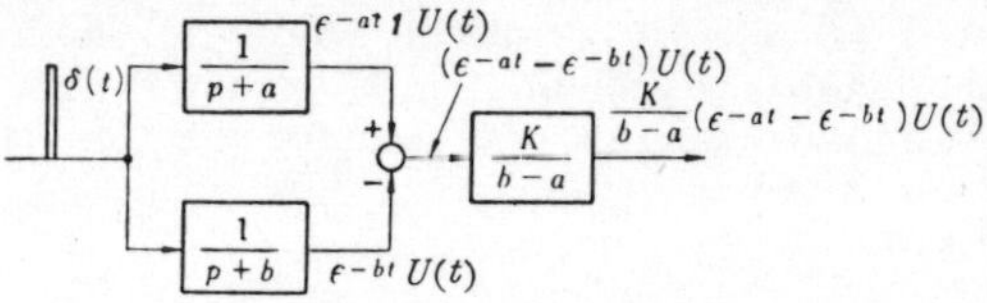

Fig. 2.25 A block diagram equivalent to the block diagram shown in Fig. 2.24

signal coming from below from the signal coming from above. From the previous results, we know that the impulse responses of the transfer functions $1/(p+a)$ and $1/(p+b)$ are $\epsilon^{-at}\,U(t)$ and $\epsilon^{-bt}\,U(t)$, respectively. Therefore, the impulse response $f(t)$ of the transfer function $F(o)$ given by equation (2.70) is

$$f(t)=\frac{K}{b-a}(\epsilon^{-at}-\epsilon^{-bt})\;U(t) \tag{2.78}$$

If we set $a=j\omega$, $b=-j\omega$, and $K=1$, then the transfer function becomes

$$F(p)=\frac{1}{(p+j\omega)(p-j\omega)}=\frac{1}{p^2+\omega^2} \tag{2.79}$$

and the impulse response of the transfer function is

$$f(t)=\frac{1}{2\,j\omega}(\epsilon^{j\omega t}-\epsilon^{-j\omega t})\;U(t) \tag{2.80}$$

$$=\frac{1}{\omega}\sin\,\omega t\;U(t) \tag{2.81}$$

In other words, a transfer function whose impulse response is $\sin\omega t\,U(t)$ is

$$F(p)=\frac{\omega}{p^2+\omega^2} \tag{2.82}$$

Let us consider the general case. Suppose that the transfer

function of a network is given in the following form:

$$F(p)=\frac{e_o(t)}{e_i(t)}=\frac{p^m+b_1p^{m-1}+b_2p^{m-2}+\cdots+b_{m-1}p+b_m}{p^n+a_1p^{n-1}+a_2p^{n-2}+\cdots\cdots+a_{n-1}p+a_n} \tag{2.83}$$

$$=\frac{N(p)}{D(p)} \tag{2.84}$$

where $N(p)$ and $D(p)$ are polynomials in p. In most automatic control systems, $n>m$, and we shall consider only this case.

If we set the denominator $D(p)$ equal to 0, we obtain

$$D(p)=p^n+a_1p^{n-1}+a_2p^{n-2}+\cdots+a_{n-1}p+a_n=0 \tag{2.85}$$

Let s_1, s_2, s_3, s_4,..., s_n be the roots of this equation. Then, the transfer function (2.84) can be written as

$$F(p)=\frac{p^m+b_1p^{m-1}+b_2p^{m-2}+\cdots\cdots+b_{m-1}p+b_m}{(p-s_1)(p-s_2)(p-s_3)\cdots\cdots(p-s_n)} \tag{2.86}$$

A value of p is called a pole if it makes the denominator of a transfer function equal to 0 (as do the roots s_1, s_2, s_3,...). If n poles of the transfer function (2.86) are distinct, it can be expanded into partial fractions:

$$F(p)=\frac{K_1}{p-s_1}+\frac{K_2}{p-s_2}+\cdots\cdots+\frac{K_n}{p-s_n} \tag{2.87}$$

provided $n>m$. The undetermined constants K_1, K_2,..., K_k,..., K_n in equation (2.87) can be determined by using a similar approach to the one used to obtain the expressions (2.75) and (2.76). The k th constant K_k is

$$\boxed{K_k=|F(p)(p-s_k)|_{p=s_k}} \tag{2.88}$$

However, for us to be able to get this value of K_k, the denominator of the transfer function must be in factored form, as in equation (2.86). If not, the expression $|F(p)(p-s_k)|_{p=s_k}$ takes the indeterminate form $\infty\times 0$ since $|F(p)|_{p=s_k}=\infty$ and $p-s_k=0$. Thus, we have to compute the limit

$$\boxed{K_k=\lim_{p\to s_k}|F(p)(p-s_k)|} \tag{2.89}$$

in this case. To compute this limit, we express $F(p)$ in the form of a quotient and rewrite (2.89) in the form

$$K_k=\lim_{p\to s_k}|F(p)(p-s_k)|=\lim_{p\to s_k}\left|\frac{N(p)(p-s_k)}{D(p)}\right| \tag{2.90}$$

We now differentiate the numerator and the denominator of this expression. If we compute the limit of the quotient of these derivatives, we can find the value of K_k.

Thus,

$$K_k = \left| \frac{\frac{d}{dp} N(p)(p-s_k)}{\frac{d}{dp} D(p)} \right|_{p=s_k} \tag{2.91}$$

$$= \left| \frac{N'(p)(p-s_k)+N(p)}{\frac{d}{dp} D(p)} \right|_{p=s_k} \tag{2.92}$$

$$= \left| \frac{N(p)}{\frac{d}{dp} D(p)} \right|_{p=s_k}$$

Therefore, we obtain

$$\boxed{K_k = \frac{N(s_k)}{D'(s_k)}} \tag{2.93}$$

From the previous discussions, we know that the impulse response of the transfer function $K_k/(p-s_k)$ is $K_k \epsilon^{s_k t} U(t)$. Therefore, the impulse response $f(t)$ of the transfer function (2.87) is

$$f(t) = (K_1\epsilon^{s_1 t} + K_2\epsilon^{s_2 t} + \cdots\cdots + K_k\epsilon^{s_k t} + \cdots\cdots + K_n\epsilon^{s_n t})\ U(t) \tag{2.94}$$

If we substitute the expressions (2.93) into this equation, we can express the impulse response $f(t)$ as follows:

$$f(t) = \frac{N(s_1)}{D'(s_1)}\epsilon^{s_1 t}\ U(t) + \frac{N(s_2)}{D'(s_2)}\epsilon^{s_2 t}\ U(t) + \cdots + \frac{N(s_k)}{D'(s_k)}\epsilon^{s_k t}\ U(t) + \cdots\cdots$$
$$+ \frac{N(s_n)}{D'(s_n)}\epsilon^{s_n t}\ U(t) \tag{2.95}$$

That is, we obtain

$$\boxed{f(t) = \sum_{k=1}^{n} \frac{N(s_k)}{D'(s_k)}\epsilon^{s_k t}\ U(t)} \tag{2.96}$$

If we use the value of K_k given by equation (2.88), then the impulse response $f(t)$ can be expressed in the form

$$\boxed{f(t) = \sum_{1}^{n} |F(p)(p-s_k)|_{p=s_k}\ \epsilon^{s_k t}\ U(t)} \tag{2.97}$$

It should be noted that the values $s_1, s_2, \ldots, s_k, \ldots, s_n$ are the poles of the transfer function and that they are distinct from one another.

As is clear from equation (2.94), the impulse response $f(t)$ can in general be considered as a combination of waves of the form ϵ^{st}. Therefore, when we compute the impulse response, we may begin with the transfer function obtained by replacing the differential operator p with the Laplace variable s in the transfer function

(2.83). Then, the transfer function takes the form

$$F(s)=\frac{s^m+b_1s^{m-1}+b_2s^{m-2}+\cdots\cdots+b_{m-1}s+b_m}{s^n+a_1s^{n-1}+a_2s^{n-2}+\cdots+a_{n-1}s+a_n} \tag{2.98}$$

Therefore, equations (2.88) and (2.89) become

$$\boxed{K_k=|F(s)(s-s_k)|_{s=s_k}} \tag{2.99}$$

and

$$\boxed{K_k=\lim_{s\to s_k}|F(s)(s-s_k)|} \tag{2.100}$$

respectively. Equation (2.97) becomes

$$\boxed{f(t)=\sum_1^n|F(s)(s-s_k)|_{s=s_k}\epsilon^{s_kt}\,U(t)} \tag{2.101}$$

To summarise, if a transfer function is given in the general form (2.83) or (2.98), its impulse response can be computed by formula (2.96) or (2.101) respectively. Formula (2.96) is often called the expansion theorem.

2.5. LAPLACE TRANSFORMS

In contrast with the preceding section, we shall study here a method of finding a transfer function whose impulse response is equal to a prescribed impulse response.

As shown in equation (2.94) or equation (2.96), the impulse response $f(t)$ of a transfer function can be expressed as a sum of signals whose forms are $K_k\epsilon^{s_kt}U(t)$

$$f(t)=(K_1\epsilon^{s_1t}+K_2\epsilon^{s_2t}+K_3\epsilon^{s_3t}+\cdots\cdots+K_k\epsilon^{s_kt}+\cdots\cdots)\,U(t) \tag{2.102}$$

If we multiply both sides of the above equation by ϵ^{-st} and if we integrate the resulting equation from $t=0$ to $t=\infty$, we obtain

$$\int_0^\infty f(t)\epsilon^{-st}\,dt=K_1\int_0^\infty\epsilon^{(s_1-s)t}\,dt+K_2\int_0^\infty\epsilon^{(s_2-s)t}\,dt+K_3\int_0^\infty\epsilon^{(s_3-s)t}\,dt$$

$$+\cdots+K_k\int_0^\infty\epsilon^{(s_k-s)t}\,dt+\cdots\cdots \tag{2.103}$$

$$=\frac{K_1}{s_1-s}\left|\epsilon^{(s_1-s)t}\right|_0^\infty+\frac{K_2}{s_2-s}\left|\epsilon^{(s_2-s)t}\right|_0^\infty+\frac{K_3}{s_3-s}\left|\epsilon^{(s_3-s)t}\right|_0^\infty$$

$$+\cdots\cdots+\frac{K_k}{s_k-s}\left|\epsilon^{(s_k-s)t}\right|_0^\infty+\cdots\cdots \tag{2.104}$$

$$=\frac{K_1}{s-s_1}+\frac{K_2}{s-s_2}+\frac{K_3}{s-s_3}+\cdots\cdots+\frac{K_k}{s-s_k}+\cdots\cdots \tag{2.105}$$

The right-hand side of this equation has the same form as (2.87). From the preceding section, we know that it is a transfer function whose impulse response is the expression for $f(t)$ given by equation (2.102). Thus, if we denote the desired transfer function by $F(s)$, we have

$$F(s)=\frac{K_1}{s-s_1}+\frac{K_2}{s-s_2}+\frac{K_3}{s-s_3}+\cdots\cdots+\frac{K_k}{s-s_k}+\cdots\cdots \tag{2.106}$$

This transfer function can be also written in the form

$$\boxed{F(s)=\int_0^\infty f(t)\epsilon^{-st}\,dt} \tag{2.107}$$

If the impulse response $f(t)$ is given, we can always use formula (2.107) to find a transfer function $F(s)$ whose impulse response is the given $f(t)$. Conversely, if a transfer function $F(s)$ is given, we can always find its impulse response $f(t)$ by use of formula (2.96) or (2.101) since $F(s)$ is the expression resulting from the substitution $p = s$ in the general form $F(p)$ of a transfer function given by equation (2.83). Therefore, it is clear that there is a one-to-one correspondence between impulse responses $f(t)$ and transfer functions $F(s)$. Accordingly, we may use $F(s)$ instead of $f(t)$ as a representation of the wave form of the impulse response. This representation is often more convenient.

In this connection $f(t)$ is called the t-representation (time representation) of the wave form of the impulse response, and $F(s)$ is called the s-representation (Laplace-variable representation) of the wave form. Formula (2.107) is used to transform the t-representation of a wave form into the s-representation. This formula is called the Laplace transformation formula and is denoted by

$$F(s)=\mathcal{L}f(t) \tag{2.108}$$

According to the theory of complex functions, the computations expressed by equations (2.96) and (2.101) can be formalized as

$$f(t)=\mathcal{L}^{-1}F(s) \tag{2.109}$$

The transformation yielding a Laplace transform is called the Laplace transformation. Conversely, the transformation that converts the s-representation $F(s)$ of a wave form into the t-representation is called the inverse Laplace transformation, and the resulting t-representation $f(t)$ is called the inverse Laplace transform. It is denoted by

$$f(t)=\frac{1}{2\pi j}\int_{-j\infty}^{+j\infty}F(s)\epsilon^{st}\,ds \tag{2.110}$$

This equation is the formula of the inverse Laplace transform. Though this formula is a neat form of the representation of $f(t)$, the actual evaluation of the integral still depends on formula (2.96) or (2.101).

2.6. EXAMPLE OF LAPLACE TRANSFORMS AND INVERSE LAPLACE TRANSFORMS

(1) EXAMPLES OF LAPLACE TRANSFORMS

The t-representation of a wave form can be converted into the s-representation by applying the Laplace transformation to the t-representation, as indicated in formula (2.107). We shall present some typical examples.

(a) The Laplace transform of the exponential function $\epsilon^{-at} U(t)$. If we denote by $F(s)$ the s-representation of the given exponential function $\epsilon^{-at} U(t)$ then, by formula (2.107),

$$F(s) = \mathcal{L}\epsilon^{-at}\,U(t) \tag{2.111}$$

$$= \int_0^\infty \epsilon^{-at}\epsilon^{-st}dt \tag{2.112}$$

$$= \int_0^\infty \epsilon^{-(s+a)t}dt \tag{2.113}$$

$$= \left| -\frac{\epsilon^{-(s+a)t}}{s+a} \right|_0^\infty \tag{2.114}$$

$$= \frac{1}{s+a} \tag{2.115}$$

Therefore,

$$\mathcal{L}\epsilon^{-at}\,U(t) = \frac{1}{s+a} \tag{2.116}$$

or

$$\mathcal{L}^{-1}\frac{1}{s+a} = \epsilon^{-at}\,U(t) \tag{2.117}$$

(b) The s-representations of the unit impulse $\delta(t)$ and the unit step signal. Without reference to formula (2.107), it is clear that the s-representation of the unit impulse $\delta(t)$ is 1 since clearly a transfer function whose impulse response is 1 must be 1. Therefore, we obtain

$$\mathcal{L}\delta(t) = 1 \tag{2.118}$$

$$\mathcal{L}^{-1}1 = \delta(t) \tag{2.119}$$

It is also clear from what was said above that the s-representation of the unit step signal $U(t)$ is $1/s$. However, let us calculate this s-representation by using formula (2.107). Applying formula (2.107) to the unit step signal $U(t)$ we have

$$\int_0^\infty U(t)\,\epsilon^{-st}dt = \left|\frac{\epsilon^{-st}}{-s}\right|_0^\infty = \frac{1}{s} \tag{2.120}$$

Therefore,

$$\mathcal{L}\,U(t) = \frac{1}{s} \tag{2.121}$$

(c) The Laplace transform of the sinusoidal wave $\sin\omega t\,U(t)$. Applying the Laplace transformation to the given sinusoidal wave $\sin\omega t\,U(t)$, we get

$$\mathcal{L}\sin\omega t\;U(t) = \mathcal{L}\frac{1}{2j}(\epsilon^{j\omega t}-\epsilon^{-j\omega t})\,U(t) \tag{2.122}$$

$$= \frac{1}{2j}\left[\int_0^\infty \epsilon^{j\omega t}\epsilon^{-st}dt - \int_0^\infty \epsilon^{-j\omega t}\,\epsilon^{-st}\,dt\right] \tag{2.123}$$

$$= \frac{1}{2j}\left[\int_0^\infty \epsilon^{-(s-j\omega)t}dt - \int_0^\infty \epsilon^{-(s+j\omega)t}\,dt\right] \tag{2.124}$$

$$= \frac{1}{2j}\left|\frac{-\epsilon^{-(s-j\omega)t}}{s-j\omega} - \frac{-\epsilon^{-(s+j\omega)t}}{s+j\omega}\right|_0^\infty \tag{2.125}$$

$$= \frac{1}{2j}\left(\frac{1}{s-j\omega} - \frac{1}{s+j\omega}\right) \tag{2.126}$$

$$= \frac{\omega}{s^2+\omega^2} \tag{2.127}$$

Therefore,

$$\mathcal{L}\sin\omega t\;U(t) = \frac{\omega}{s^2+\omega^2} \tag{2.128}$$

(d) The Laplace transform of the wave $t\,U(t)$ that increases at a constant rate. Applying the Laplace transformation to the given wave $t\,U(t)$ we get

$$\mathcal{L}t\,U(t) = \int_0^\infty t\epsilon^{-st}\,dt \tag{2.129}$$

$$= \left|\frac{-t\epsilon^{-st}}{s}\right|_0^\infty - \int_0^\infty \frac{\epsilon^{-st}}{s}dt \tag{2.130}$$

$$= 0 + \frac{1}{s}\left|\frac{-\epsilon^{-st}}{s}\right|_0^\infty \tag{2.131}$$

$$= \frac{1}{s^2} \tag{2.132}$$

Therefore, we obtain

$$\mathcal{L}t\;U(t) = \frac{1}{s^2} \tag{2.133}$$

(e) The s-representation of the wave shown in Fig. 2.26. Let $f(t)$

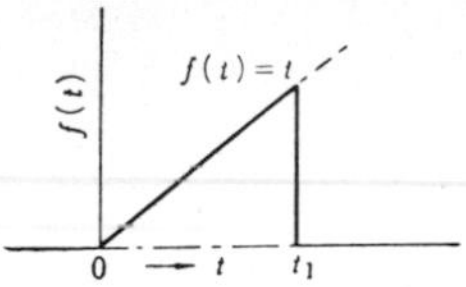

Fig. 2.26

be the t-representation of the wave shown in Fig. 2.26. Then, the function $f(t)$ is defined in

$$\left.\begin{aligned} f(t)&=t \qquad t_1>t>0 \\ &=0 \qquad t>t_1 \end{aligned}\right\} \tag{2.133}$$

Denoting by $F(s)$ the s-representation of the given wave, we get

$$F(s)=\mathcal{L}f(t) \tag{2.134}$$

$$=\int_0^{t_1} t\epsilon^{-st}dt \tag{2.135}$$

$$=\left|\frac{-t\epsilon^{-st}}{s}\right|_0^{t_1}+\frac{1}{s^2}\left|-\epsilon^{-st}\right|_0^{t_1} \tag{2.136}$$

$$=-\frac{t_1\epsilon^{-st_1}}{s}+\frac{1}{s^2}(-\epsilon^{-st_1}+1) \tag{2.137}$$

$$=\frac{1}{s^2}(1-\epsilon^{-st_1})-\frac{t_1\epsilon^{-st_1}}{s} \tag{2.138}$$

(2) SPECIAL EXAMPLES OF INVERSE LAPLACE TRANSFORMS

The s-representation of a wave can be converted into the t-representation by application of the inverse Laplace transformation, and the Laplace transform can be computed by use of (2.96) or (2.101). Some simple examples have already been presented in Section 2.4. Thus, we shall discuss here only special examples.

(a) The t-representation of the wave whose s-representation is $1/(s+a)^2$. The given s-representation has two poles. However, they are both equal to $-a$; that is, the given s-representation has a double pole. When an s-representation has a multiple pole, we cannot apply formula (2.96) or (2.101) directly to the given s-representation. Therefore, we first compute the t-representation $f'(t)$ of a wave with an s-representation:

$$F'(s)=\frac{1}{(s+a)(s+a+\Delta)} \tag{2.139}$$

then we calculate the limit of $f'(t)$ as $\Delta \to 0$ for the t-representation of the given wave.

The t-representation $f'(t)$ is computed by use of formula (2.101):

$$f'(t)=\mathcal{L}^{-1}F'(s) \tag{2.140}$$

$$=\mathcal{L}^{-1}\frac{1}{(s+a)(s+a+\Delta)} \tag{2.141}$$

$$=\left|\frac{1}{s+a+\Delta}\right|_{s=-a}\epsilon^{-at}\,U(t)+\left|\frac{1}{s+a}\right|_{s=-(a+\Delta)}\epsilon^{-(a+\Delta)t}\,U(t) \tag{2.142}$$

$$=\frac{1}{\Delta}\epsilon^{-at}\,U(t)-\frac{1}{\Delta}\epsilon^{-(a+\Delta)t}\,U(t) \tag{2.143}$$

$$=\frac{\epsilon^{-at}-\epsilon^{-(a+\Delta)t}}{\Delta}\,U(t) \tag{2.144}$$

Therefore, if we denote by $f(t)$ the t-representation of the wave whose s-representation is $F(s)$, then $f(t)$ can be computed as follows:

$$f(t)=\lim_{\Delta\to 0} f'(t) \tag{2.145}$$

$$=\lim_{\Delta\to 0}\frac{\epsilon^{-at}-\epsilon^{-(a+\Delta)t}}{\Delta}\,U(t) \tag{2.146}$$

$$=\lim_{\Delta\to 0}\frac{\dfrac{d}{d\Delta}(\epsilon^{-at}-\epsilon^{-(a+\Delta)t})}{\dfrac{d}{d\Delta}\Delta}\,U(t) \tag{2.147}$$

$$=\lim_{\Delta\to 0}(t\epsilon^{-(a+\Delta)t})\,U(t) \tag{2.148}$$

$$=t\epsilon^{-at}\,U(t) \tag{2.149}$$

Thus, we obtain

$$\mathcal{L}^{-1}\frac{1}{(s+a)^2}=t\epsilon^{-at}\,U(t) \tag{2.150}$$

(b) The t-representation of the wave whose s-representation is $(s+b)/(s+a)^2$. The given s-representation $(s+b)/(s+a)^2$ can be written in the form

$$\frac{s+b}{(s+a)^2}=\frac{s+a+b-a}{(s+a)^2} \tag{2.151}$$

$$=\frac{1}{s+a}+\frac{b-a}{(s+a)^2} \tag{2.152}$$

Therefore, the inverse Laplace transform of $(s+b)/(s+a)^2$ is

$$\mathcal{L}^{-1}\frac{s+b}{(s+a)^2}=\mathcal{L}^{-1}\frac{1}{s+a}+\mathcal{L}\frac{b-a}{(s+a)^2} \tag{2.153}$$

$$=\epsilon^{-at}1+(b-a)t\epsilon^{-at}\,U(t) \tag{2.154}$$

$$=\{1+(b-a)t\}\,\epsilon^{-at}\,U(t) \tag{2.155}$$

Consequently,

$$\mathcal{L}^{-1}\frac{s+b}{(s+a)^2}=\{1+(b-a)t\}\,\epsilon^{-at}\,U(t) \tag{2.156}$$

(c). The t-representation of the wave whose s-representation is $s^{-2}(s+1)^{-1}$. The given s-representation $s^{-2}(s+1)^{-1}$ can be expanded into partial fractions as follows:

$$\frac{1}{s^2(s+1)}=\frac{K_1}{s^2}+\frac{K_2}{s}+\frac{K_3}{s+1} \tag{2.157}$$

To find the value of K_1, we multiply both sides of equation (2.157) by s^2. Then,

$$\frac{1}{s+1}=K_1+sK_2+\frac{s^2K_3}{s+1} \tag{2.158}$$

If we set $s=0$ in this equation, the value of K_1 is

$$K_1=1 \tag{2.159}$$

Differentiation of equation (2.158) yields

$$\frac{-1}{(s+1)^2}=K_2+\frac{2s(s+1)-s^2}{(s+1)^2}K_3 \tag{2.160}$$

If we again set $s=0$, the value of K_2 is found to be

$$K_2=-1 \tag{2.161}$$

Repeating this procedure, we find that

$$K_3=1 \tag{2.162}$$

Therefore, the inverse Laplace transform of the given s-representation $s^{-2}(s+1)^{-1}$ is

$$\mathcal{L}^{-1}\frac{1}{s^2(s+1)}=\mathcal{L}^{-1}\frac{1}{s^2}-\mathcal{L}^{-1}\frac{1}{s}+\mathcal{L}^{-1}\frac{1}{s+1} \tag{2.163}$$

$$=t\,U(t)-U(t)+\epsilon^{-t}\,U(t) \tag{2.164}$$

$$=(t-1+\epsilon^{-t})\,U(t) \tag{2.165}$$

Table 2.1 shows the relations between the t- and s- representations of some basic waves; that is, it shows some basic Laplace transforms and inverse Laplace transforms.

2.7 APPLICATION OF LAPLACE TRANSFORMS TO AUTOMATIC CONTROL THEORY

(1) REPRESENTATION OF SIGNAL TRANSMISSIONS AND TRANSFER FUNCTIONS

It is clear from what was said above that the s-representation of a wave that is given by its t-representation $f(t)$ has the same property as that of the transfer function $F(s)$. We can use this fact to represent a signal transmission in a simple manner.

TABLE 2.1 BASIC LAPLACE TRANSFORMS AND INVERSE LAPLACE TRANSFORMS

Wave forms	*t*-representation	*s*-representation
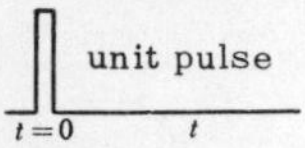	$\delta(t)$	1
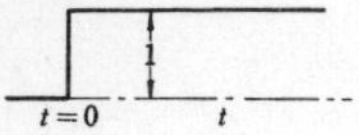	$U(t)$	$\frac{1}{s}$
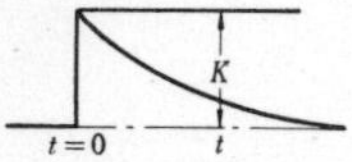	$K\epsilon^{-\alpha t}\ U(t)$	$\frac{K}{s+\alpha}$
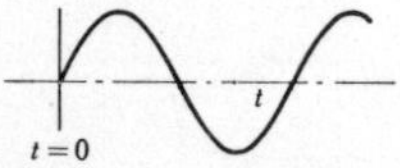	$\sin \omega t\ U(t)$	$\frac{\omega}{s^2+\omega^2}$
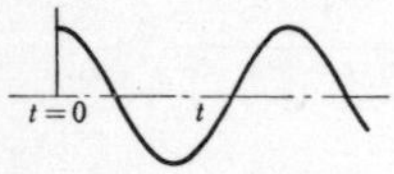	$\cos \omega t\ U(t)$	$\frac{s}{s^2+\omega^2}$
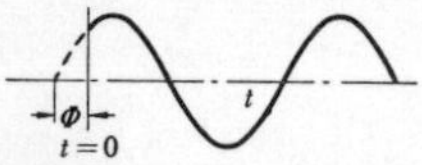	$K \sin(\omega t+\Phi)\ U(t)$	$K\frac{s \sin \Phi+\omega \cos \Phi}{s^2+\omega^2}$
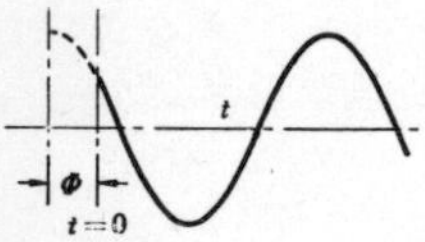	$K \cos(\omega t+\Phi)\ U(t)$	$K\frac{s \cos \Phi+\omega \sin \Phi}{s^2+\omega^2}$
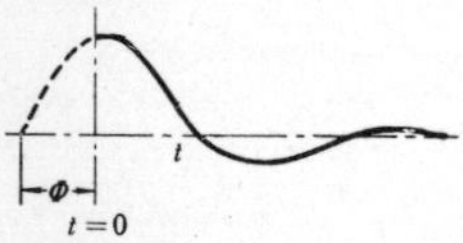	$K\epsilon^{-\alpha t} \sin(\omega t+\Phi)\ U(t)$	$K\frac{(s+\alpha)\sin \Phi+\omega \cos \Phi}{(s+\alpha)^2+\omega^2}$
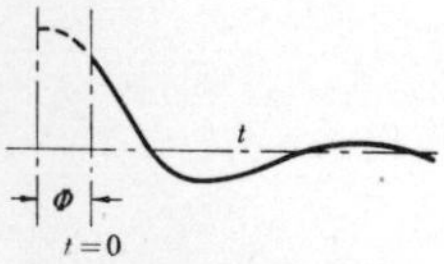	$K\epsilon^{-\alpha t} \cos(\omega t+\Phi)\ U(t)$	$K\frac{(s+\alpha)\cos \Phi+\omega \sin \Phi}{(s+\alpha)^2+\omega^2}$
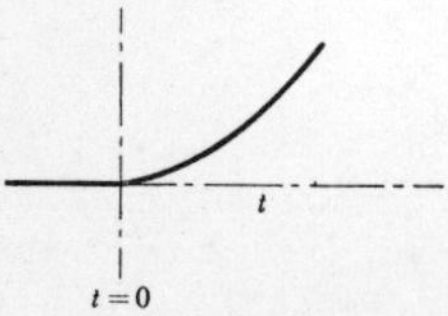	$t^n\ U(t)$	$\frac{n!}{s^{n+1}}$

For example, consider the block diagram shown in Fig. 2.27. Suppose that an input signal $\epsilon^{-at}U(t)$ is applied to the transfer function $1/(p+b)$. If we wish to express the corresponding output signal by a t-representation, a certain amount of computation is necessary. However, if the s-representation of the input signal is given, the s-representation of the corresponding output signal is easily found as the algebraic product of the transfer function and the s-representation of the input signal, as illustrated in Fig. 2.27 (b). Representations of this type are frequently used to express the performance mechanisms of automatic control systems. Let us discuss this representation in a more general case. Suppose that a transfer function is given and that an input signal and the corresponding output signal are given by the t-representations $f_i(t)$ and $f_o(t)$ respectively. If we denote the s-representations corresponding to $f_i(t)$ and $f_o(t)$ by

$$F_i(s) = \mathcal{L}f_i(t)$$

$$F_o(s) = \mathcal{L}f_o(t)$$

we may express the relation between $f_i(t)$ and $f_o(t)$ by the block diagram shown in Fig. 2.28(b), instead of that shown in Fig. 2.28 (a). We then obtain

$$F_o(s) = F_i(s)F(s)$$

Therefore, the transfer function $F(s)$ can be expressed as

$$F(s) = \frac{F_o(s)}{F_i(s)} = \frac{\mathcal{L}f_o(t)}{\mathcal{L}f_i(t)} \tag{2.166}$$

That is, the transfer function $F(s)$ can in general be found from $f_i(t)$ and $f_o(t)$. Equation (2.166) is a definition of a transfer function. Here, $f_i(t)$ and $f_o(t)$ must be 0 for $t < 0$.

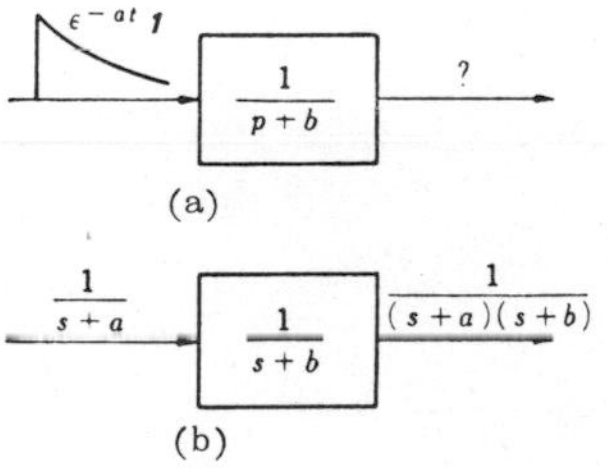

Fig. 2.27 Representation of signal transmission: (a) t-representation and; (b) s-representation

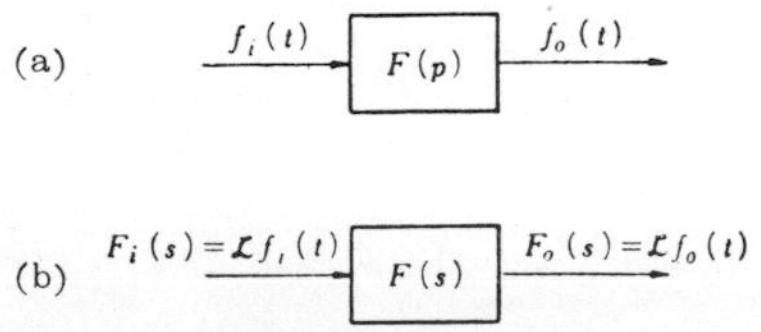

Fig. 2.28 Definition of a transfer function

D

(2) TRANSFER FUNCTION OF DEAD TIME

Consider an element such that the output signal is a wave which results from a shift of the input signal by a time τ as shown in Fig. 2.29. Using the definition (2.166) of a transfer function, let us compute the transfer function of this element.

Let $F_i(s)$ and $F_o(s)$ be the s-representations of the input and output signal, respectively. Then,

$$F_i(s) = \mathcal{L} f_i(t) \tag{2.167}$$

$$F_o(s) = \mathcal{L} f_i(t-\tau) \tag{2.168}$$

$$= \int_0^\infty f_i(t-\tau)\epsilon^{-st}dt \tag{2.169}$$

If we set $t - \tau = T$, then

$$F_o(s) = \int_{-\tau}^\infty f_i(T)\epsilon^{-s(\tau+T)}dT \tag{2.170}$$

$$= \epsilon^{-s\tau}\left(\int_0^\infty f_i(T)\epsilon^{-sT}dT + \int_{-\tau}^0 f_i(T)\epsilon^{-sT}dT\right) \tag{2.171}$$

Here, the function $f_i(t-\tau) = f_i(T)$ is 0 for $0 < t < \tau$ or, equivalently, for $-\tau < T < 0$. Therefore, the second term in equation (2. 171) is 0. Consequently,

$$F_o(s) = \epsilon^{-s\tau}\int_0^\infty f_i(T)\epsilon^{-sT}dT \tag{2.172}$$

$$= \epsilon^{-s\tau}\mathcal{L} f_i(T) \tag{2.173}$$

If we write equation (2.173) in terms of t, we obtain

$$F_o(s) = \epsilon^{-s\tau}\mathcal{L} f_i(t) \tag{2.174}$$

Therefore, the transfer function $F(s)$ of the given system is

$$F(s) = \frac{F_o(s)}{F_i(s)} = \frac{\epsilon^{-s\tau}\mathcal{L} f_i(t)}{\mathcal{L} f_i(t)} = \epsilon^{-s\tau} \tag{2.175}$$

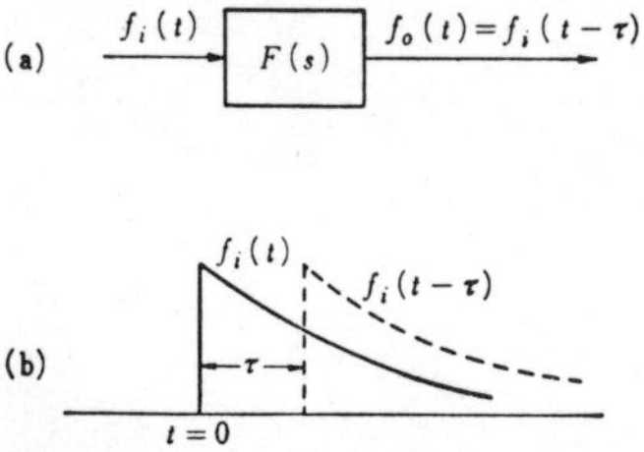

Fig. 2.29 Transient characteristics of dead time

(3) ANALYSIS OF TRANSIENT CHARACTERISTICS

It may be easily inferred from the above that the Laplace transformation can be used for analysis of transient characteristics. As an example, consider a network whose transfer function is

$$F(s) = \frac{d}{(s+b)(s+c)} \tag{2.176}$$

as shown in Fig. 2.30. Let us compute the output signal when the input signal is

$$e_i = A(1-\epsilon^{-at})\ U(t) \tag{2.177}$$

If the Laplace transformation to the input signal is e_i, we obtain

$$\mathcal{L}e_i = \mathcal{L}A(1-\epsilon^{-at})\ U(t) \tag{2.178}$$

$$= A\mathcal{L}\,1 - A\mathcal{L}\epsilon^{-at}\ U(t) \tag{2.179}$$

$$= \frac{A}{s} - \frac{A}{s+a} \tag{2.180}$$

$$= \frac{Aa}{s(s+a)} \tag{2.181}$$

Therefore, the block diagram in Fig. 2.30 can be replaced by the block diagram in Fig. 2.31 (a); furthermore, it can be written as the block diagram in Fig. 2.31 (b). Here, the symbol $\overset{+}{\underset{-}{\bigcirc}}$ stands for subtraction of the signal, as mentioned in section 2.4. If we denote by $F(s)$ the s-representation of the output signal in Fig. 2.31 (b), then

$$F(s) = \frac{Aad}{s(s+a)(s+b)(s+c)} \tag{2.182}$$

This expression can be expanded into the following partial fractions:

$$F(s) = \frac{K_0}{s} + \frac{K_1}{s+a} + \frac{K_2}{s+b} + \frac{K_3}{s+c} \tag{2.183}$$

Here, the values of the undetermined constants K_0, K_1, K_2, and K_3 are computed by the usual procedure:

$$\left.\begin{aligned} K_0 &= \frac{Aad}{(0+a)(0+b)(0+c)} = \frac{Ad}{bc} \\ K_1 &= \frac{Aad}{-a(-a+b)(-a+c)} = \frac{-Aad}{a(b-a)(c-a)} \\ K_2 &= \frac{Aad}{-b(-b+a)(-b+c)} = \frac{-Aad}{b(a-b)(c-b)} \\ K_3 &= \frac{Aad}{-c(-c+a)(-c+b)} = \frac{-Aad}{c(a-c)(b-c)} \end{aligned}\right\} \tag{2.184}$$

Therefore, the block diagram shown in Fig. 2.31 (b) can be equivalently transformed into the diagram shown in Fig. 2.32. In order to compute the t-representation $f(t)$ of the output signal, we apply the inverse Laplace transformation to the s-representation $F(s)$, that is, to the transfer function. We then obtain

$$f(t)=\mathcal{L}^{-1}F(s) \tag{2.185}$$

$$=\mathcal{L}^{-1}\frac{Aad}{s(s+a)(s+b)(s+c)} \tag{2.186}$$

$$=\mathcal{L}^{-1}\left(\frac{K_0}{s}+\frac{K_1}{s+a}+\frac{K_2}{s+b}+\frac{K_3}{s+c}\right) \tag{2.187}$$

$$=(K_0+K_1\epsilon^{-at}+K_2\epsilon^{-bt}+K_3\epsilon^{-ct})\ U(t) \tag{2.188}$$

Transient characteristics in general can be analysed in this manner.

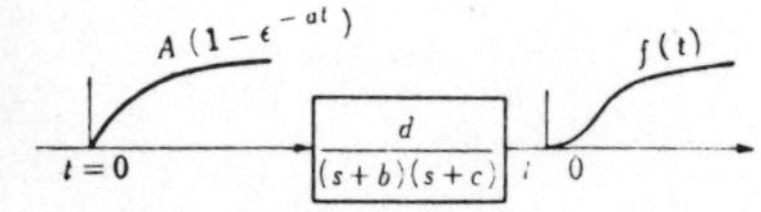

Fig. 2.30 An example of transient characteristics analysis

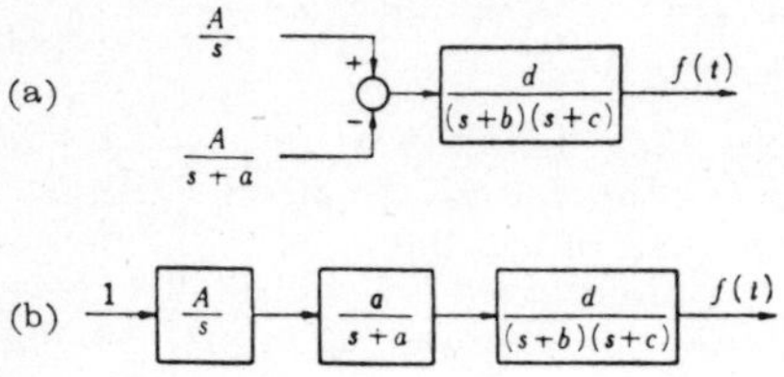

Fig. 2.31 Manipulation of a transfer function

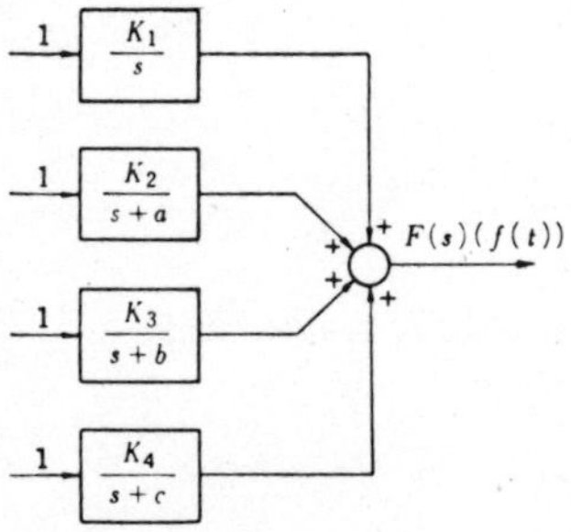

Fig. 2.32 Manipulation of a transfer function

(4) LAPLACE TRANSFORM OF A DIFFERENTIAL EQUATION

The Laplace transformation can be applied not only to waves but also to differential equations. In fact, we have already made use of the Laplace transform of a differential equation when computing a transfer function. Here, we shall study this subject in detail.

The Laplace transform of a differential equation is obtained by applying the Laplace transformation to each term of the differential equation. In general, each term of a differential equation is either the derivative or the integral of a function of time $f(t)$, in other words, an expression of the form $d^n/(dt)^n f(t)$ or $\int f(t)\,dt$. Therefore, we shall study primarily the Laplace transforms of derivatives and integrals of wave functions.

As a preliminary, we shall derive some simple formulae. Since the formula for the Laplace transform is

$$F(s)=\int_0^\infty f(t)\epsilon^{-st}\,dt \tag{2.189}$$

it can easily be seen that the following formulae hold:

$$\boxed{\mathcal{L}\{f_a(t)+f_b(t)\}=\mathcal{L}f_a(t)+\mathcal{L}f_b(t)} \tag{2.190}$$

$$\boxed{\mathcal{L}Af(t)=A\mathcal{L}f(t)} \tag{2.191}$$

where A is a constant.

The above procedure should be slightly modified when we apply the Laplace transformation to a derivative or an integral of a time function (signal wave). With the signal waves that have been treated up to now, the signal has the value 0 for $t<0$, is discontinuous at $t=0$, and has various values for $t>0$, as shown in Fig. 2.33 (a). If we denote by $f(t)$ a wave of this type, then the signal wave shown in Fig. 2.33 (a) will be represented by the equation

$$f(t)=\epsilon^{-at}\,U(t) \tag{2.192}$$

Let us now consider a signal wave that is continuous at $t=0$, as shown in Fig. 2.33 (b). If we denote this signal wave by $f^*(t)$, then the signal wave in Fig. 2.33 (b) will be represented by the equation

$$f^*(t)=\epsilon^{-at} \tag{2.193}$$

As comparison of equations (2.192) and (2.193) clearly indicates, $f(t)$ is related to $f^*(t)$ by the following equation:

$$f(t)=f^*(t)\;U(t) \tag{2.194}$$

where $U(t)$ is the unit step signal.

First we compute the Laplace transform of $d/(dt)\,f^*(t)$, where $f^*(t)$ is also continuous at $t=0$:

$$\mathcal{L}\frac{d}{dt}f^*(t)=\int_0^\infty \frac{d}{dt}f^*(t)\epsilon^{-st}\,dt \tag{2.195}$$

$$=\Big|f^*(t)\epsilon^{-st}\Big|_0^\infty+s\int_0^\infty f^*(t)\epsilon^{-st}\,dt \tag{2.196}$$

$$=-f^*(0)+s\mathcal{L}f^*(t) \tag{2.197}$$

Thus, we obtain the formula

$$\boxed{\mathcal{L}\frac{d}{dt}f^*(t)=s\mathcal{L}f^*(t)-f^*(0)} \tag{2.198}$$

For the signal wave $f(t)=f^*(t)\,U(t)$ ($=0$ for $t<0$), which is frequently used in automatic control theory, we obtain the formula

$$\boxed{\mathcal{L}\frac{d}{dt}f(t)=s\mathcal{L}f(t)} \tag{2.199}$$

by setting $f^*(0)=0$ in formula (2.198).

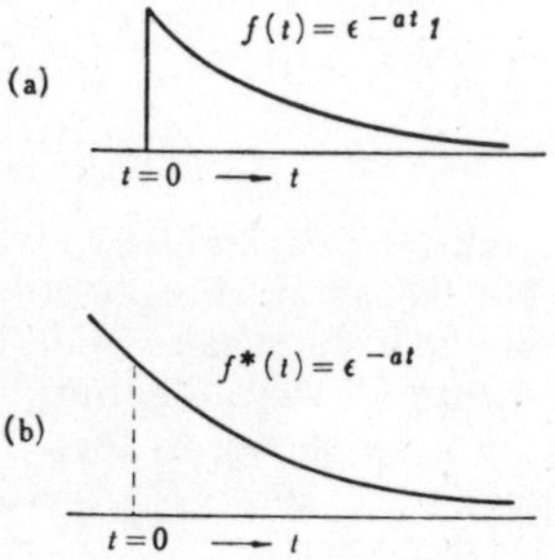

Fig. 2.33 Waves representation

We can also derive formulae for $\mathcal{L}\{\int f^*(t)\,dt\}$ and $\mathcal{L}\{\int f(t)\,dt\}$. For the signal $f^*(t)$, we proceed as follows:

$$\mathcal{L}\{\int f^*(t)dt\}=\int_0^\infty\{\int f^*(t)dt\}\epsilon^{-st}\,dt \tag{2.200}$$

$$=-\left|\int f^*(t)dt\frac{\epsilon^{-st}}{s}\right|_0^\infty+\frac{1}{s}\int_0^\infty f^*(t)\epsilon^{-st}\,dt \tag{2.201}$$

$$=\frac{1}{s}\left|\int f^*(t)dt\right|_{t=0}+\frac{1}{s}\mathcal{L}f^*(t) \tag{2.202}$$

We introduce the notation

$$\left|\int f^*(t)dt\right|_{t=0}=f^*(\overset{(-1)}{0}) \tag{2.203}$$

Using this notation, formula (2.202) becomes

$$\boxed{\mathcal{L}\{\int f^*(t)dt\}=\frac{1}{s}\mathcal{L}f^*(t)+\frac{1}{s}f^*(\overset{(-1)}{0})} \tag{2.204}$$

For the signal $f(t)=f^*(t)\,U(t)$, which is 0 for $t<0$, we have the corresponding formula

$$\boxed{\mathcal{L}\{\int f(t)dt\}=\frac{1}{s}\mathcal{L}f(t)} \tag{2.205}$$

as in case of the Laplace transform of a derivative.

Table 2.2 gives several formulae derived in a similar manner. Since the transfer functions are obtained by the substitution of s for $d/dt \equiv p$, the input and the output signals associated with the transfer functions must be waves whose amplitudes are 0 for $t<0$ like the wave of equation (2.192) shown in Fig. 2.33 (a).

TABLE 2.2 BASIC LAPLACE TRANSFORM FORMULAE

Formulae for a wave $f^*(t)$ that is continuous at $t = 0$	Formulae for the wave $f(t)$ that is 0 for $t<0$ and discontinuous at $t = 0$
$\mathcal{L}\{f_a^*(t)+f_b^*(t)\}=\mathcal{L}f_a^*(t)+\mathcal{L}f_b^*(t)$	as in first column.
$\mathcal{L}Af^*(t)=A\mathcal{L}f^*(t)$	as in first column.
$\mathcal{L}\frac{df^*(t)}{dt}=sF(s)-f^*(0)$	$\mathcal{L}\frac{df(t)}{dt}=sF(s)$
$\mathcal{L}\frac{d^2f^*(t)}{dt^2}=s^2F(s)-sf^*(0)-f^*(\overset{(1)}{0})$	$\mathcal{L}\frac{d^2f(t)}{dt^2}=s^2F(s)$
$\mathcal{L}\int^t f^*(t)dt=\frac{1}{s}F(s)+\frac{1}{s}f^*(\overset{(-1)}{0})$	$\mathcal{L}\int^t f(t)dt=\frac{1}{s}F(s)$
$\mathcal{L}\frac{d^nf^*(t)}{dt^n}=s^nF(s)-s^{n-1}f^*(0)-s^{n-2}f^{*\prime}(0)\cdots$	$\mathcal{L}\frac{d^nf(t)}{dt^n}=s^nF(s)$
	$\mathcal{L}f(t-\tau)=F(s)\epsilon^{-\tau s}$

(5) RELATIONS OF INITIAL AND FINAL VALUES: TRANSIENT RESPONSE

In the study of the transient characteristics of an automatic control system or of an element of an automatic control system, the output signal corresponding to the unit step input signal is of greatest importance in several aspects. This output is called the transient (or indicial) response of an automatic control system or of an element.

Let us find the transient response of a network whose transfer function is given in the general form $F(s)$. The s-representation of the unit step signal, which is the input signal to the transient response is $\mathcal{L}\ U(t) = 1/s$. If we denote by $F_0(s)$ the s-representation of the output signal for the unit step input signal, then $F_0(s)$ is, as shown in Fig. 2.34,

$$F_o(s)=\frac{1}{s}F(s) \tag{2.206}$$

where $F(s)$ is the transfer function of the network. Therefore, the transient response $f_0(t)$ is

$$f_o(t)=\mathcal{L}^{-1}F_o(s)=\mathcal{L}^{-1}\frac{1}{s}F(s) \tag{2.207}$$

Suppose that the transfer function $F(s)$ is explicitly given by the equation

$$F(s)=\frac{N(s)}{(s+a_1)(s+a_2)(s+a_3)\cdots\cdots} \tag{2.208}$$

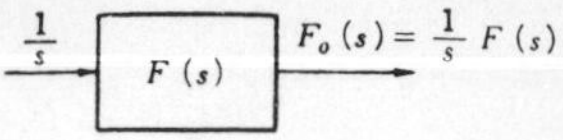

Fig. 2.34 Transient response of the transfer function *F(s)*

Then, the s-representation of the transient response is

$$F_o(s) = \frac{1}{s}F(s) = \frac{N(s)}{s(s+a_1)(s+a_2)(s+a_3)\cdots\cdots} \tag{2.209}$$

$$= \frac{A_0}{s} + \frac{A_1}{s+a_1} + \frac{A_2}{s+a_2} + \frac{A_3}{s+a_3} + \cdots \tag{2.210}$$

Therefore, the t-representation of the transient response is

$$f_o(t) = \mathcal{L}^{-1}F_o(s) = \mathcal{L}^{-1}\left(\frac{A_0}{s} + \frac{A_1}{s+a_1} + \frac{A_2}{s+a_2} + \frac{A_3}{s+a_3} + \cdots\cdots\right) \tag{2.211}$$

$$= (A_0 + A_1\epsilon^{-a_1t} + A_2\epsilon^{-a_2t} + A_3\epsilon^{-a_3t} + \cdots\cdots)U(t) \tag{2.212}$$

Table 2.3 shows the transient responses of the simpler transfer functions encountered in automatic control theory.

The value of a transient response at $t = 0$ is called the initial value, and the value of a transient response at $t = \infty$ is called the final or steady-state value.

If we denote the initial value of the transient response (2.212) by B_0, then B_0 can be computed by setting $t = 0$ in equation (2.212):

$$B_0 = A_0 + A_1 + A_2 + A_3 + \cdots\cdots \tag{2.213}$$

By setting $t = \infty$ in equation (2.212), we can also compute the final value B_∞ to be

$$B_\infty = A_0 \tag{2.214}$$

These initial and final values can also be computed by using other formulae. The final value B_∞ (which is equal to A_0) can be found from formula (2.100) as follows:

$$B_\infty = A_0 = \lim_{s\to 0}\left|sF_o(s)\right| \tag{2.215}$$

$$= \lim_{s\to 0}\left|F(s)\right| \tag{2.216}$$

In order to compute B_0, we multiply both sides of equation (2.210) by s. Then,

$$sF_0(s) = F(s) = A_0 + A_1\frac{s}{s+a_1} + A_2\frac{s}{s+a_2} + A_3\frac{s}{s+a_3} + \cdots\cdots \tag{2.217}$$

Taking the limit of this equation as $s \to \infty$, we obtain

$$\lim_{s\to\infty}\left|sF_o(s)\right| = \lim_{s\to\infty}\left|A_0 + A_1\frac{s}{s+a_1} + A_2\frac{s}{s+a_2} + A_3\frac{s}{s+a_3} + \cdots\cdots\right| \tag{2.218}$$

$$= A_0 + A_1 + A_2 + A_3 + \cdots\cdots \tag{2.219}$$

$$= B_0 \tag{2.220}$$

Therefore, to find the initial value B_0, we need only compute

$$B_0 = \lim_{s \to \infty} \left| sF_o(s) \right| \tag{2.221}$$

$$= \lim_{s \to \infty} \left| F(s) \right| \tag{2.222}$$

TABLE 2.3 TRANSIENT RESPONSES OF THE SIMPLER TRANSFER FUNCTIONS

transfer function	transient response		
	s-representation	t-representation	wave form of transient response
$\frac{1}{s}$	$\frac{1}{s^2}$	$t\,U(t)$	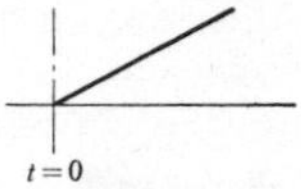
$\frac{1}{s^2}$	$\frac{1}{s^3}$	$\frac{t^2}{2}\,U(t)$	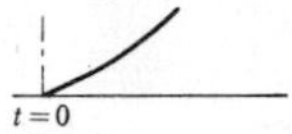
$\frac{1}{1+sT}$	$\frac{1}{s(1+sT)} = \left(\frac{1}{s} - \frac{1}{s+\frac{1}{T}}\right)$	$(1-\epsilon^{-\frac{t}{T}})\,U(t)$	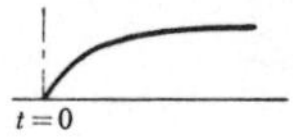
$\frac{\omega^2_n}{s^2+2\zeta\omega_n s+\omega_n^2}$	$\frac{\omega^2_n}{s(s^2+2\zeta\omega_n s+\omega^2_n)}$	$\frac{\epsilon^{-\zeta\omega_n t}}{\sqrt{1-\zeta^2}}\cos\left(\sqrt{1-\zeta^2}\,\omega_n t - \tan^{-1}\frac{\sqrt{1-\zeta^2}}{\zeta}\right)$	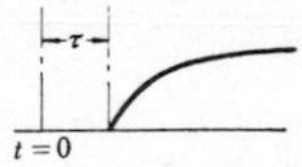
$\frac{1}{s}\epsilon^{-s\tau}$	$\frac{1}{s^2}\epsilon^{-s\tau}$	$(t-\tau)\,U(t)\,(t-\tau)$	
$\frac{\epsilon^{-s\tau}}{1+sT_1}$	$\left\{\frac{\epsilon^{-s\tau}}{s(1+sT_1)} = \left(\frac{1}{s} - \frac{1}{s+\frac{1}{T_1}}\right)\epsilon^{-s\tau}\right\}$	$\left(1-\epsilon^{-\frac{t-\tau}{T_1}}\right)U(t)(t-\tau)$	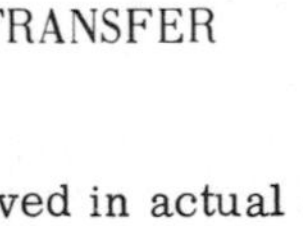

2.8. REPRESENTATION OF DISTURBANCES AND TRANSFER FUNCTIONS OF DISTURBANCES

In general, a variety of disturbances are involved in actual automatic control systems, differing in type as well as intensity. However, we shall not need to consider all of them. In an actual case, it is often permissible to treat the disturbance with the greatest influence on the controlled variable as if it were the only disturbance. Most commonly, this disturbance is the load variation.

To analyse the behaviour of an automatic control system under the influence of a disturbance, we need the following two things. First, it is necessary to represent the disturbance in terms of a signal. Second, it is necessary to specify the effect of the disturbance on the controlled variable; that is, we need to specify the transfer function where the input is the disturbance and the output is the effect of the disturbance on the controlled variable.

If the disturbance is a variation of the signal such as a variation of voltage, current, force, velocity, fluid flow, or heat flow, the disturbance already has a signal representation which is the variation of the signal. However, if the disturbance is a variation of the network constants or of on-off switches, it should be represented by an equivalent signal variation.

As an example, consider a network consisting of a d.c. generator with internal resistance R_i and a d.c. motor, as shown in Fig. 2.35. The d.c. motor is the load in this case, and the value of the load constant (the internal resistance R_m of the armature of the d.c. motor) is invariant. However, if the counter e.m.f. of the armature varies as shown in Fig. 2.36, it affects the voltage across the output terminals t and t'. If we denote by e_D the variation of the counter e.m.f. observed at a certain instant with respect to the counter e.m.f. at the prior instant, then e_D can be regarded as a voltage source as shown in Fig. 2.37. This variation e_D is the disturbance in this case. However, it will not be observed directly since it is in the voltage across the output terminals.

Figure 2.37 shows only the variation of the voltage at each part of the network. Let us investigate the relation between these voltage variations. If we denote by e_{tD} the variation of the voltage across the output terminals caused by the disturbance e_D, then e_{tD} is

$$e_{tD}=\frac{R_i}{R_i+R_m}e_D \tag{2.223}$$

If e_{to} is the variation of the voltage across the output terminals caused by the increase e_o in the e.m.f. of the d.c. generator, then

$$e_{to}=\frac{R_m}{R_i+R_m}e_o \tag{2.224}$$

Therefore, the variation e_t of the voltage across the output terminals is expressed by the equation

$$e_t=e_{to}+e_{tD}=\frac{R_m}{R_i+R_m}e_o+\frac{R_i}{R_i+R_m}e_D \tag{2.225}$$

This relation is represented clearly by the block diagram shown in Fig. 2.38.

As shown in Fig. 2.38, $R_i/(R_i+R_m)$ is the transfer function from the disturbance to the voltage across the output terminals or to the controlled variable. In general, such a transfer function is called a disturbance transfer function.

Let us consider a disturbance of another kind. Consider the network shown in Fig. 2.39, where the disturbance is a switch-

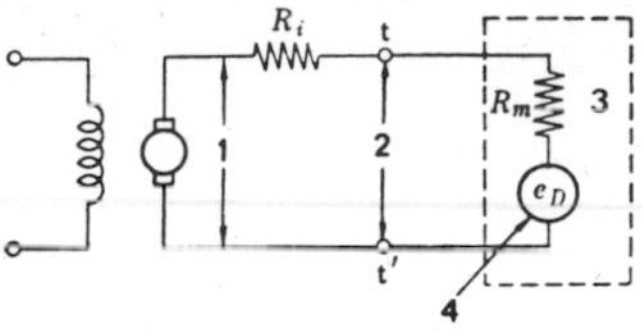

1 - *e.m.f. of generator*; 2 - *voltage across output terminals* 3 - *load*; 4 - *variation of the counter e.m.f. of the motor (disturbance)*

Fig. 2.35 Example of a voltage variation disturbance

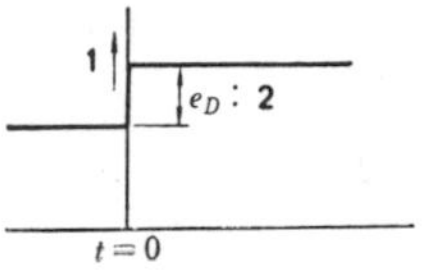

1 - *counter e.m.f.*; 2 - *disturbance*

Fig. 2.36 Disturbance of the network shown in Fig. 2.35

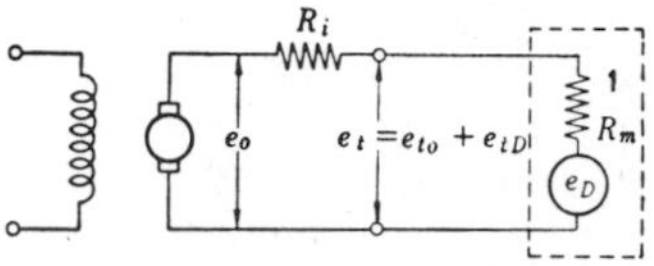

1 - *load*

Fig. 2.37 Effect of the disturbance and the variation in the generator e.m.f. on the output terminal voltage

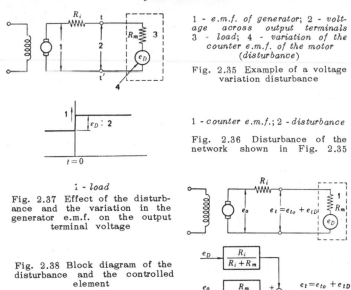

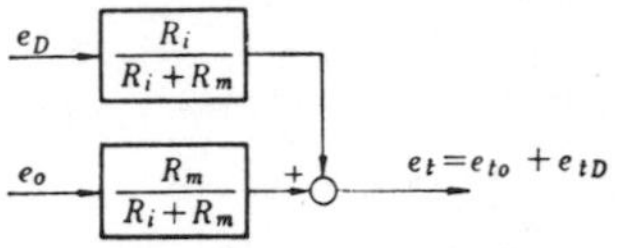

Fig. 2.38 Block diagram of the disturbance and the controlled element

closing. A switch-closing itself is not a signal. Therefore, it is necessary to represent the switch-closing in terms of a voltage or current variation in order to investigate the effect of the disturbance. Consider a voltage source (an electric source that generates an e.m.f. and has internal resistance 0) whose e.m.f. is equal to the voltage observed across the switch terminals when the switch is open. (This voltage is equal to the e.m.f. E_0 of the generator in this example.) If we replace the switch by this voltage source in the given network, the load current for this voltage source will be 0, and hence the distribution of voltage and current in the network will be exactly the same as before closing the switch. If we let the e.m.f. of the voltage source be 0, the resultant network will be equivalent to the given network with the switch closed since the internal resistance of the voltage source is 0. That is, closing the switch in the given network is equivalent to varying the e.m.f. of the voltage source (see Fig. 2.41) in the network obtained by replacing the switch with the voltage source. Note that this equivalence is valid only when the switch is closed. When the switch is opened, we consider an equivalent network obtained by replacing the switch with a source that generates a current independently of the load and has internal admittance 0, as shown in Fig. 2.42. This current source should be such that the generated current is equal to the current

$$I_0 = \frac{E_0}{R_i + R_l} \tag{2.226}$$

that flows through the switch when it is closed. Opening the switch is now equivalent to making the generated current (2.226) zero, as shown in Fig. 2.43.

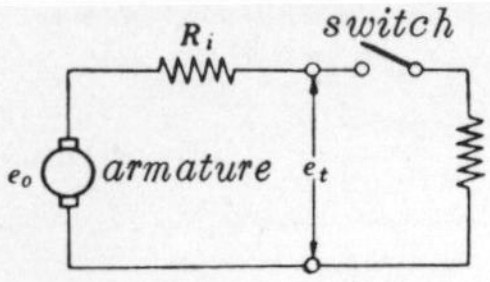

Fig. 2.39 A disturbance in the form of switch-closing

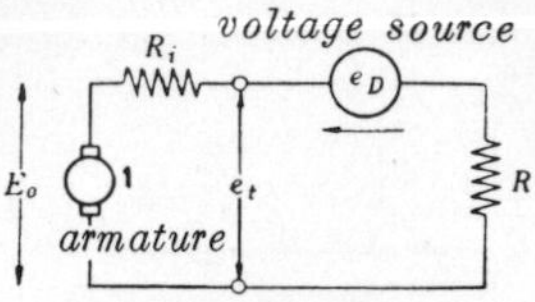

Fig. 2.40 A network equivalent to the given network with a disturbance in the form of switch-closing

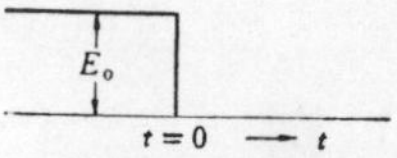

Fig. 2.41 A variation e_D of the voltage source, equivalent to the disturbance

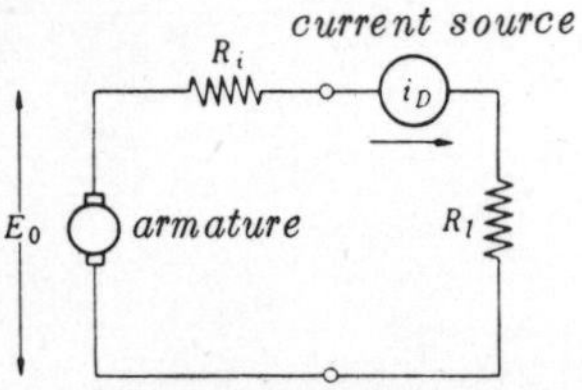

Fig. 2.42 A network equivalent to the given network with a disturbance in the form of switch-opening

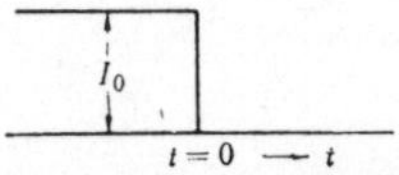

Fig. 2.43 Variation of the generated current of the current source in Fig. 2.42

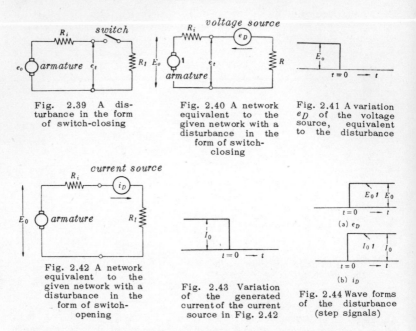

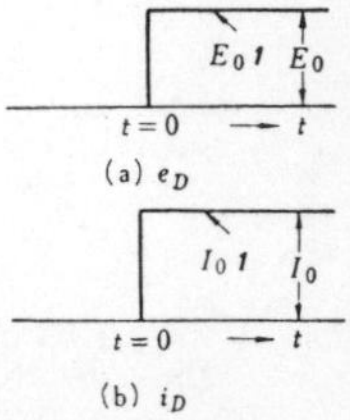

Fig. 2.44 Wave forms of the disturbance (step signals)

Figures 2.41 and 2.43 show respectively the wave forms of the e.m.f. of the voltage source and the generated current of the current source, respectively. As the disturbance, we take the variation of the e.m.f. or the generated current from the original electromotive voltage or the generated current at the prior instant. Therefore, we should take the wave shown in Fig. 2.44 (a) as the signal wave of the disturbance instead of the wave shown in Fig. 2.41. Consequently, the disturbance should be the voltage $E_0 U(t)$ acting in the direction indicated by the broken-line arrow in Fig. 2.40. Similarly, when representing the disturbance in terms of current, we should take as the disturbance the current $I_0 U(t)$ which has the wave form shown in Fig. 2.44 (b). The current $I_0 U(t)$ is assumed to flow in the direction indicated by the broken-line arrow in Fig. 2.42.

Let us now investigate the effects of the disturbance voltage or current and the variation of the generator voltage on the voltage across the output terminals.

For example, in the case of Fig. 2.40, the disturbance is $e_D = E_0 U(t)$. Denoting by e_{tD} the variation of the voltage across the output terminals due to the disturbance e_D, we have

$$e_{tD}=\frac{R_i}{R_i+R_l}e_D=\frac{R_i}{R_i+R_l}E_0\,\mathbf{1} \tag{2.227}$$

Accordingly, the relation between the disturbance e_D and the corresponding variation e_{tD} of the output voltage will be represented by the block diagram shown in Fig. 2.45. In the case of

Fig. 2.42 (that is, when the switch is opened), the disturbance is the current i_D. If we again denote by e_{tD} the variation of the output voltage due to the disturbance i_D, the relation between i_D and e_{tD} will be represented by the block diagram shown in Fig. 2.46 (a). If we use the value of I_0 given by equation (2.226), then the block diagram in Fig. 2.46 (a) can be transformed into an equivalent block diagram (shown in Fig. 2.46 (b)) equal to the block diagram shown in Fig. 2.45.

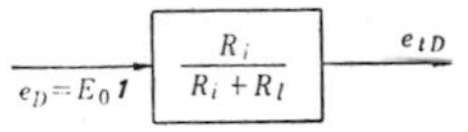

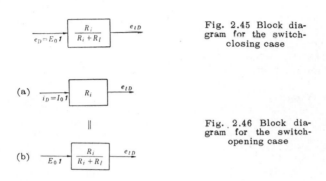

Fig. 2.45 Block diagram for the switch-closing case

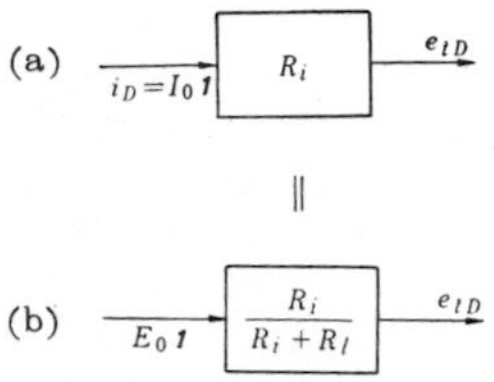

Fig. 2.46 Block diagram for the switch-opening case

It is clear that the output voltage e_t varies not only according to the disturbance but also according to the variation of the generator voltage. We consider first the state after the switch is closed. Denoting by e_o the voltage across the generator and by e_{to} the variation in the voltage across the output terminals, we obtain

$$e_{t0} = \frac{R_l}{R_i + R_l} e_0 \tag{2.228}$$

Combining this relation and the relation shown in Fig. 2.45, we obtain the block diagram shown in Fig. 2.47. In a similar manner, we obtain the block diagram shown in Fig. 2.48 for the case in which the switch is open.

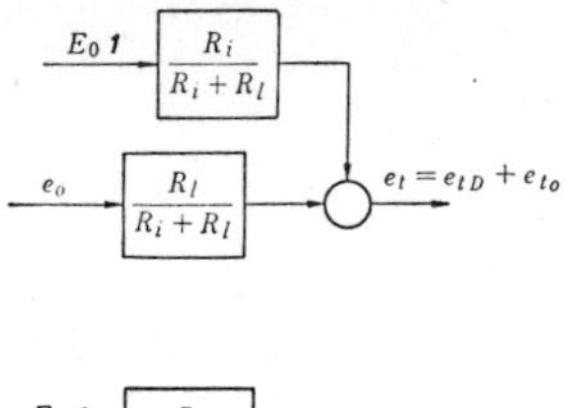

Fig. 2.47 Block diagram showing the relation between the disturbance and the controlled element; (switch closed)

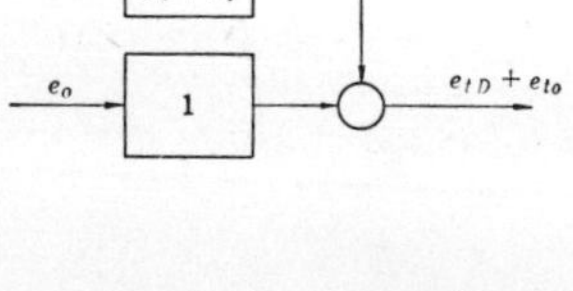

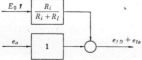

Fig. 2.48 Block diagram showing the relation between the disturbance and the controlled element; (switch open)

These examples illustrate the following: If the disturbance itself is a signal variation (as shown in Fig. 2.35), then the transfer function of each element in Fig. 2.38 remains unchanged regardless of the type of disturbance. However, if the disturbance is a switch-opening or a switch-closing (as shown in Fig. 2.39), then the transfer function of the controlled element changes according to whether the disturbance is a switch-opening or a switch-closing, as a comparison of Fig. 2.47 and 2.48 indicates. The reason is that the load resistance is ∞ or R_e accordingly as the switch is opened or closed. Therefore, if the load resistance varies continuously, the corresponding constant used in the transfer function becomes a function of time, and hence analysis of the network becomes extremely complicated.

In these two examples, the transfer functions of the disturbances were not functions of s. In general, however, they are functions of s.

For example, consider the network shown in Fig. 2.49, where the load consists of the resistance R_l and the inductance L_l. If the switch-closing is replaced by an equivalent voltage source (the e.m.f. $E_0\,U(t)$ in the given network, we obtain the network shown in Fig. 2.50. Let e_D be the disturbance voltage equivalent to the switch-closing (the given disturbance). Denoting by e_{tD} the variation of the output voltage caused by the disturbance e_{tD}, we obtain

$$e_{tD}=\frac{R_i}{R_i+R_l+sL_l}e_D=\frac{\frac{R_i}{R_i+R_l}}{1+s\frac{L_l}{R_i+R_l}}E_0\,U(t) \tag{2.229}$$

$$=\frac{\frac{R_i}{R_i+R_l}}{1+sT_D}E_0\,U(t) \tag{2.230}$$

where

$$T_D=\frac{L_l}{R_i+R_l} \tag{2.231}$$

Let $Y(s)$ be a transfer function whose input signal is $e_D=E_0U(t)$ and whose output signal is e_{tD}. Then, $Y(s)$ is clearly the transfer function of the disturbance. Its value is

$$Y(s)=\frac{e_{tD}}{E_0U(t)}=\frac{\frac{R_i}{R_i+R_l}}{1+sT_D} \tag{2.232}$$

$$=\frac{Y_o}{1+sT_D} \tag{2.233}$$

where

$$Y_o=\frac{R_l}{R_i+R_l} \tag{2.234}$$

In most cases, a transfer function of a disturbance is represented by an expression of the form (2.233). The constant T_D is called the disturbance time constant, and Y_o is called the steady-state variation ratio.

Denoting by e_0 a variation in the generator voltage and by e_{t0}

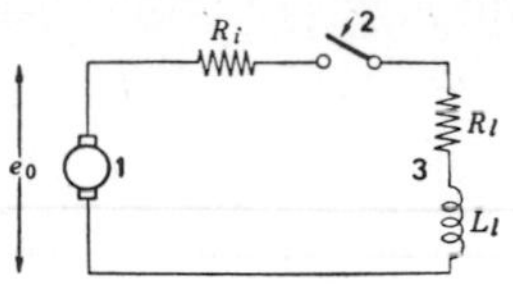

1 - *armature*; 2 - *closing*; 3 - *load*

Fig. 2.49 A network whose load includes an inductance

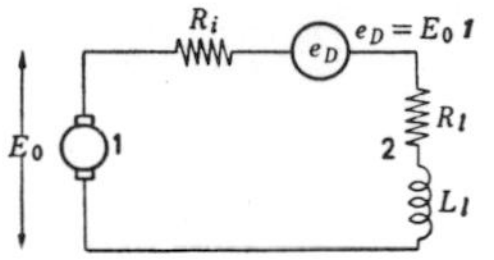

1 - *armature*; 2 - *load*

Fig. 2.50 A network equivalent to that shown in Fig. 2.49

the variation in the voltage across the load terminals (in the loaded state) caused by e_o, we obtain

$$e_{lo} = \frac{R_l + sL_l}{R_i + R_l + sL_l} e_0 \tag{2.235}$$

Therefore, if we denote by $F(s)$ the transfer function whose input signal is e_o and whose output signal is e_{to}, we have

$$F(s) = \frac{e_{to}}{e_o} \tag{2.236}$$

$$= \frac{R_l + sL_l}{R_i + R_l + sL_l} \tag{2.237}$$

$$= \frac{\dfrac{R_l}{R_i + R_l} + s\dfrac{L_l}{R_i + R_l}}{1 + s\dfrac{L_l}{R_i + R_l}} \tag{2.238}$$

$$= \frac{1 - Y_o + sT_D}{1 + sT_D} \tag{2.239}$$

Here, T_D and Y_o are as defined by equations (2.231) and (2.234). Therefore, the relation between the disturbance e_D, the variation e_o of the generator voltage, and the corresponding variation e_t of the controlled variable can be expressed by the block diagram shown in Fig. 2.51.

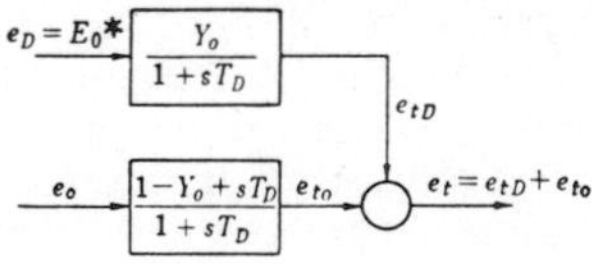

* $= U(t)$

Fig. 2.51 Block diagram showing the relation between the disturbance and the controlled variable when the load includes an inductance

2.9. BLOCK DIAGRAMS OF AUTOMATIC CONTROL SYSTEMS AND A METHOD OF CONSTRUCTING THEM

A block diagram explicitly shows the input signal, the transfer function, the output signal and the path for the signal transmission as shown in Figs. 2.47, 2.48, and 2.51. Therefore, block diagrams are convenient representations when we are concerned only with signal transmissions. They are especially convenient for representing complicated signal transmissions such as those of automatic control systems.

We now present a complete set of rules for constructing a block diagram.

1. A transfer function enclosed by a block symbol ▭, but ▭ never applies to a signal regardless of its t-representation or s-representation.
2. A block has two arrows attached indicating the direction of the signal transmission. No signal is transmitted in the opposite direction.
3. Addition of signals is defined as shown in Fig. 2.52 (a). That is, the signal quantity indicated by the arrow pointing away from the circle is the algebraic sum of the signal quantities indicated by the arrows pointing to the circle. Subtraction of signals is defined as in Fig. 2.52 (b). The signal quantity to be subtracted is indicated by the arrow with the minus sign.

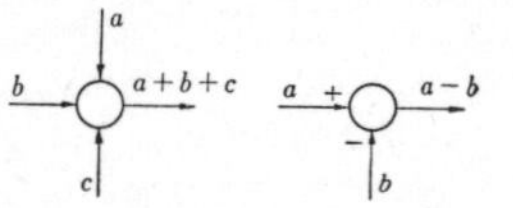

(a) addition (b) subtraction

Fig. 2.52 Addition and subtraction of signals

4. If a signal travels along a branched path, it is represented by the symbol shown in Fig. 2.53.

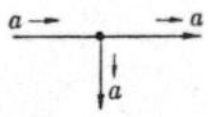

Fig. 2.53 A branching point

5. If it is necessary to distinguish a block diagram for the t-representation of a signal from that for the s-representation, we use $F(p)$ for the transfer function written in the block diagram for the t-representation and $F(s)$ for the s-representation.

As mentioned in Chapter I, an automatic control system forms a closed loop and a signal circulates around this closed loop. Signals fed to the closed-loop system from the outside consist of the reference input and the disturbance. The signal that is transmitted from the closed-loop system to the outside is the controlled variable. As can be seen from the preceding section, the disturbance is not a physical element in the closed-loop system, but it affects the behaviour of the system through the disturbance transfer function. From these facts, we may construct the general form of the block diagram of an automatic control system, as shown in Figs. 2.54 and 2.55. These block diagrams represent an automatic control system that forms a single closed loop. However, the block diagram of an automatic control system that forms a multiple closed loop can usually be reduced to the general block diagram shown in Figs. 2.54 or 2.55. Fig. 2.54 shows the general block diagram for the t-representation, and Fig. 2.55 shows that for the s-representation. The block diagrams for the s-representation will be most frequently used in practice.

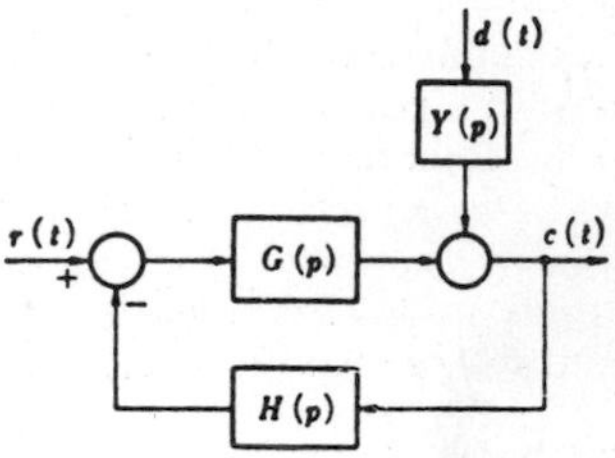

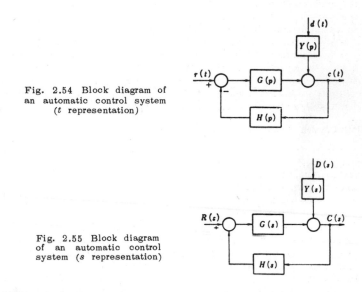

Fig. 2.54 Block diagram of an automatic control system (t representation)

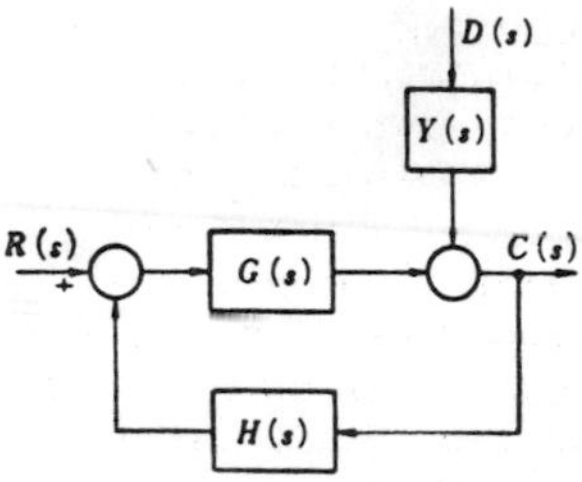

Fig. 2.55 Block diagram of an automatic control system (s representation)

The notations $R(s)$, $D(s)$, and $C(s)$ in Fig. 2.55 stand for the reference input signal, the disturbance signal, and the controlled variable (in s-representation) respectively. The transfer function $G(s)$ is called the forward transfer function, $H(s)$ the feedback transfer function, and $Y(s)$ the disturbance transfer function. Here, $F(s)=G(s)H(s)$ is the transfer function of the entire closed loop of the automatic control system and is called the open loop transfer function of the system.

In most cases, the disturbance transfer function $Y(s)$ is given by

$$Y(s)=\frac{Y_o}{1+sT_D} \tag{2.240}$$

as shown above (c.f. equation (2.233)). The forward transfer function $G(s)$ is represented by the following function in general:

$$G(s)=\frac{K(1+sT_1')(1+sT_2')(1+sT_3')\cdots}{s^n(1+sT_1)(1+sT_2)(1+sT_3)\cdots\cdots} \tag{2.241}$$

The constant K in this expression is often called the gain constant. It is usually positive though on rare occasions it may be negative. The constants T_1, T_2, T_3... and T_1', T_2', T_3'... are time constants. These too are usually positive real numbers, but they may sometimes be complex and on rare occasions they may be negative real numbers. The exponent n is a positive integer. For most automatic regulators, n is zero though again, for special types of automatic regulators, n may be 1. For a servomechanism which is a follow-up control system, n is usually 1. Also n may on occasion take values greater than 1.

An automatic control such that $n = 0$ is called a proportional or static control. An automatic control with $n \geq 1$ is called an integral control or an astatic control. An automatic control such that $n = k$ for some integer k is referred to as a type-k automatic control. The steady-state transient characteristics of automatic control systems depend largely on the value of n.

The feedback transfer function $H(s)$ is usually a constant in actual automatic control systems. In particular, a unity feedback transfer function is often used. If $H(s) = 1$, the automatic control system is called a unity feedback system. The feedback transfer function sometimes takes the following forms:

$$H(s) = \frac{K}{1+sT_h}, sT_h, \frac{sT_h}{1+sT_h} \tag{2.242}$$

Accordingly, the overall transfer function $F(s)$ takes the form

$$F(s) = G(s)H(s) = \frac{K(1+sT_1')(1+sT_2')(1+sT_3')\cdots}{s^n(1+sT_1)(1+sT_2)(1+sT_3)\cdots\cdots} \tag{2.243}$$

Quite frequently, the degrees of the denominators of the open loop transfer function $F(s)$ and the forward transfer function $G(s)$ are much greater than the degrees of the numerators. (In fact, the numerators are often constants.) Therefore, as s increases to large values, the denominators of $F(s)$ and $G(s)$ increase more rapidly than do the numerators. Consequently, the values of $|F(s)|$ and $|G(s)|$ both tend to 0:

$$\lim_{s\to\infty} |F(s)| = 0, \qquad \lim_{s\to\infty} |G(s)| = 0 \tag{2.244}$$

Physically, the value of s represents the ratio of the changes in the phenomena. Therefore, a large value of s means a rapid variation in a signal. For example, if the signal is sinusoidal, an increase in the value of s means an increase in the frequency of the sinusoidal signal. Similarly, for a signal with slow variation, the Laplace variable s is small.

As s tends to 0 in equation (2.243), the limit is

$$\lim_{s\to 0} \left|F(s)\right| = \lim_{s\to 0} \left|\frac{K}{s^n}\right| \tag{2.245}$$

Therefore, [62.1] for $n = 0$, and [62.2] for $n \geq 1$. In general, the open loop transfer function $F(s)$ and the forward transfer function

$G(s)$ of an automatic control system are designed so to have either a large or an infinite limiting value as $s \to 0$.

2.10. MANIPULATION OF BLOCK DIAGRAMS

The automatic control systems which have been treated up to now are limited to the type of system that forms a single closed loop. However, many automatic control systems actually form a multiple closed-loop system. Moreover, a disturbance is not only involved on the output side but also between the active elements. In these cases, it is necessary to transform the given block diagram into the simplest equivalent block diagram before investigating the characteristics of the automatic control system.

Table 2.4 shows the basic manipulations used to simplify a complicated block diagram. Manipulations (4) and (5) will be justified in the following section. The others were discussed in the previous sections.

As an example, consider the block diagram shown in Fig. 2.56. This block diagram can be transformed to the equivalent block diagram shown in Fig. 2.57 by using manipulation (6). Then, by manipulation (4), the block diagram in Fig. 2.57 can be simplified to the block diagram shown in Fig. 2.58, which represents a single closed-loop system. Finally, this block diagram can be transformed into a simple one by use of manipulation (5), as shown in Fig. 2.59.

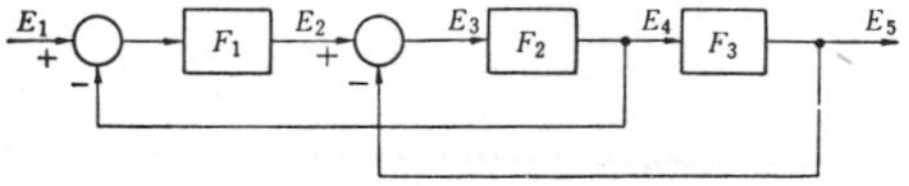

Fig. 2.56 A complicated block diagram

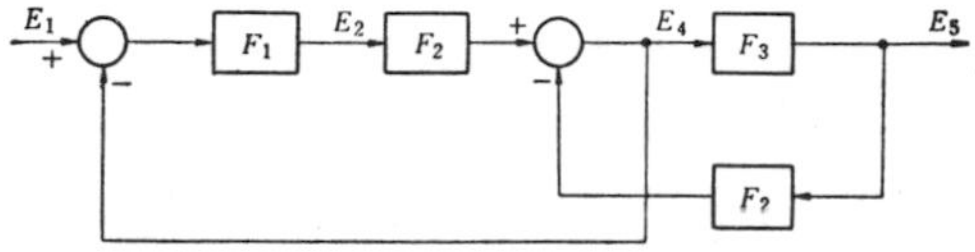

Fig. 2.57 Simplification of the block diagram in Fig. 2.56

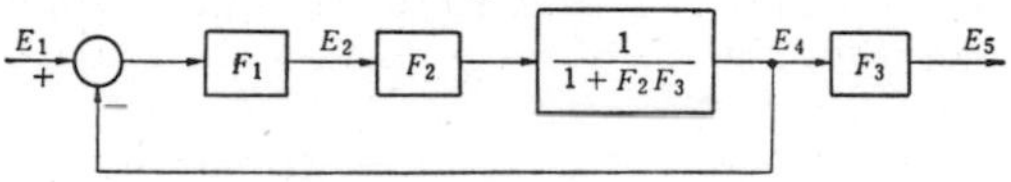

Fig. 2.58 Simplification of the block diagram in Fig. 2.57

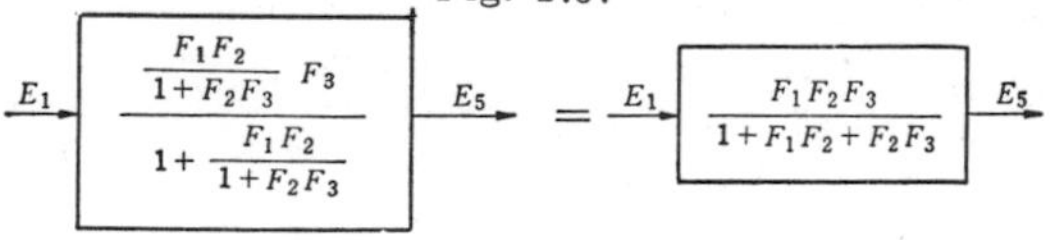

(a) (b)

Fig. 2.59 The block diagram after simplification is complete

TABLE 2.4 BASIC MANIPULATIONS OF BLOCK DIAGRAMS

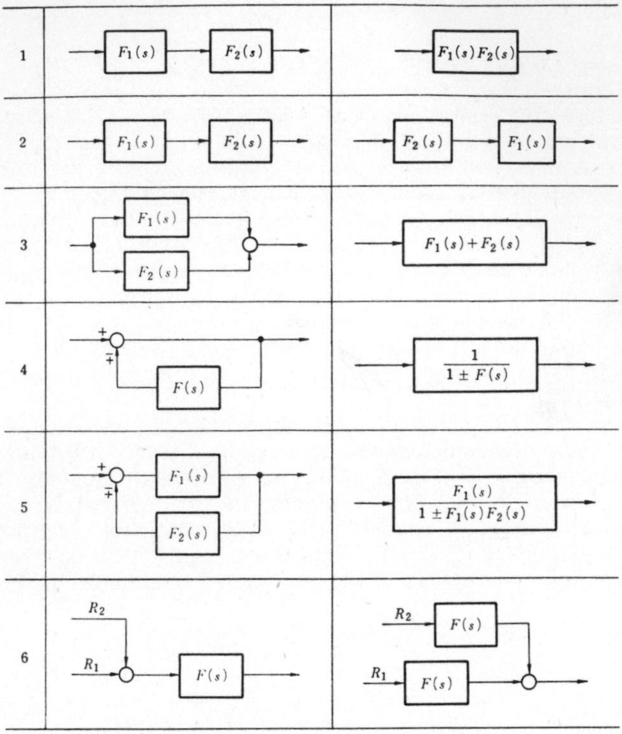

EXERCISE PROBLEMS

1. Suppose that we are given two networks (a) and (b), and two input signals $e_i = E_i exp\, j\omega t$ and $e_i = E_i exp\, (\alpha t + j\omega)t$ (where $\alpha < 0$). For each network and for each input, find the ratio e_o / e_i, where e_o is the corresponding output signal. Since the ratio e_o / e_i is a complex number, it can be represented by a vector on the complex plane. Plot the vector for each and compare the graphs.

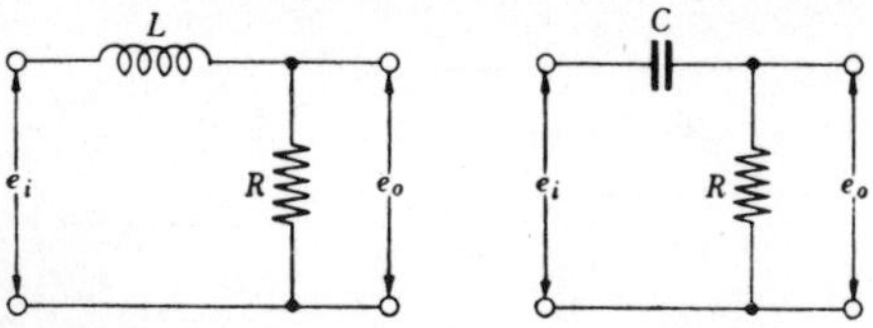

(a) (b)

2. Suppose that we are given three networks (a), (b), and (c) and an input signal of the form

$$e_i = 50\, e^{(\alpha + j\omega)t} \; [\mathrm{V}]$$

For each network, compute the output signal for the following three cases:

(i) $\alpha=-15,\ \omega=30,$ (ii) $\alpha=0,\ \omega=30,$ (iii) $\alpha=+15,\ \omega=30$

In the given networks, we assume that (a), (b) and (c) below

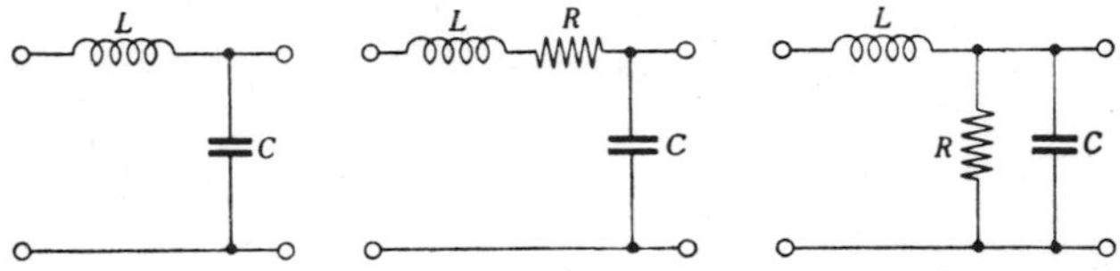

(a) (b) (c)

3. Networks (a), (b), (c), and (d), shown below, are often used to compensate for certain transient characteristics of automatic control systems. For each network, find the transfer function and express it in a form containing time constants.

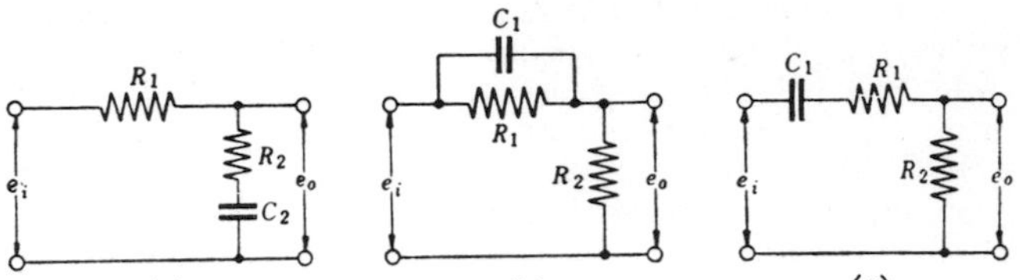

(a) (b) (c)

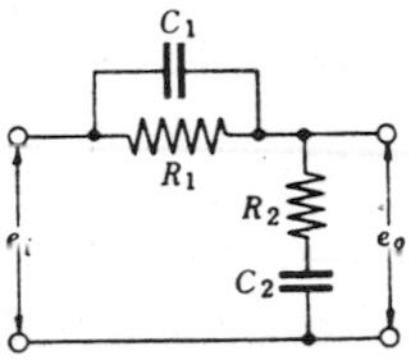

(d)

4. Consider the system shown below. The output signal of the d.c. motor is supplied to a load through the gear train. Take as the input signal to the given system the voltage applied to the d.c. motor; as the output signal, take the angular velocity ω_o of the loaded shaft. Then compute the transfer function of the given system. Here, it is assumed that the field current of the d.c. motor is constant and that the system constants are given as follows: $R_i = 0.15$ [Ω] = resistance of the armature network of the d.c. motor; $J_M = 0.2$ [$Kg-m^2$] = total moment of inertia acting on the armature shaft; $N = 1.27$ [v-sec/rad] or [N-m/A] = the ratio e_c / ω_a, where e_c is the e.m.f. of the armature and ω_a is the angular velocity of the armature or the ratio τ / i_a where τ is the armature torque and i_a is the armature current (these ratios being equal); v = 5:1 = gear ratio for reduction of the angular velocity; $J_L = 5.0$ [$Kg-m^2$] = moment of inertia of the loaded shaft; $D = 10$ [$N-m$-sec/rad] = damping coefficient of the load, that is, the ratio of the torque required to rotate the load to the angular velocity of the load.

We neglect the energy losses in the gears and in the unloaded motor.

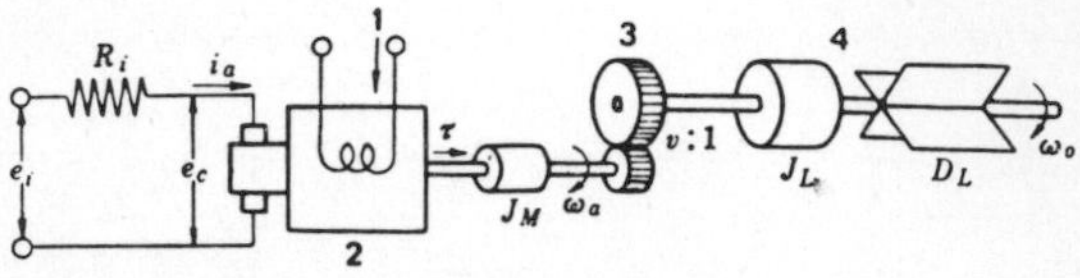

1 - *constant*; 2 - *direct current motor*; 3 - *gears*; 4 - *load*

5. The network shown below is a device used to effect a large amplification of a d.c. current by means of a d.c. motor. This device is called an amplidyne. The large d.c. amplification is achieved by having the armature current i_f of the generator G_1 excite the field of G_1. Find the transfer function of this network when the input signal is e_i and the output signal is e_o. Find the value of R_f such that the d.c. amplification coefficient is infinite. Then find the transfer function. Here, the network constants are as follows: $R_e = 50$ [Ω] = field resistance of the generator G. ; $L_e = 8.0$ [H] = inductance of the current control field of the generator G_1 ; $k_1 = 150$ [Ω] = $\Delta e_1 / \Delta i_e$, where Δi_e is a variation of the field current (i.e. of the generator G_1) and Δe_1 is the variation of the armature voltage caused by Δ_{ie} ; $k_i' = 7.0$ [Ω] = $\Delta e_1' / \Delta i_f$, where Δi_f is a variation of the armature current i_f and $\Delta e_1'$ is the variation of the armature e.m.f. caused by Δi_f ; $R_f = 10$ [Ω]; $L_f = 2.5$ [H]; $k_2 = 7.5$ [Ω]; the value for the generator G_2 corresponding to k_1.

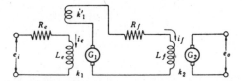

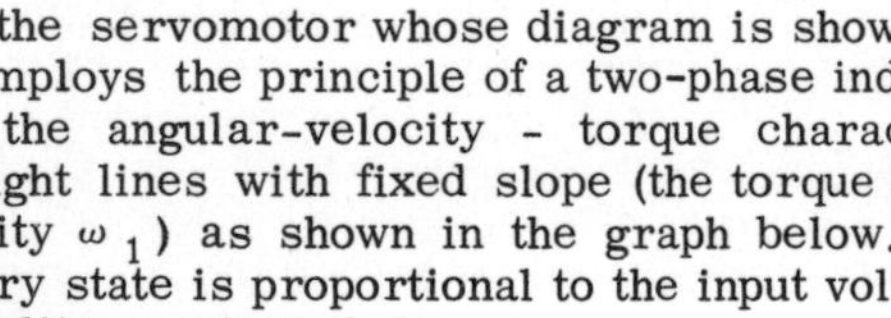

6. Consider the servomotor whose diagram is shown below. This servomotor employs the principle of a two-phase induction motor. Suppose that the angular-velocity - torque characteristics are given by straight lines with fixed slope (the torque is τ_1 for the angular velocity ω_1) as shown in the graph below. If the torque in the stationary state is proportional to the input voltage e_i, then the proportionality constant k is

$$k = \frac{\tau_s}{e_i}$$

where τ_s is the torque [N] in the stationary state and e_i is the input voltage [V] in the stationary state. If J is the moment of inertia of the rotating part of the motor, find the transfer function of the servomotor and the time constant, when e_i is the input signal and ω is the output signal.

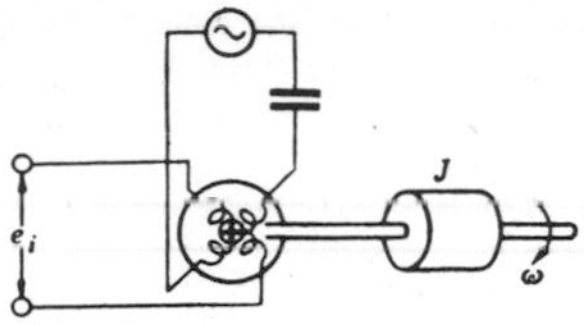

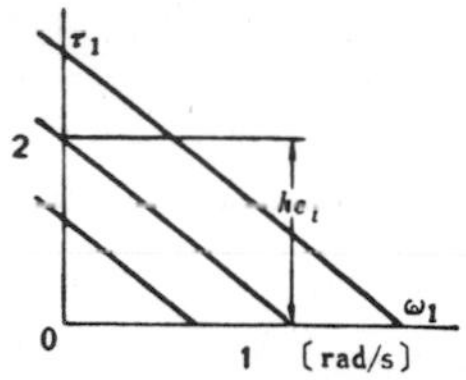

1 - *angular velocity*; 2 - *torque*

7. The oil-pressure motor and the pilot valve shown in Fig. 2.5 do not perform ideally in practice. The actual performance is shown below in Fig. (a). The difference P between the pressure in the cylinder compartment above the piston of the motor, and the pressure in the cylinder compartment below it, is plotted on the horizontal axis, and the flow in the pipe is plotted on the vertical axis. As shown in (a) below, the performance of this servo mechanism cannot be represented by straight lines. However, it can be approximated by a family of lines having a fixed slope as shown in Fig. (b) except for large values of P. For a more accurate representation of the performance, the force exerted on the piston rod of the motor is plotted on the horizontal axis instead of the pressured difference P and the velocity of the piston rod is plotted on the vertical axis instead of the flow Q. Then, the velocity of the piston rod decreases in proportion to the weight of the load when

1 - Q (*flow quantity*); 2 - *variation of* x_i (*positive value*); 3 - P (*pressure*) 4 - *change in* x_i (*negative value*)

(a)

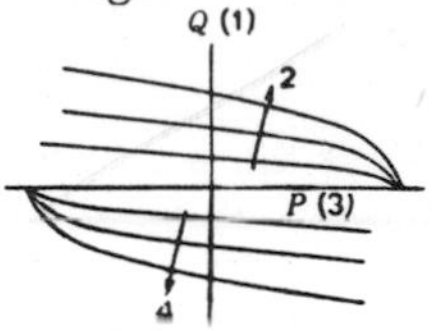

1 - v (*velocity of piston rod*) [m/sec] 2 - *change in* x_i; 3 - f (*force exerted on piston rod*) [N]

(b)

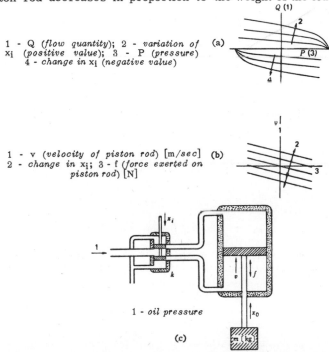

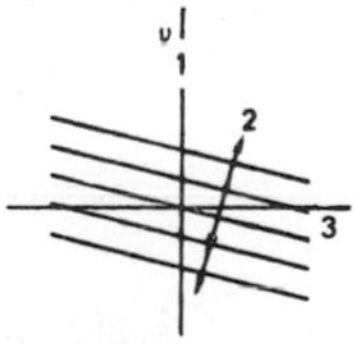

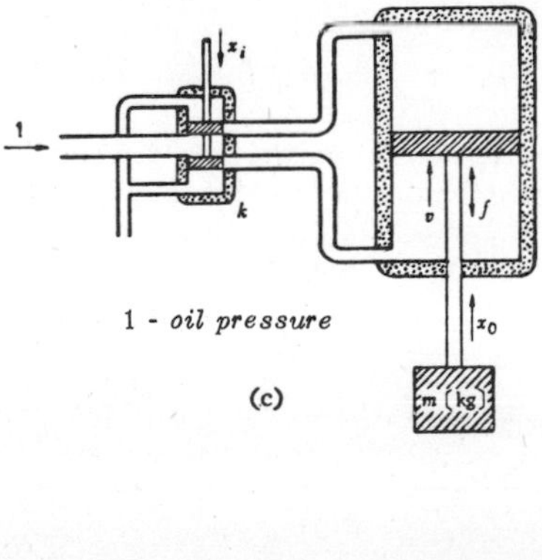

1 - *oil pressure*

(c)

it is loaded. Therefore, the given servomechanism is equivalent to an ideal system consisting of a dash-pot and piston rod that performs almost ideally by transmitting the force to the load through the dash-pot. Suppose that the weight of the load is m [Kg] as shown in Fig. (c). Find the transfer function when the input signal is the displacement x_i of the piston of the pilot valve and the output signal is the corresponding displacement x_o of the loaded piston rod of the motor. Here, we assume that the slopes of the lines in Fig. (b) are D (where $D = \Delta f / \Delta v$ = constant) and that the constant $k = \Delta v / \Delta x_i$ is given, where Δx_i is a change in x_i and Δv is the corresponding change in the velocity of the unloaded piston rod.

8. Find the t-representation of each of the following waves given in s-representation:

(i) $\dfrac{2}{(s+1)(s+5)}$ (ii) $\dfrac{2s+10}{s^2+10s+24}$

(iii) $\dfrac{s+1}{s^2(s+2)(s+3)}$ (iv) $\dfrac{3s^2+8s+8}{s^3+7s^2+14s+8}$

(v) $\dfrac{1}{s(s+1)(s+3)^2}$ (vi) $\dfrac{\epsilon^{-0.5s}}{s}$

(vii) $\dfrac{s+2}{(s+5)[(s+1)^2+4]}$ (viii) $\dfrac{3\epsilon^{-s}}{1+2s}$

9. Use the Laplace transformation to find the s-representation of each of the following waves given in t-representation:

(i) $\cos\omega t\ U(t)$ (ii) $\sin(\omega t+\phi)\ U(t)$

(iii) $\dfrac{d}{dt}\left(\cos\omega t\ U(t)\right)$ (iv) $5\epsilon^{3(\tau-t)}\ U(t)\ (t-\tau)$

10. Find the s-representations of the waves shown in the figures below.

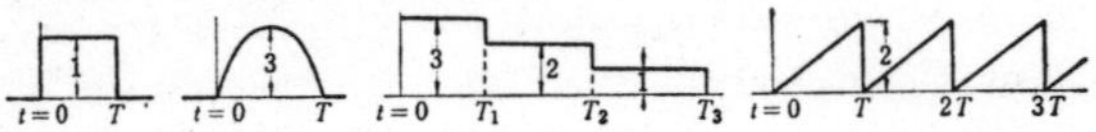

(a) (b) (c) (d)

11. Find the Laplace transforms of each of the following differential equations:

(i) $L\dfrac{di(t)}{dt}+Ri(t)+\dfrac{1}{C}\displaystyle\int i(t)dt=U(t)$

(ii) $M\dfrac{d^2x(t)}{dt^2}+D\dfrac{dx(t)}{dt}+Kx(t)=F_0\cos\omega_0 t\ U(t)$

(iii) $3\dfrac{d^2\theta}{dt^2}+8\dfrac{d\theta}{dt}+5\theta=10\ U(t)$

(iv) $5\dfrac{dx}{dt}+6x+12\displaystyle\int x dt=t\epsilon^{-3t}\ U(t)$

12. Consider the network shown below. Find the transient response e_t of the network when the switch is closed and when it is open.

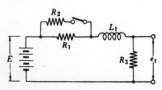

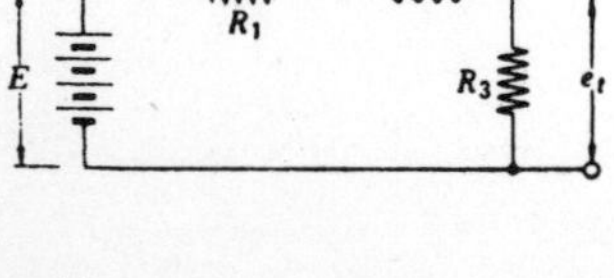

13. Consider the network shown above. Construct a block diagram showing clearly the relation between the disturbance caused by the switch-closing, the variation e_o of the generator voltage, and the voltage across the output terminals when we close the switch. (Construct a block diagram similar to Fig. 2.47.) Do the same when the switch is opened. Here, we assume that E_0 is the generator voltage and that the variation e_o of E_0 is extremely small in comparison with E_0.

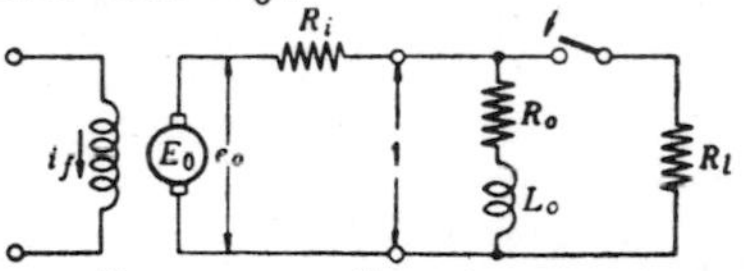

1 - *voltage across the output terminals*

14. Consider the network shown in the diagram below. This network is obtained by replacing R_o and L_o by an unloaded motor in the network of problem (13). Do as in Problem (13) for this network. Assume that the following constants are given: the moment of inertia J of the rotating part of the unloaded motor, the internal resistance R_m, the ratio $e_c/\omega = N$, where e_c is the armature voltage and ω is the angular velocity of the armature.

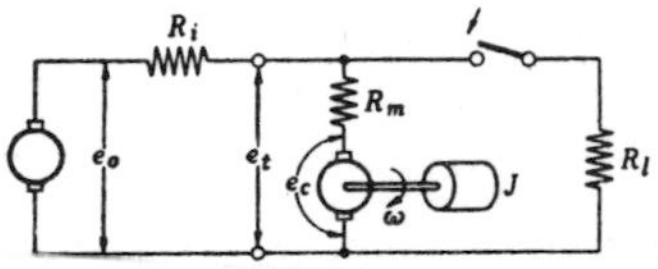

15. Considor the water-heating device shown in the diagram. The water is heated continuously. Find the variation in the temperature of the outflowing water when the rate of flow changes instantaneously from Q_1 to Q_2. Here, the volume of the water in the vessel is V [m³], the specific heat of the water is h [cal/m³-c°], the temperature of the supplied water is T_i, and the temperature of the outflowing water corresponding to the rate of flow Q_1 is T_1. We assume that the temperature T_1 is constant, that the electric heater supplies heat at a constant rate H [cal/sec] to the water in the vessel, that the water in the vessel is automatically maintained at a constant level, and that the water in the vessel is kept stirred. Also, we neglect heat conduction.

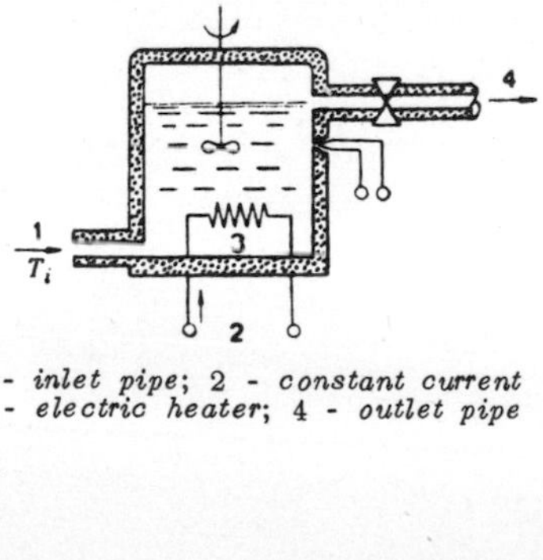

1 - *inlet pipe*; 2 - *constant current*
3 - *electric heater*; 4 - *outlet pipe*

16. Consider the stationary-type Leonard's rolling mill shown in the diagram below. This diagram shows the automatic speed control of the rolling mill. Construct the block diagram showing the relation between the output voltage e_m of the mercury-arc rectifier, the voltage e_ω developed by the tachometer generator, and the disturbance caused by the insertion of the materials between the rollers. Here, the notations in the diagram are as follows: L_i = inductance of the armature network in the motor; R_i = resistance of the armature network in the motor; N = ratio of the armature voltage of the motor to the angular velocity of the armature; J = total moment of inertia about the rotation shaft; D = damping coefficient equivalent to the no-load loss in the rotation shaft; N_T = ratio of the angular velocity of the tachometer generator to the generated voltage. We also assume that the torque required for the pressing is τ_0 and that it has a constant value independent of the angular velocity ω of the rotation shaft.

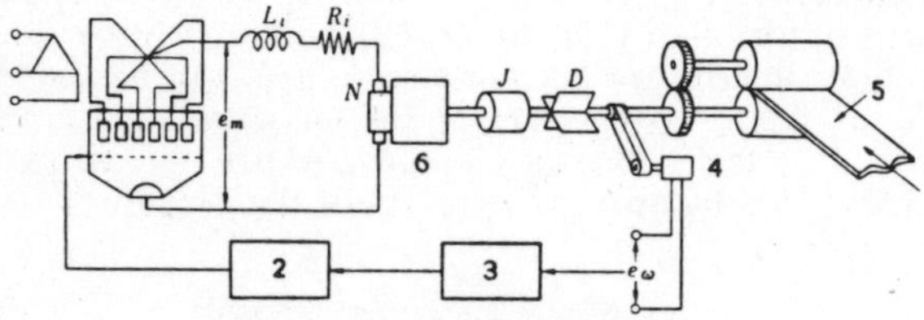

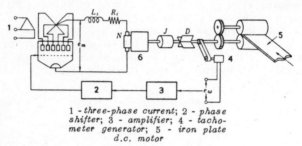

1 - *three-phase current*; 2 - *phase shifter*; 3 - *amplifier*; 4 - *tachometer generator*; 5 - *iron plate d.c. motor*

17. Find the transfer function in the block diagrams below when the input signal is the reference input signal and the output signal is the controlled variable.

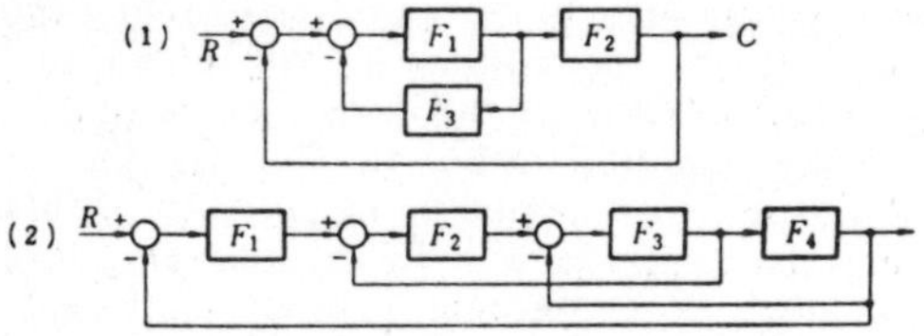

18. Transform the block diagrams shown below into the form of the basic block diagram shown in Fig. 2.55.

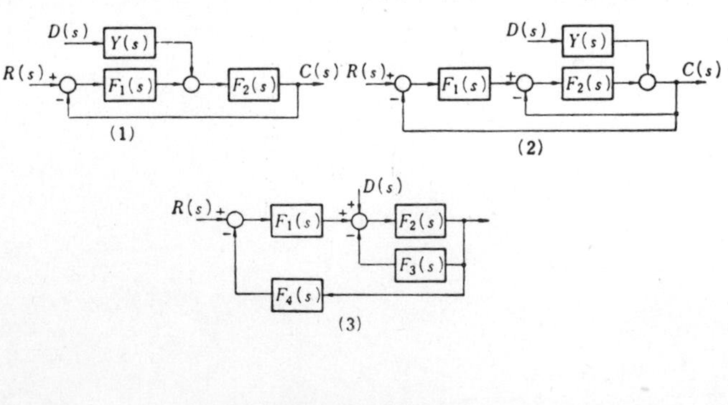

3

Automatic Control Systems Fundamental Analysis

3.1. CLASSIFICATION OF PERFORMANCE OF AUTOMATIC CONTROL SYSTEMS

Performances of automatic control systems can be classified into two categories, namely, steady-state performance and transient performance. The steady-state performance is the performance achieved by an automatic control system when the input signal or some other signal applied to the system from the outside either remains unchanged or varies in a uniform manner. This is an important point with an automatic control system. It is relatively easy to analyse the steady-state performance of a given automatic control system or to design an automatic control system with a prescribed steady-state performance.

The transient performance is the performance of an automatic control system when the signals applied to the system from the outside vary arbitrarily. It is not easy in general to analyse the transient performance of a given automatic control system unless the given system is extremely simple. Furthermore, it is more difficult to design an automatic control system with a prescribed transient performance. However, this problem has to be solved in order to design a satisfactory automatic control system.

In this chapter, we shall discuss the basic methods for analysing or roughly estimating the performance of an automatic control system. As a standard technique for the analysis of the performances, we shall use the approach used in Section 2.8. Specifically, we take a certain equilibrium state of the automatic control as a reference and observe the deviation from that reference state in order to evaluate the characteristics of the automatic control system. This approach is very useful since it simplifies the problem considerably.

3.2. IDEAL PERFORMANCE

For an automatic control system that forms a single closed-loop system, as shown in the general block diagram of Fig. 2.54 or 2.55, we shall derive the fundamental equation showing the relation between the reference input signal, the disturbance, and the controlled variable.

Observing the block diagram in Fig. 2.54, the signal feedback from the output side to the signal side is $H(p)c(t)$. Therefore, the input signal to the forward transfer function $G(p)$ is $r(t) - H(p)c(t)$. The sum of this signal multiplied by $G(p)$ and the disturbance multiplied by $Y(p)$ must be equal to $c(t)$:

$$(r(t)-H(p)\cdot c(t))G(p)+Y(p)d(t)=c(t) \tag{3.1}$$

If we solve this equation for $c(t)$, we obtain

$$c(t)=\frac{G(p)r(t)+Y(p)d(t)}{1+H(p)G(p)} \tag{3.2}$$

Since $H(p)G(p)$ is the open-loop transfer function, we may denote it by $F(p)$. Then,

$$c(t)=\frac{G(p)r(t)+Y(p)d(t)}{1+F(p)} \tag{3.3}$$

Since p is a short notation for d/dt, equation (3.3) is simply a differential equation.

If we apply the Laplace transformation to both sides of equation (3.3), we obtain

$$C(s)=\frac{G(s)R(s)+Y(s)D(s)}{1+F(s)} \tag{3.4}$$

which is the s-representation of equation (3.3). The block diagram corresponding to this equation is that shown in Fig. 2.55. This equation, in form (3.3) or (3.4), plays a basic role in the examination of various characteristics of an automatic control system. Therefore, it is called the 'fundamental equation' in automatic control system theory.

Equations (3.2), (3.3), and (3.4) are general forms of the fundamental equation which hold for any automatic control system. For certain automatic control systems, the fundamental equation may be simplified.

Let us find the fundamental equation of an automatic regulating system. Since the reference input to an automatic regulating system is constant by definition, the deviation from the equilibrium state is always zero. That is, we have $R(s) = 0$ (equivalently $r(t) = 0$) in the block diagram of Fig. 2.55 or in equation (3.4). Consequently, the block diagram of an automatic regulating system is the one shown in Fig. 3.1 (a), and the fundamental equation of this system is

$$C(s)=\frac{Y(s)D(s)}{1+F(s)} \tag{3.5}$$

where $F(s)=H(s)G(s)$ is the open-loop transfer function. The block diagram in Fig. 3.1 (a) can be simplified to the equivalent block diagram shown in Fig. 3.1 (b), in which the transfer functions are combined into one expression.

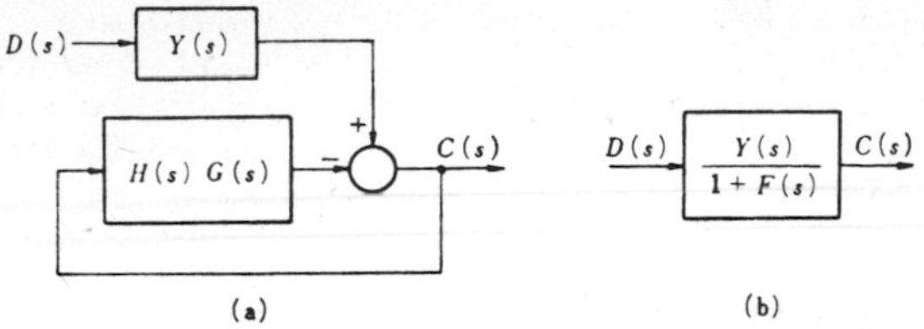

Fig. 3.1 Block diagrams of an automatic regulating system

If $F(s) = \infty$ for a certain s belonging to a domain that is used in practice, then $C(s) = 0$, moreover $C(s)$ is always 0 regardless of the disturbance $D(s)$. This state is a state in which the automatic regulating system performs ideally; it is called the ideal state of the automatic regulating system.

In a follow-up control system, the reference input signal and the disturbance both vary as time passes. However, a variation of the reference signal affects the controlled variable much more than does the variation of the disturbance in general. Therefore, the disturbance is usually neglected in a follow-up control. In other words, it is generally true that if an automatic control system performs satisfactorily for a variation of the reference input signal, it also performs satisfactorily with the disturbance. Therefore, for a follow-up control system, we assume that $D(s) = 0$ in the basic block diagram shown in Fig. 2.55 or in the corresponding fundamental equation. That is, the block diagram of a follow-up control system is the one shown in Fig. 3.2 (a), and the fundamental equation is

$$C(s) = \frac{G(s)}{1+F(o)} R(s) \tag{3.6}$$

The block diagram in Fig. 3.2 (a) can be simplified to the equivalent block diagram shown in Fig. 3.1 (b), and the relation between the

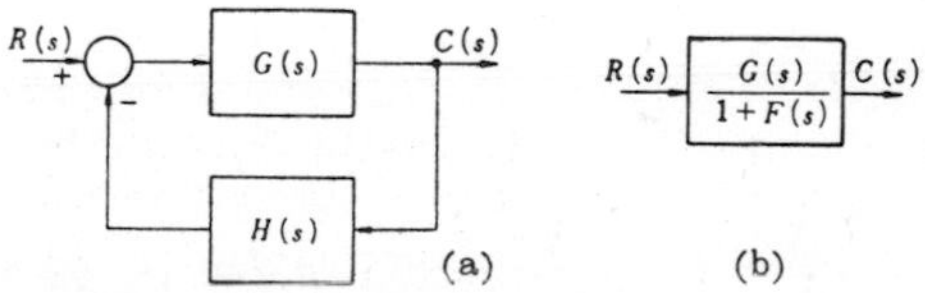

Fig. 3.2 Block diagram of follow-up control system

reference input signal and the controlled variable can be represented by one transfer function, as shown in Fig. 3.2 (b).

The function $F(s)$ used in equation (3.6) is the open-loop transfer function $F(s) = G(s)H(s)$. If we assume that $G(s) = \infty$ for some s as before, then equation (3.6) becomes

$$C(s) = \frac{G(s)R(s)}{1+H(s)G(s)} = \frac{R(s)}{H(s)} \tag{3.7}$$

This state is a state in which the follow-up control system performs ideally and is called the ideal state of a follow-up control system. In particular, if $H(s)=1$, that is, if the system is a unity feedback system, the controlled variable is identical with the reference input signal.

FUNDAMENTAL ERROR RESPONSE

If the forward transfer function $G(s)$ were to take the value ∞ for some complex number s belonging to a domain that is used in practice, the automatic control system would perform ideally, as mentioned before. However, this ideal situation cannot be expected in actual automatic control systems, since in practice there are always some disturbances associated with controlled variables.

For an automatic regulating system, the controlled variable $C(s)$ is 0 in an ideal state. Therefore, if any disturbance is involved in the controlled variable, the signal of the disturbance itself becomes the error. Denoting by $E(s)$ the s-representation of the error, we have

$$E(s)=C(s) \tag{3.8}$$

$$=\frac{1}{1+F(s)}Y(s)D(s) \tag{3.9}$$

For a follow-up control system, the controlled variable $C(s)$ is equal to $R(s)/H(s)$ in the ideal state. Therefore,

$$E(s)=\frac{R(s)}{H(s)}-C(s) \tag{3.10}$$

$$=\frac{R(s)}{H(s)}-\frac{G(s)R(s)}{1+F(s)} \tag{3.11}$$

$$=\left(1-\frac{G(s)H(s)}{1+F(s)}\right)\frac{R(s)}{H(s)} \tag{3.12}$$

$$=\left(1-\frac{F(s)}{1+F(s)}\right)\frac{R(s)}{H(s)} \tag{3.13}$$

$$=\frac{1}{1+F(s)}\cdot\frac{1}{H(s)}R(s) \tag{3.14}$$

Equation (3.9) is the expression of the error for an automatic regulating control, and equation (3.14) is the expression of the error for a follow-up control system. However, the two equations have the same form and hence can be represented by one block diagram as shown in Fig. 3.3. The function $D(s)$ or $R(s)$ is the s-representation of the input signal applied to the transfer function $1/(1+F(s))$. It will represent different waves according to the individual system under consideration. Nonetheless, it is tedious (and not very meaningful) to compute the error for each different wave. It is better to compute the error for a fixed wave chosen as the standard input signal for purposes of comparing the characteristics of automatic control systems, specifying the characteristics for the design of automatic control systems, or developing a general theory concerning the error. The unit step signal $U(t)$ shown in Fig. 2.22 is most commonly used for this. We set

$$d(t) = r(t) = 1 \tag{3.15}$$

or

$$D(s) = R(s) = 1/s \tag{3.16}$$

In fact, disturbances or reference input variations in actual controls are often unit step signals. It is also easy to apply the unit step signal as a disturbance or as a reference input signal to an automatic control system for experimental purposes. The experimental results can be used to compute or infer the characteristics of the system for other signals.

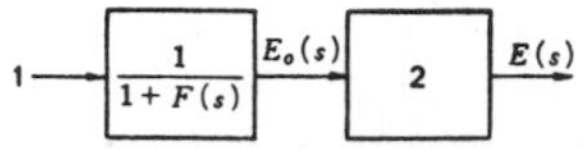

1 - D(s) *or* R(s); 2 - Y(s) *or* 1/H(s)

Fig. 3.3 Block diagram of error

If we use the unit step signal for the disturbance or reference input variation, the block diagram for error computation is uniquely represented as shown in Fig. 3.4 whether the control is of the automatic-regulation or follow-up type. Moreover, the corresponding output signal of the transfer function $1/(1+F(s))$ is also unique regardless of the type of control, and it depends only on the structure of the closed-loop system. Therefore, this output signal is uniquely denoted by $e_0(t)$, which is the t-representation, or by $E_0(s)$, which is the s-representation. It is called the fundamental error response or simply the error response. It is clear that the fundamental error response in automatic regulation is the control variation of the controlled variable when the disturbance transfer function $Y(s)$ is 1. The block diagram in this case is as shown in Fig. 3.5. Thus, if the fundamental error shown in this block diagram is known for an automatic control system, the error response $e(t)$ or $E(s)$ of the controlled variable can easily be computed by using the fundamental error.

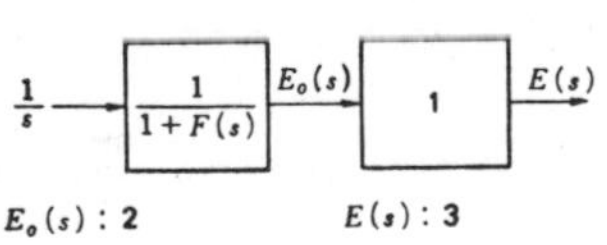

1 - Y(s) *or* 1/H(s); 2 - *fundamental error response*; 3 - *error response of controlled variable*

Fig. 3.4 Block diagram showing error responses when the unit step signal is used (as the input signal in Fig. 3.3)

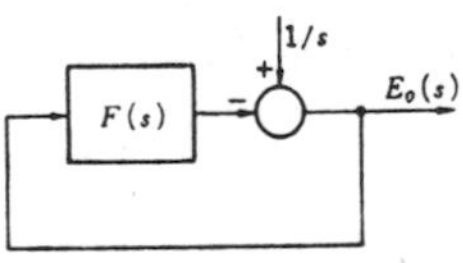

Fig. 3.5 Block diagram of fundamental error response

Suppose that the overall transfer function $F(s)$ is given in the form (2.243). Let us compute the fundamental error. From what was said above, the s-representation $E_o(s)$ of the fundamental response is (c.f. Fig. 3.4):

$$E_o(s)=\frac{1}{1+F(s)}\cdot\frac{1}{s} \tag{3.17}$$

Substituting the expression for $F(s)$ given by (2.243) into equation (3.17), we get

$$E_o(s)=\frac{1}{1+\frac{K(1+sT_1')(1+sT_2')\cdots}{s^n(1+sT_1)(1+sT_2)\cdots}}\cdot\frac{1}{s} \tag{3.18}$$

$$=\frac{s^n(1+sT_1)(1+sT_2)\cdots\cdots}{s^n(1+sT_1)(1+sT_2)\cdots+K(1+sT_1')(1+sT_2')\cdots}\cdot\frac{1}{s} \tag{3.19}$$

To convert $E_o(s)$ to the t-representation, it is necessary, as mentioned in the preceding chapter, to factor the denominator of the expression on the right-hand side of (3.19). That is, it is necessary to solve the equation for s.

$$s^n(1+sT_1)(1+sT_2)\cdots+K(1+sT_1')(1+sT_2')\cdots=0 \tag{3.20}$$

This equation is precisely the equation

$$1+F(s)=0 \tag{3.21}$$

which is obtained by equating the denominator in (3.17) to 0. Equation (3.21) is called the characteristic equation of the automatic control system, and the roots of the characteristic equation are called the characteristic roots. If r_1, r_2, r_3,.. are the roots of equation (3.20), then equation (3.19) can be written in the form

$$E_o(s)=\frac{As^n(1+sT_1)(1+sT_2)\cdots}{(s-r_1)(s-r_2)(s-r_3)\cdots(s-r_m)\cdots}\cdot\frac{1}{s} \tag{3.22}$$

where

$$A=\frac{1}{T_1T_2T_3\cdots\cdots} \tag{3.23}$$

If the given system is a proportional control system, then $n=0$ and hence the fundamental error response $E_o(s)$ is

$$E_o(s)=\frac{A(1+sT_1)(1+sT_2)\cdots}{s(s-r_1)(s-r_2)\cdots(s-r_m)\cdots} \tag{3.24}$$

Expanding this expression into partial fractions, we obtain

$$E_o(s)=\frac{E_0}{s}+\frac{E_1}{s-r_1}+\frac{E_2}{s-r_2}+\cdots\cdots+\frac{E_m}{s-r_m}+\cdots \tag{3.25}$$

Here, E_0, E_1, E_2,..., E_m,...can be found from formula (2.99) or (2.100) as discussed previously. Therefore, the t-representation $e_o(t)$ of the fundamental error will be obtained by applying the inverse Laplace transformation to $E_o(s)$ given in equation (3.25)

$$e_o(t)=\mathcal{L}^{-1}E_o(s)=\mathcal{L}^{-1}\frac{E_0}{s}+\mathcal{L}^{-1}\frac{E_1}{s-r_1}+\mathcal{L}^{-1}\frac{E_2}{s-r_2}+\cdots+\mathcal{L}^{-1}\frac{E_m}{s-r_m}+\cdots$$
$$=E_0\,U\,(t)+E_1\epsilon^{r_1t}\,U\,(t)\,1+E_2\epsilon^{r_2t}+\cdots\cdots+E_m\epsilon^{r_mt}\,U(t)+\cdots\cdots \tag{3.26}$$

The signal $E_0U(t)$ in the above expression is a fixed quantity called the steady-state error component of the fundamental error response. The signal

$$E_1\epsilon^{r_1t}+E_2\epsilon^{r_2t}+\cdots\cdots+E_m\epsilon^{r_mt}+\cdots$$

is a time-dependent variable quantity called the transient error component of the fundamental error response.

Let us consider the case of $n=1$ in equation (3.22). That is, we shall examine the fundamental error response of the type 1 integral control system. The fundamental error response $E_o(s)$ in this case is

$$E_o(s)=\frac{A(1+sT_1)(1+sT_2)\cdots}{(s-r_1)(s-r_2)(s-r_3)\cdots(s-r_m)\cdots} \tag{3.27}$$

If we compute the t-representation $e_o(t)$ of this fundamental error response by the application of the inverse Laplace transformation as before, we obtain

$$e_o(t)=E_1\epsilon^{r_1t}\,1+E_2\epsilon^{r_2t}\,1+E_3\epsilon^{r_3t}\,1+\cdots+E_m\epsilon^{r_mt}\,1+\cdots \tag{3.28}$$

This equation shows that the fundamental error response of a type 1 integral control system has no steady-state error component but only a transient error component. The same conclusion can be made for integral systems of type higher than 1.

If the t-representation $e_o(t)$ of the fundamental error response or the partial-fraction expansion (3.25) of the s-representation $E_o(s)$ of the fundamental error response is found as above, the error response $e\,(t)$ or $E\,(s)$ of the controlled variable can be easily computed. If the given control system is an automatic regulating system, the error response of the controlled variable can be computed as the output signal of the disturbance transfer function $Y(s)$ when the fundamental error response is used as the input signal to the transfer function. If the given system is a follow-up control system, the error response of the controlled variable can be computed as the output signal of the feedback transfer function $1/H(s)$ when the fundamental error response is used as the input signal to the transfer function, as shown in Fig. 3.6.

$$Y(s)=\frac{Y_D}{1+sT_D} \tag{3.29}$$

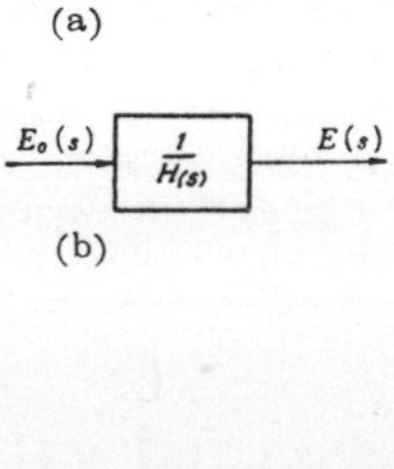

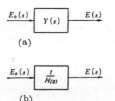

Fig. 3.6 (a) Error response of the controlled variable of an automatic regulating system; (b) error response of the controlled variable of a follow-up control system

For example, if the disturbance transfer function $Y(s)$ is the s-representation of the fundamental error response $E_0(s)$ is

$$E_o(s)=\frac{E_0}{s}+\frac{E_1}{s-r_1}+\frac{E_2}{s-r_2} \tag{3.30}$$

Then, the error response of the controlled variable can be computed by computing the error response of the controlled variable for each term in (3.30) and adding the results. Denoting by $E(s)$ the s-representation of the error response of the controlled variable, we get

$$E(s)=\frac{Y_D}{1+sT_D}E_o(s)=\frac{Y_D/T_D}{s+1/T_D}E_o(s) \tag{3.31}$$

$$=\frac{Y_D/T_D}{s+1/T_D}\left(\frac{E_0}{s}+\frac{E_1}{s-r_1}+\frac{E_2}{s-r_2}\right) \tag{3.32}$$

$$=\frac{Y_D}{T_D}\left(\frac{E_0}{s(s+1/T_D)}+\frac{E_1}{(s-r_1)(s+1/T_D)}+\frac{E_2}{(s-r_2)(s+1/T_D)}\right) \tag{3.33}$$

Here, the general term is

$$\frac{E_m}{(s-r_m)(s+1/T_D)}=\frac{E_mT_D}{1+r_mT_D}\left(\frac{1}{s-r_m}-\frac{1}{s+1/T_D}\right) \tag{3.34}$$

Therefore,

$$E(s)=Y_D\left\{E_0\left(\frac{1}{s}-\frac{1}{s+1/T_D}\right)+\frac{E_1}{1+r_1T_D}\left(\frac{1}{s-r_1}-\frac{1}{s+1/T_D}\right)+\frac{E_2}{1+r_2T_D}\left(\frac{1}{s-r_2}-\frac{1}{s+1/T_D}\right)\right\} \tag{3.35}$$

$$=Y_D\left\{\frac{E_0}{s}+\frac{E_1}{(1+r_1T_D)(s-r_1)}+\frac{E_2}{(1+r_2T_D)(s-r_2)}-\frac{1}{s+1/T_D}\left(E_0+\frac{E_1}{1+r_1T_D}+\frac{E_2}{1+r_2T_D}\right)\right\} \tag{3.36}$$

Hence, the t-representation $e(t)$ of the error response of the controlled variable is

$$e(t)=\mathcal{L}^{-1}E(s)=Y_D\left\{\left(E_0+\frac{E_1}{1+r_1T_D}\epsilon^{r_1t}+\frac{E_2}{1+r_2T_D}\epsilon^{r_2t}\right)-\left(E_0+\frac{E_1}{1+r_1T_D}+\frac{E_2}{1+r_2T_D}\right)\epsilon^{-\frac{t}{T_D}}\right\}1 \tag{3.37}$$

3.4. STEADY-STATE PERFORMANCE

As mentioned already, the (fundamental) error response of the controlled variable of an automatic control system can be separated into two errors: the steady-state error, which is independent of time, and the transient error, which varies as time passes. In this section, we shall discuss only the steady-state error. Since analysis of the steady-state error is relatively simple, we shall compute the steady-state error for two disturbances besides the unit step signal disturbance, namely, a signal that varies at a constant rate (as shown in Fig. 3.7(b) and a signal that varies with a constant acceleration (as shown in Fig. 3.7(c)).

(1) STEADY-STATE ERROR WITH A UNIT STEP-SIGNAL DISTURBANCE

The fundamental response to a disturbance whose variation is a unit step signal is given by equation (3.26) or (3.28), and the corresponding error response of the controlled variable is given, for instance, by equation (3.37). The characteristic roots r_1, r_2,... r_m associated with these equations are in general complex. If their real parts are all negative, the limit of the transient response $t = \infty$ is 0, and the corresponding error response of the controlled variable is equal to the steady-state error. That is, for all the real parts of the characteristic roots to be negative means that the automatic control system is stable. Otherwise the automatic control system has no practical value, and hence it is pointless to compute the steady-state error.

The steady-state error component of the fundamental error response can be computed as the limit of expression (3.26) as $t \to \infty$. That is, the steady-state error component is E_0. In general,

$$E_0 = |E_o(s)s|_{s=0} \tag{3.38}$$

from formula (2.216). If we substitute expression (3.17) into equation (3.38), we obtain

$$E_0 = \left. \frac{1}{1+F(s)} \cdot \frac{1}{s} \cdot s \right|_{s=0} = \frac{1}{1+F(0)} \tag{3.39}$$

Since E_0 is the steady-state error component of the fundamental error response, the corresponding error response of the controlled variable can be computed by multiplying E_0 by $Y(0) = Y_0$ or $1/H(0)$ depending on whether the given system is an automatic regulating system or a follow-up control system. This can be seen from equation (3.31).

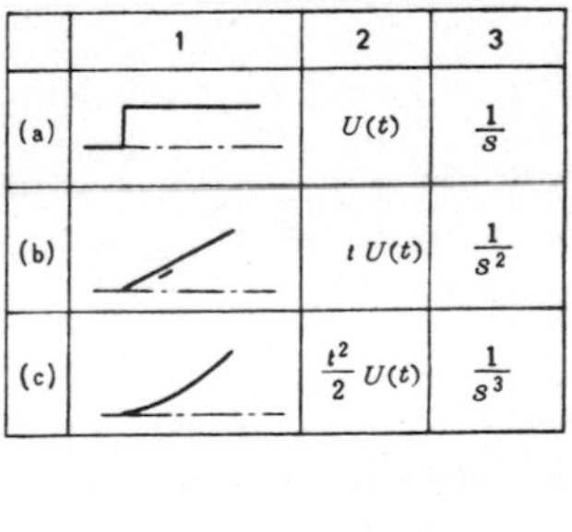

	1	2	3
(a)		$U(t)$	$\frac{1}{s}$
(b)		$t\,U(t)$	$\frac{1}{s^2}$
(c)		$\frac{t^2}{2}U(t)$	$\frac{1}{s^3}$

1 - *signal wave*; 2 - *t-representation*; 3 - *s-representation*

Fig. 3.7 Signal wave of disturbance used as input signals for steady-state error analysis

The value of $F(0)$ in equation (3.31) may vary depending on the form of $F(s)$. If the open loop transfer function $F(s)$ is of the form given by equation (2.243), we have

$$F(s)=\frac{K(1+sT_1')(1+sT_2')(1+sT_3')\cdots}{s^n(1+sT_1)(1+sT_2)(1+sT_3)\cdots\cdots} \tag{3.40}$$

and if $n = 0$ (that is, if the automatic control system under consideration is a proportional control system), then $F(0) = K$ is a finite constant. Therefore, the steady-state error component E_0 of the fundamental error response is

$$E_0=\frac{1}{1+K} \tag{3.41}$$

which is again a finite constant. On the other hand, if $n > 1$, that is, if the system under consideration is an integral control system, then $F(0) = \infty$, and hence the steady-state error component E_0 of the fundamental error response is zero. Summarizing these results, we conclude that the steady-state error component of the fundamental error response to a unit step signal input is a finite constant for a proportional control system, as shown in equation (3.41), and is theoretically zero for an integral control system.

(2) STEADY-STATE ERRORS FOR DISTURBANCES

The s-representation of a disturbance that varies at a constant rate is $1/s^2$. Therefore, the s-representation E_0 of the fundamental error response is

$$E_0(s)=\frac{1}{1+F(s)}\cdot\frac{1}{s^2} \tag{3.42}$$

If we convert this equation into a t-representation, we get

$$E_0=|E_0(s)\cdot s|_{s=0} \tag{3.43}$$

$$=\left|\frac{1}{1+F(s)}\cdot\frac{1}{s^2}\cdot s\right|_{s=0} \tag{3.44}$$

$$=\left|\frac{1}{s(1+F(s))}\right|_{s=0} \tag{3.45}$$

$$=\left|\frac{1}{sF(s)}\right|_{s=0} \tag{3.46}$$

If the open-loop transfer function $F(s)$ is of the form (3.40) and if $n = 0$, then $|sF(s)|_{s=0} = 0$, and hence E_0 is ∞ (from equation (3.46)). Therefore, this system is theoretically not controllable. If $n=1$, then $|sF(s)|_{s=0} = K$, and hence,

$$E_0=\frac{1}{K} \tag{3.47}$$

If $n \geq 2$, then $|sF(s)|_{s=0} = \infty$, and hence the steady-state error component E_0 is zero.

Summarising these results, we draw the following conclusion. If the disturbance varies at a constant rate, a proportional control system has no practical value, since the steady-state error is infinite. On the other hand, a type-1 integral control system has a finite steady-state error $1/K$ as shown in equation (3.47). Therefore, in order to reduce the steady-state error, the value of K has to be increased. The constant K used here is the gain constant appearing in equation (2.241). It is also called an error coefficient because of the foregoing. If $n \geq 2$, that is, if the system is an integral control system of type higher than 1, the theoretical value of the steady-state error is zero.

Similarly, the steady-state error for an input signal that varies with a constant acceleration is also easily computed. We only state the result. For a type-0 or type-1 control system; the steady-state error is infinite. For an automatic control system of type higher than 2, the steady-state error is zero.

It is clear from the error analysis in this section that an integral control system is superior to a proportional control system as far as the steady-state performance is concerned. The performance of a higher-type integral control system is better than that of a lower-type one in this respect. On the other hand, it becomes more difficult to get a superior transient performance as the type number increases. Therefore, in practice it is desirable to increase n only to a certain value.

3.5. INFERENCE OF THE TRANSIENT PERFORMANCE

As we have seen, it is relatively simple to compute the steady-state error. On the other hand, it is much more difficult to express the transient error accurately. As briefly mentioned above, it is necessary to solve the characteristic equation for the characteristic roots in order to compute the error response. Since the characteristic equation is an algebraic equation, it is extremely simple to solve the characteristic equation if its degree is no greater than 2. However, as the degree increases, solution of the characteristic equation becomes more difficult. Therefore, this method is not practical for automatic control systems with characteristic equations of high degree. Consequently, we are almost forced to use the special methods discussed in Chapter V when analysing the error responses of such automatic control systems. In fact, it is not sufficient just to find the error response or transient error for automatic control engineering. We also need to determine what design improvements are required to convert an unsatisfactory automatic control system into one that performs with the prescribed transient response or error response. For this purpose, it is more important to find the relation between the error response and the structure of the automatic control system than to compute the error response accurately.

The transient response of an automatic control system of order no greater than 2 can be computed easily and accurately. An automatic control system whose characteristic equation is of a degree higher than 2 has a different block diagram and transfer function from those of a second-order system. However, the transient response of the system is, in many cases, quite similar to that of a second-order system. In particular, a well-designed practical automatic control system has a transient response much like that of a second-order system. Consequently, when we wish to analyse the transient response of a higher-order automatic control system, we may instead analyse the transient response of a second-order system approximating to that of the higher-order system, instead of computing the transient response of the latter directly.

In fact, we may assert that the essential problem in the analysis or synthesis of a transient response is that of finding out how well a higher-order system is approximated by a suitable second-order system. We usually use the following two methods:
1. The frequency response method, 2. The root configuration method. These methods will be discussed in detail in later chapters. We shall only outline them here.

If we use a sinusoidal wave of unit amplitude as the input signal to a network and if we vary its angular frequency ω from 0 to ∞, then the amplitude and phase angle of the output sinusoidal wave will vary accordingly. These variations in the amplitude and phase angle are referred to by the term frequency response. The frequency response of a system is closely related to the transient response of the system. In general, the transient response can be found from the frequency response and vice versa. Consequently, if the transient response of a second-order system is similar to that of a higher-order system, the frequency response of the second-order system will also be similar to that of the higher-order system. Although it is quite difficult to find the transient response of a higher-order system directly, it is not so difficult to compute the frequency response. This fact will be used for finding the transient response of a higher-order system indirectly. Thus, to find the transient response of a higher-order system, we first compute the frequency response of the higher-order system. Then, we find a second-order system whose frequency response is similar to that of the higher-order system. The transient response of this second-order system will also be similar to that of the given higher-order system. This is the principle according to which the frequency response method is used to approximate a higher-order system by means of a second-order system.

The number of characteristic roots of a characteristic equation must be equal to the degree of the characteristic equation. In general, they are complex numbers and can be plotted on the complex plane, as shown in Fig. 3.8. The fact that the transient response of a higher-order system is similar to that of a second-order system means that two particular characteristic roots (out of all the characteristic roots) have the dominant effect on the transient response of the given higher-order system and that all other characteristic roots have no significant effect. If so, the given higher-order system can be well approximated by a second-order system whose characteristic roots are those two. Such roots are called the dominant roots. It is not always easy to find the dominant roots exactly. However, it is not difficult to compute approximate values of the dominant roots or to determine an effective domain to which the dominant roots belong. Moreover, it is relatively simple to design an automatic control system with certain prescribed dominant roots that can be accurately set up (see Chapter VIII).

The frequency response method and the root configuration method have different advantages and disadvantages, depending on the purposes for which they are used. However, they are both used for

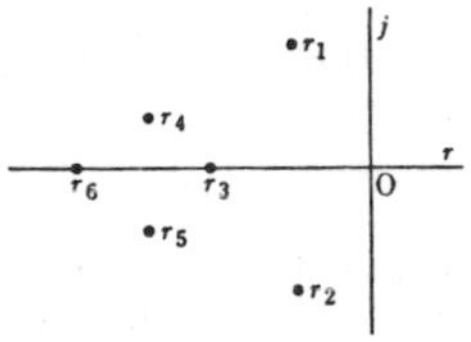

Fig. 3.8 Root configuration on the complex plane

the common purpose of approximating the characteristics of a higher-order system to the characteristics of a suitable second-order system.

3.6. RESPONSE OF A SECOND-ORDER SYSTEM

It has just been shown that a higher-order system is usually approximated by a suitable second-order system by means of either the frequency response method or the root configuration method when the transient response of the higher-order system is to be investigated. We shall now compute the error response or the transient response of a second-order automatic control system.

Since we wish to know only the transient error, we do not need to consider the steady-state error. Consequently, we shall choose a second-order system with no steady-state error and shall investigate the error response and the transient response of this network. We may choose a type-1 integral control system as shown in Fig. 3.9 for such a second-order system (see p. 79).

It is clear that the block diagram in Fig. 3.9 (a) is for computing the error response and the block diagram in Fig. 3.9 (b) is for computing the transient response. If we denote by $E_0(s)$ the s-representation of the error response, then, from the block diagram in Fig. 3.9 (a), we have

$$E_0(s)=\frac{1/s}{1+\dfrac{K}{s(1+sT)}} \tag{3.48}$$

$$=\frac{sT+1}{s^2T+s+K} \tag{3.49}$$

$$=\frac{s+\dfrac{1}{T}}{s^2+\dfrac{s}{T}+\dfrac{K}{T}} \tag{3.50}$$

To normalise this equation we use the following transformations:

$$\omega_n=\sqrt{\frac{K}{T}},\quad \zeta=\frac{1}{2\sqrt{KT}} \tag{3.51}$$

The number ω_n is called the specific angular frequency or the undamped natural angular frequency, and the number ζ is called the damping ratio. The transformations given by equations (3.51) can be written in the form

$$T=\frac{1}{2\zeta\omega_n},\quad K=\frac{\omega_n}{2\zeta} \tag{3.52}$$

If we apply these transformations to equation (3.50), we obtain

$$E_o(s)=\frac{s+2\zeta\omega_n}{s^2+2\zeta\omega_n s+\omega_n^2} \tag{3.53}$$

In order to find the t-representation $e_o(t)=\mathcal{L}^{-1}E_o(s)$ of the error response, we need to solve the characteristic equation

$$s^2+2\zeta\omega_n s+\omega_n^2=0 \tag{3.54}$$

The roots of this equation, that is the characteristic roots r are

$$r=-\zeta\omega_n\pm\sqrt{\zeta^2\omega_n^2-\omega_n^2} \tag{3.55}$$

$$=(-\zeta\pm\sqrt{\zeta^2-1})\omega_n \tag{3.56}$$

If $\zeta>1$, we have two real roots. If we denote them by $-\alpha_1$ and $-\alpha_2$, we have

$$-\alpha_1=(-\zeta+\sqrt{\zeta^2-1})\omega_n \tag{3.57}$$

$$-\alpha_2=(-\zeta-\sqrt{\zeta^2-1})\omega_n \tag{3.58}$$

Consequently, equation (3.53) can be rewritten as

$$E_o(s)=\frac{s+\alpha_1+\alpha_2}{(s+\alpha_1)(s+\alpha_2)} \tag{3.59}$$

$$=\frac{1}{\alpha_2-\alpha_1}\left(\frac{\alpha_2}{s+\alpha_1}-\frac{\alpha_1}{s+\alpha_2}\right) \tag{3.60}$$

Therefore, the fundamental error response $e_o(t)$ is

$$e_o(t)=\frac{1}{\alpha_2-\alpha_1}\left(\mathcal{L}^{-1}\frac{\alpha_2}{s+\alpha_1}-\mathcal{L}^{-1}\frac{\alpha_1}{s+\alpha_2}\right) \tag{3.61}$$

$$=\frac{1}{\alpha_2-\alpha_1}(\alpha_2\epsilon^{-\alpha_1 t}-\alpha_1\epsilon^{-\alpha_2 t}) \tag{3.62}$$

If $\zeta>1$ in equation (3.54), the characteristic roots are complex numbers. Denoting them by $-\alpha_0\pm j\omega_0$, we have from equation (3.56)

$$\left.\begin{aligned}-\alpha_0+j\,\omega_0&=(-\zeta+j\sqrt{1-\zeta^2})\omega_n\\-\alpha_0-j\,\omega_0&=(-\zeta-j\sqrt{1-\zeta^2})\omega_n\end{aligned}\right\} \tag{3.63}$$

Therefore,

$$\left.\begin{aligned}\alpha_0&=\zeta\omega_n\\\omega_0&=\omega_n\sqrt{1-\zeta^2}\end{aligned}\right\} \tag{3.64}$$

The number α_0 is called a damping factor, and the number ω_0 is called a damped angular frequency. Substituting the values given by equation (3.64) into equation (3.53), we get

$$E_o(s)=\frac{s+2\alpha_0}{\{s-(-\alpha_0+j\omega_0)\}\{s-(-\alpha_0-j\omega_0)\}} \quad (3.65)$$

$$=\frac{s+2\alpha_0}{(s+\alpha_0-j\omega_0)(s+\alpha_0+j\omega_0)} \quad (3.66)$$

$$=\frac{\frac{1}{2}\left(1-j\frac{\alpha_0}{\omega_0}\right)}{s+\alpha_0-j\omega_0}+\frac{\frac{1}{2}\left(1+j\frac{\alpha_0}{\omega_0}\right)}{s+\alpha_0+j\omega_0} \quad (3.67)$$

Now, we set

$$\gamma_0=\frac{\alpha_0}{\omega_0} \quad (3.68)$$

This number γ_0 is called a damping coefficient. If we substitute this expression into equation (3.67), we obtain

$$E_o(s)=\frac{1}{2}\left(\frac{1-j\gamma_0}{s+\alpha_0-j\omega_0}+\frac{1+j\gamma_0}{s+\alpha_0+j\omega_0}\right) \quad (3.69)$$

Therefore, the t-representation $e_o(t)$ of the fundamental error response in this case is

$$e_o(t)=\mathcal{L}^{-1}E_o(s) \quad (3.70)$$

$$=\frac{1}{2}\{(1-j\gamma_0)\epsilon^{(-\alpha_0+j\omega_0)t}+(1+j\gamma_0)\epsilon^{(-\alpha_0-j\omega_0)t}\} \quad (3.71)$$

$$=\epsilon^{-\alpha_0 t}\left(\frac{\epsilon^{j\omega_0 t}+\epsilon^{-j\omega_0 t}}{2}+\gamma_0\frac{\epsilon^{j\omega_0 t}-\epsilon^{-j\omega_0 t}}{2j}\right) \quad (3.72)$$

$$=\epsilon^{-\alpha_0 t}(\cos\omega_0 t+\gamma_0\sin\omega_0 t) \quad (3.73)$$

$$=\sqrt{1+\gamma_0^2}\,\epsilon^{-\alpha_0 t}\cos(\omega_0 t-\tan^{-1}\gamma_0) \quad (3.74)$$

$$=\sqrt{1+\gamma_0^2}\,\epsilon^{-\gamma_0\omega_0 t}\cos(\omega_0 t-\tan^{-1}\gamma_0) \quad (3.75)$$

This expression shows that the fundamental error response in this case is a damped cosinusoidal wave.

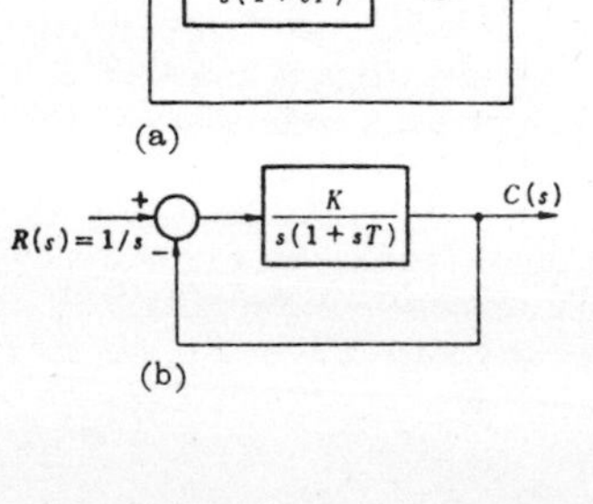

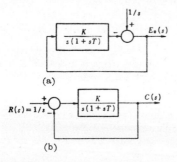

Fig. 3.9 Fundamental error response and transient response of a standard second-order system: (a) block diagram for computing the fundamental error response; (b) block diagram for computing the transient response

If we substitute the expressions (3.64) into equation (3.75), we can write equation (3.75) in ζ and ω_n as follows:

$$e_0(t) = \frac{\epsilon^{-\zeta\omega_n t}}{\sqrt{1-\zeta^2}} \cos\left(\sqrt{1-\zeta^2}\,\omega_n t - \tan^{-1}\frac{\zeta}{\sqrt{1-\zeta^2}}\right) \tag{3.76}$$

As clearly shown by the last two equations, the error response of a second-order system is completely determined by the damping coefficient γ_0 and the damped angular frequency ω_0 or by the undamped natural angular frequency ω_n and the damping ratio ζ. The constants, ω_0 and ω_n are always used in the forms $\omega_0 t$ and $\omega_n t$ (that is, multiplied by the time). Therefore, a variation of ω_0 or ω_n means a change in the time scale. That is, ω_0 or ω_n represents the speed of the error response. If we plot $\omega_0 t$ on the horizontal axis and the error response on the vertical axis, then the curve of the error response will be completely determined by γ_0 alone or by only ζ alone. That is, the damping coefficient γ_0 and the damping ratio represent the shape of the error response wave. Fig. 3.10 shows various waves of the error response of an automatic control system in practical use. They are plotted for various values of γ_0 on a sheet where $\omega_0 t$ is plotted on the horizontal axis.

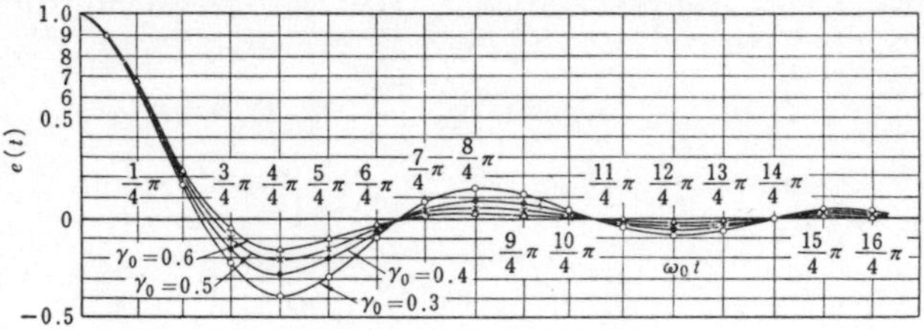

Fig. 3.10 Fundamental error response of a standard second-order system

We have just computed the error response $e_o(t)$ of a standard second-order system. Using the usual technique, we can find the transient response $c_o(t)$ from the error response:

$$c_o(t) = U(t) - e_o(t) \tag{3.77}$$

$$= \{1 - \sqrt{1+\gamma_0^2}\,\epsilon^{-\gamma_0\omega_0 t}\cos(\omega_0 t - \tan^{-1}\gamma_0)\}\ 1 \tag{3.78}$$

As clearly shown in Fig. 3.10, if the error response is oscillatory, the response takes the value 0 at a certain instant and then takes a value larger or smaller than 0. The ratio of the maximum value of the error response to the error response at $t = 0$ (in Fig. 3.10, the error response at $t = 0$ is 1) is called the overshoot.

Let us compute the overshoot from equation (3.75). First we substitute $\omega t = \theta$ in equation (3.75) and differentiate the resulting expression with respect to 0. Equating this derivative to zero, we obtain

$$\frac{de_o(t)}{d\theta}=\frac{d}{d\theta}\{\sqrt{1+\gamma_0^2}\epsilon^{-\gamma_0\theta}\cos(\theta-\tan^{-1}\gamma_0)\} \quad (3.79)$$

$$=-\sqrt{1+\gamma_0^2}\,\gamma_0\epsilon^{-\gamma_0\theta}\cos(\theta-\tan^{-1}\gamma_0)-\sqrt{1+\gamma_0^2}\,\epsilon^{-\gamma_0\theta}\sin(\theta-\tan^{-1}\gamma_0)=0 \quad (3.80)$$

This equation is solved as follows:

$$\epsilon^{-\gamma_0\theta}\{\gamma_0\cos(\theta-\tan^{-1}\gamma_0)+\sin(\theta-\tan^{-1}\gamma_0)\}=0 \quad (3.81)$$

$$\frac{\sin(\theta-\tan^{-1}\gamma_0)}{\cos(\theta-\tan^{-1}\gamma_0)}=\tan(\theta-\tan^{-1}\gamma_0)=-\gamma_0 \quad (3.82)$$

$$\theta-\tan^{-1}\gamma_0=-\tan^{-1}\gamma_0+n\pi \quad (3.83)$$

Therefore,

$$\theta=n\pi \quad (3.84)$$

Here, the number n must be an integer. However, it is clear from Fig. 3.10 that we should take $n = 1$ for the overshoot. Therefore, we substitute $\theta = \pi$ in equation (3.75) to find the overshoot. Then,

$$\Theta_m=|\sqrt{1+\gamma_0^2}\epsilon^{-\gamma_0\theta}\cos(\theta-\tan^{-1}\gamma_0)|_{\theta=\pi} \quad (3.85)$$

$$=\sqrt{1+\gamma_0^2}\epsilon^{-\gamma_0\pi}\cos(\pi-\tan^{-1}\gamma_0) \quad (3.86)$$

$$=-\sqrt{1+\gamma_0^2}\epsilon^{-\gamma_0\pi}\cos(\tan^{-1}\gamma_0) \quad (3.87)$$

$$=-\epsilon^{-\gamma_0\pi} \quad (3.88)$$

The reason the overshoot is negative is clear from the error response curve in Fig. 3.10. Equation (3.88) indicates that the overshoot of a second-order system is completely determined by the damping coefficient γ_0.

The quantitative relation between the damping ratio, the damping coefficient γ_0, and the overshoot θ_m of the second-order system represented by the block diagram in Fig. 3.9 is presented in Fig. 6.1.

EXERCISE PROBLEMS

1. Consider an automatic control system represented by the block diagram below. We assume that the reference input is constant and that the disturbance is 100%. What percentage variation will occur in the controlled variable corresponding to the disturbance in the steady state?

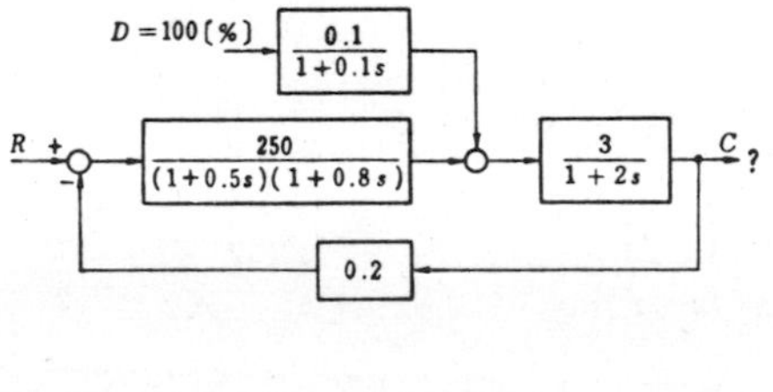

2. The diagram below shows an automatic voltage regulator. We wish to have 1% variation in the output terminal voltage e_o of the primary generator when the regulator is loaded by closing the switch *Sw*. What should be the suitable amplification coefficient A of the amplifier? Here, the system constants are as follows:

R_i = 0.1 [Ω] = internal resistance of the primary generator;
R_l = 0.1 [Ω] = load resistance;
B = 0.5 = feedback transfer function.

We assume that the d.c. amplification coefficient between the voltage applied to the field winding of the excitor and the electromotive force e_a of the primary generator is 1.

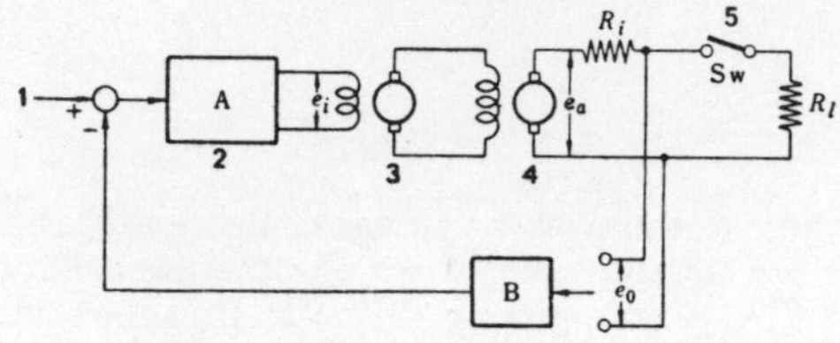

1 - R (*constant*); 2 - *amplifier*; 3 - *excitor*
4 - *primary generator*; 5 - *switch*

3. The block diagrams below show the performance mechanisms of typical electronic industrial controllers. Find the equivalent transfer function (= $c(s)/R(s)$) for each block diagram. We assume that the amplification coefficient A of the amplifier is infinite.

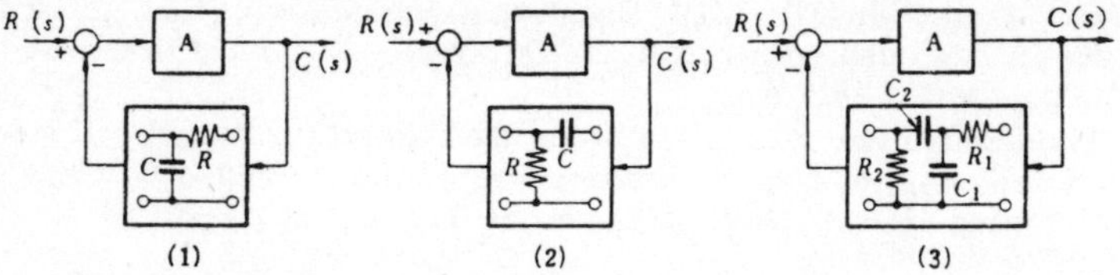

4. The networks shown in the diagrams below are used in an analogue computer to find the transfer functions of the industrial controllers of problem (3). These networks are all negative feedback systems. Construct the block diagram of each network as shown in Fig. 3.2(a), and find the equivalent transfer function for each block diagram. We assume that the amplification coefficients of the amplifiers are all $-\infty$.

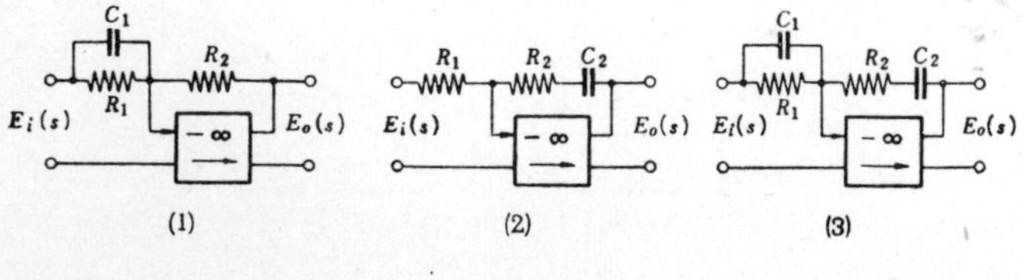

5. The amplifier shown in Fig. (a) below is called a cathode follower; that shown in Fig. (b) is called an anode. The internal resistances of both amplifiers are small when observed from the output terminals. Find the internal resistances of both amplifiers. We assume that the mutual conductance of the vacuum tube is gm = 10 m Ω and that the plate resistance (the internal resistance of the vacuum tube) is infinite.

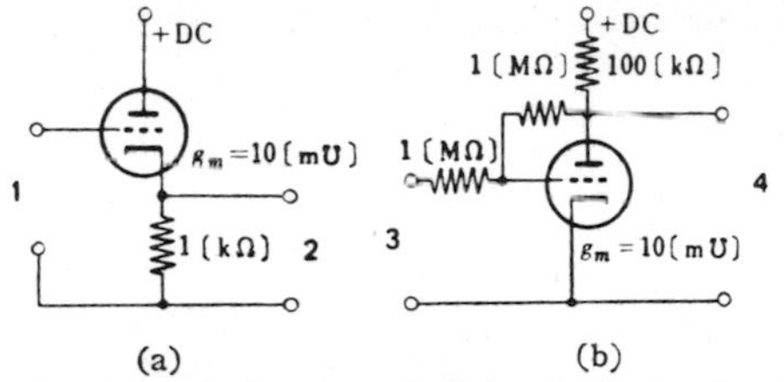

1 - *input terminals*; 2 - *output terminals*; 3 - *input terminals*; 4 - *output terminals*

6. The diagram below shows a d.c. voltage regulator that uses vacuum tubes. Here, V_3 is a voltage-regulating tube, and the voltage e_s applied to the tube is held at 100 [V]. V_2 is a d.c. amplifier that uses twin triode tubes, amplifies $e_s - e_o$ thirty times, and supplies the amplified voltage to the grid of the tube V_1. The internal resistance of the tube V_1 is R_i = 500 [Ω], and the amplifying coefficient of the tube V_1 is μ = 3.2. We assume that R_s is the equivalent internal resistance of the rectifier and that R_3 = 300 [Ω]. Find the variation of the output terminal voltage when the no-load voltage across the output terminals of the rectifier varies by 40 [V]. Find the equivalent internal resistance of the network when viewed from the output terminals toward the electric source.

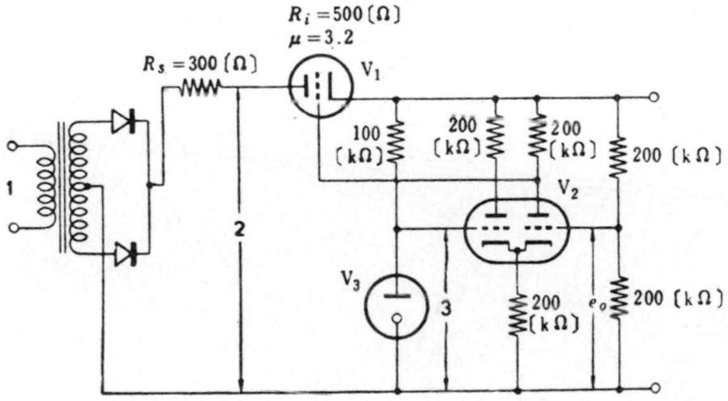

1 - *a.c. electric source*; 2 - *output terminals of* 3 - e_s = 100 [*v*] (*constant*)

7. The diagram below shows an oil-pressure servomechanism that uses a pilot valve. It is often used as a single unit or as an active element of an automatic control system. Find the transient response of this system; that is, find the output displacement for an instantaneous 1 cm variation in the input displacement. We assume that

the oil pressure applied to the pilot valve is constant and that the relationship between the stem displacement x_e [cm] in the pilot valve and the rate of flow q [cm^3/sec] of the oil transport to the oil-pressure motor is given by

$$q = 5 \times 10^2 \, x_e$$

We also assume that the effective cross section of the piston of the oil-pressure motor is 10 [cm^2] and that the dividing ratio of the lever is 1:9.

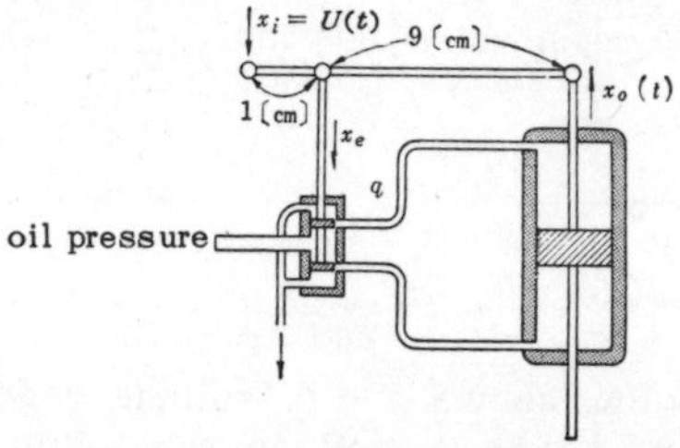

8. The diagram above shows a jet-type oil-pressure servomotor. Find the undamped natural angular frequency ω_n and the damping ratio of this system. Here the system constants are as follows:
$k_1 = p/x_e$, where p is the difference between the oil-pressures in the cylinder compartments above and below the piston and x_e is the displacement of the jet pipe;
A = effective cross section of the piston of the oil-pressure motor;
m = mass of the load.

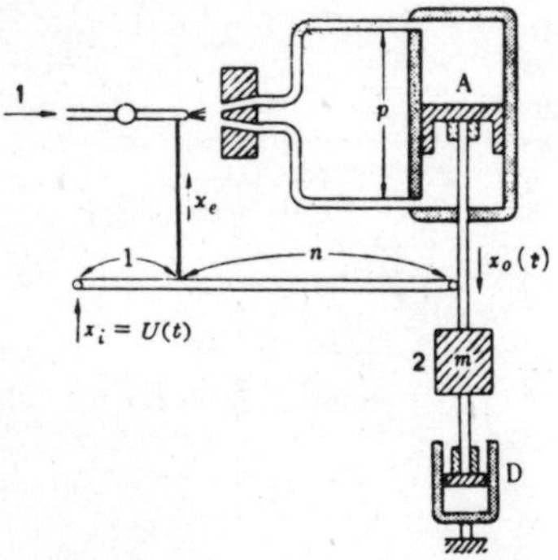

1 oil pressure
2 load

D = damping constant of the load
n = advantage ratio of the lever

9. Consider the system shown in the diagram on the page opposite. Construct the block diagram of this system and find the transfer function when x_i is the input signal and x_o is the output signal. The system constants are as shown in the diagram. We assume that

$k = q / x_e$ where q is the rate of flow of the oil to the cylinder and x_e is the displacement of the stem of the pilot valve.

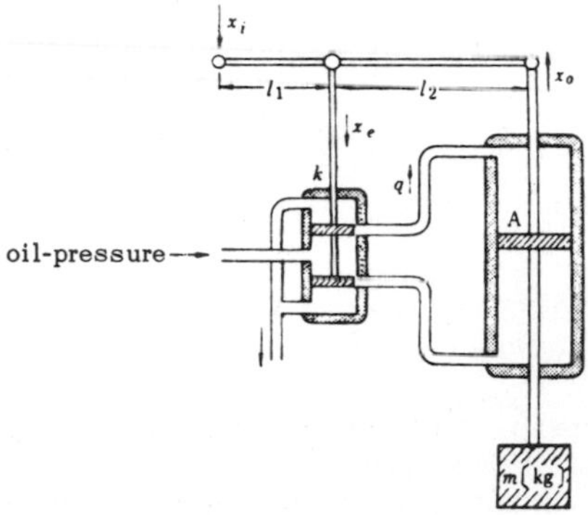

10. Consider the following three open-loop transfer functions:

(i) $\frac{5(1+2s)}{s(1+4s)}$

(ii) $\frac{5(1+6s)(1+s)}{s(1+4s)(1+s)}$

(iii) $\frac{5}{s(1+4s)}$

Automatic control systems with these open-loop transfer functions are second-order systems. The three have different response characteristics. Construct the block diagram of each, regarding them as unity feedback systems. Find the transient response of each and sketch the transient response curve. Point out the differences between them.

11. The diagram shown below shows a jet-type oil-pressure control of a d.c. motor. Find the fundamental error response of this system and of the controlled variable to an instantaneous change in the load torque τ_0, and plot them to obtain the response curves. Here we assume that the torque τ $[N-m]$ of the d.c. motor is proportional to the field current i_f and that the proportional constant is k_0. The damping coefficient of the rotation shaft of the d.c. motor is D. We neglect the moment of inertia. (In many cases, we cannot neglect the moment of inertia.) The ratio of the output voltage e_p of the potentiometer P_2 to the rotation angle θ_c of the wiper is given by $e_p / \theta_c = k_p$. We assume the same relation for the potentiometer P_1.

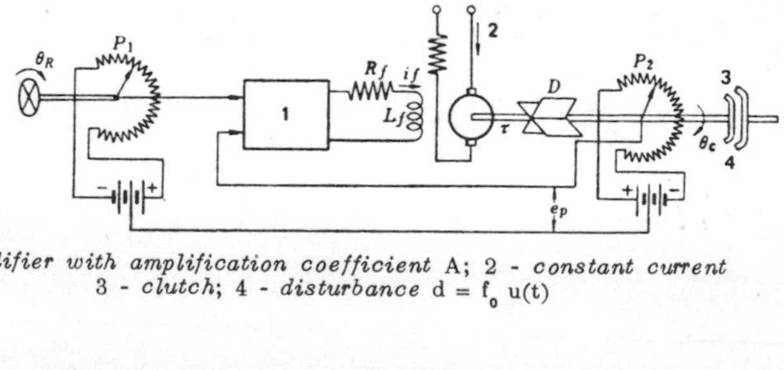

1 - *amplifier with amplification coefficient* A; 2 - *constant current*
3 - *clutch*; 4 - *disturbance* $d = f_0\, u(t)$

12. In the block diagram below, find the error response of the controlled variable to the disturbance. We assume that $T = 0.2$

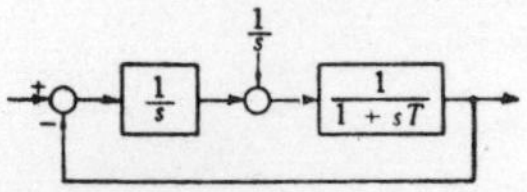

13. The fundamental error response $e_0(t)$ is given by the equation

$$e_0(t) = 1.12\, \epsilon^{-2.5t} \cos(5t - 26.8°)$$

and the disturbance transfer function $Y(s)$ is given by the equation

$$Y(s) = \frac{0.5}{1+2s}$$

Find the corresponding error response of the controlled variable and the overshoot of this system.

14. The block diagram given below shows an automatic control system which has a local feedback path. Find the damping ratio ζ of this system when the dashed-line block is removed from the block diagram. Next, assume that the dashed-line block exists as shown in the diagram. What is the value of T for which $\zeta = 1$?

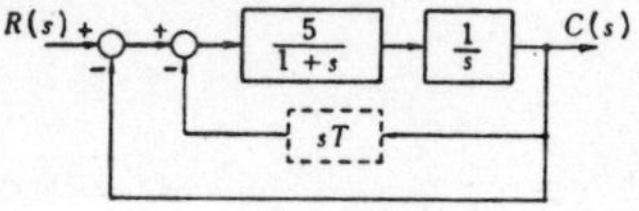

4

Frequency Response of Automatic Control Systems

4.1. RELATION BETWEEN FREQUENCY RESPONSE AND TRANSIENT RESPONSE

As mentioned in the preceding chapter, the frequency response method is one way of investigating the transient response of an automatic control system. We shall discuss this method in detail. In order to justify the effectiveness of the frequency response method, we need to show that there is a close relation between the frequency response and the transient response and that the transient response can be evaluated by computing the frequency response.

As stated previously, the frequency response of a system is the signal-transmission characteristic of the system when a sinusoidal input signal is applied. The value of the frequency response depends on the angular frequency of the sinusoidal input and can be expressed quantitatively as follows:

Consider a network whose transfer function is $F(p)$ and suppose that a sinusoidal signal $A_i\epsilon^{j\omega t}$ is applied to the network as an input signal. If we denote by $A_o\epsilon^{j(\omega t+\phi)}$ the output signal to the sinusoidal input, then

$$A_o\epsilon^{j(\omega t+\phi)} = F(j\omega)A_i\epsilon^{j\omega t} \tag{4.1}$$

where $F(j\omega)$ is obtained by substituting $j\omega$ for p in $F(p)$. The value $F(j\omega)$ is the frequency response of this network. It is clear that $F(j\omega)$ is a vector. That is, $F(j\omega)$ is a value consisting of a magnitude and a phase angle. Therefore, to express the frequency response completely, we need to specify how the magnitude and the phase angle vary according to the angular frequency of the sinusoidal input signal.

As the first step in studying the relation between the transient response and the frequency response, let us find the relation between the frequency response and the impulse response.

Consider a system whose transfer function is $F(p)$ and suppose that a unit impulse $\delta(t)$ is applied to the system as an input signal (see Fig. 4.1). The output signal $f(t)$ for the unit impulse input signal can be computed by applying the inverse Laplace transformation to the transfer function $F(p)$.

That is,

$$f(t)=\mathcal{L}^{-1}F(s) \tag{4.2}$$

where $F(s)$ is obtained by substituting s for p in $F(p)$.

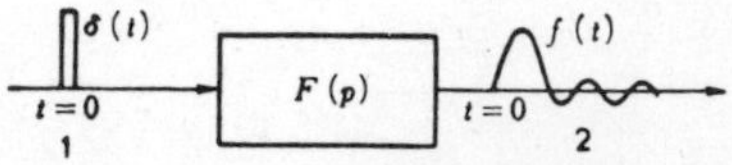

1 - *input signal*; 2 - *output signal*

Fig. 4.1 An impulse response

Let us investigate the properties of the unit impulse that is used as the input signal in Fig. 4.1. This impulse can be regarded as the periodic rectangular wave shown in Fig 4.2 with an extremely large half-period $T/2$, an extremely large amplitude I_m, and an extremely small width τ. The pulse of Fig. 4.2 can be expanded in a Fourier series:

$$I=\sum_{n=0}^{\infty}\left\{\frac{2I_m}{(2n+1)\pi}\sin\left((2n+1)\frac{2\pi}{T}\tau\right)\cos(2n+1)\frac{2\pi}{T}t\right\}$$
$$+\sum_{n=0}^{\infty}\left\{\frac{2I_m}{(2n+1)\pi}\left(1-\cos(2n+1)\frac{2\pi}{T}\tau\right)\sin(2n+1)\frac{2\pi}{T}t\right\} \tag{4.3}$$

If we let $\tau\to\infty$ and $\tau\to 0$ maintaining $I_m\tau$ equal to 1 (where $I_m\tau$ is the area under one rectangular pulse), then 1 in equation (4.3) represents the unit impulse $\delta(t)$. We then have

$$\lim_{\frac{\tau}{T}\to 0}\left\{\sin(2n+1)\frac{2\pi}{T}\tau\right\}=(2n+1)\frac{2\pi}{T}\tau \tag{4.4}$$

$$\lim_{\frac{\tau}{T}\to 0}\left\{\cos(2n+1)\frac{2\pi}{T}\tau\right\}=1 \tag{4.5}$$

$$I_m=\frac{1}{\tau} \tag{4.6}$$

Therefore, the unit impulse $\delta(t)$ is represented by the following equation:

$$I=\delta(t)=\sum_{n=0}^{\infty}\left\{\frac{2I_m}{(2n+1)\pi}(2n+1)\frac{2\pi}{T}\tau\cos(2n+1)\frac{2\pi}{T}t\right\} \tag{4.7}$$

$$=\frac{4}{T}\sum_{n=0}^{\infty}\cos(2n+1)\frac{2\pi}{T}t \tag{4.8}$$

The quantity $2\pi/T$ is the angular frequency of the fundamental harmonic. Denoting $2\pi/T$ by ω_0, we have

$$\delta(t)=\frac{4}{T}\sum_{n=0}^{\infty}\cos(2n+1)\omega_0 t \tag{4.9}$$

This equation shows that, if we expand the unit impulse $\delta(t)$ in a Fourier series, the amplitude of every high harmonic is equal to $4/T$. Since the angular frequency ω_0 or the frequency $f_0=\omega_0/2\pi$ of the fundamental harmonic has an extremely small value, a high harmonic is very close to the adjacent high harmonic. Therefore, the unit impulse $\delta(t)$ can be regarded as the superposition of all cosinusoidal waves each of which has an amplitude $4/T$ and a frequency between 0 and ∞. Curves obtained by plotting the amplitude of each component harmonic or the phase angle of each component harmonic against the frequency or angular frequency are called frequency spectra. From the above discussion, it is clear that the frequency spectra of the unit impulse $\delta(t)$ are as shown in Fig. 4.3. Figure 4.3(a) presents the frequency spectrum of the harmonic amplitude. It shows that the amplitudes of all harmonics are equal to a fixed value independent of the frequency. Figure 4.3(b) presents the frequency spectrum of the harmonic phase and shows that the phase angles of all harmonics are equal to zero regardless of the frequency.

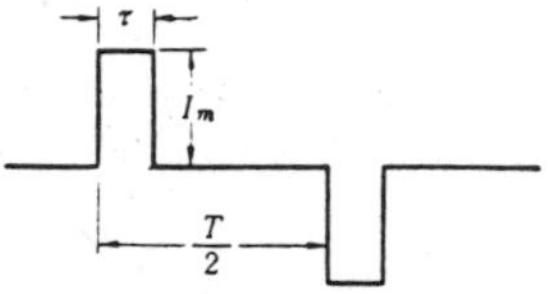

Fig. 4.2 A rectangular pulse wave

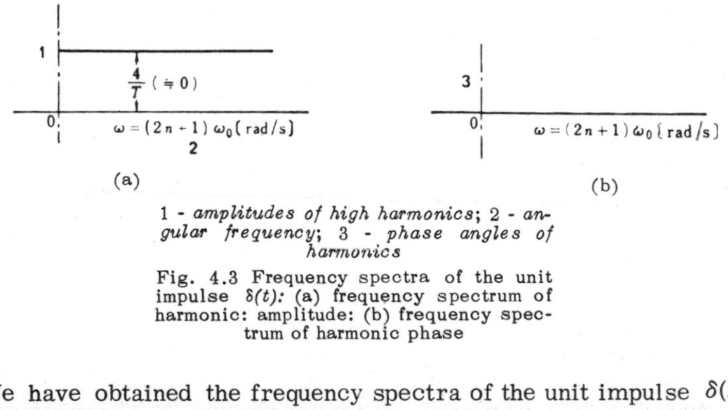

1 - *amplitudes of high harmonics*; 2 - *angular frequency*; 3 - *phase angles of harmonics*

Fig. 4.3 Frequency spectra of the unit impulse $\delta(t)$: (a) frequency spectrum of harmonic: amplitude: (b) frequency spectrum of harmonic phase

We have obtained the frequency spectra of the unit impulse $\delta(t)$ by a Fourier expansion. Using the same method, we can construct the frequency spectra of the ouput signal $f(t)$. That is, we regard $f(t)$ as a periodic wave whose half-period is infinite, and we obtain the Fourier expansion of $f(t)$. Using this Fourier expansion, we can construct the frequency spectra of $f(t)$ by the same method as before. Fig. 4.4 (a) shows the frequency spectrum of harmonic amplitude and Fig. 4.4 (b) shows that of a harmonic phase.

Figure 4.1 illustrates the fact that, if the unit impulse $\delta(t)$ is applied to the transfer function $F(p)$ as an input signal, the corresponding output signal is $f(t)$. This fact can also be expressed as follows: if a signal wave whose frequency spectra are as shown in Fig. 4.3 is applied to the transfer function $F(p)$ as an input signal, then the corresponding output signal is the signal wave whose frequency spectra are as shown in Fig. 4.4. If we wish to find the frequency spectra of $f(t)$ shown in Fig. 4.4, we can construct the frequency spectra directly from the frequency spectra of the input signal shown in Fig.4.3 and the transfer function $F(p)$ without using the Fourier expansion of $f(t)$. Specifically, if we let $I(j\omega)$ be the vector representation of the amplitude and the phase angle of the harmonic for an arbitrary angular frequency ω in the frequency spectra of the input signal, then the output signal of $F(p)$ for the input signal $I(j\omega)$ is $F(j\omega).I(j\omega)$. Therefore, if we plot the values of $F(j\omega).I(j\omega)$ for the values of ω from 0 to ∞, we obtain the frequency spectra of $f(t)$. Since $I(j\omega)$ represents the frequency spectra of the unit impulse, it has the constant value

$$I(j\omega) = \frac{4}{T}\underline{/0}$$

independently of the value of ω, as previously mentioned. Thus, the frequency spectrum $F(j\omega).I(j\omega)$ of the impulse response $f(t)$ of the transfer function $F(p)$ is proportional to $F(j\omega)$. Here $F(j\omega)$ is the function resulting from the substitution $p = j\omega$ in the transfer function $F(p)$. It is the frequency response of the transfer function $F(p)$.

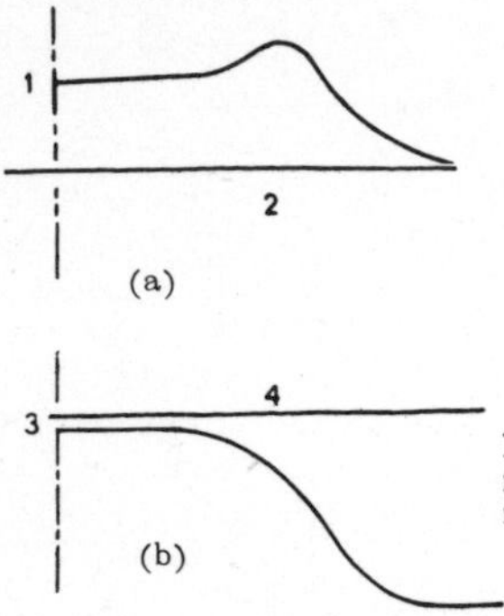

1 - *harmonic amplitude*; 2 - ω [*rad/sec*] *or* f [*cycles/sec*]; 3 - *phase angles of component harmonics*; 4 - ω [*rad/sec*] *or* f [*cycles/sec*]

Fig. 4.4 Frequency spectra of the output signal $f(t)$: (a) frequency spectrum of the harmonic amplitude; (b) frequency spectrum of the harmonic phase

We have shown that the impulse response of a transfer function can be represented by the frequency spectrum of the response and that the frequency spectrum has a form similar to that of the frequency response of the transfer function. If necessary, the impulse response can be obtained by superposition of the harmonics associated with the frequency spectrum of the impulse response. Hence, the frequency spectrum may be considered as another representation of the impulse response. Therefore, it is clear that, if the frequency response of a transfer function is given, the impulse response of the transfer function is uniquely determined. Once the impulse response is known, it is not difficult to find the transient response, as stated above.

Consequently, the transient response of an automatic control system can be indirectly evaluated by computing the frequency response instead of computing the transient response directly. In fact, accurate computation of the transient response is quite complicated for most automatic control systems. On the other hand, it is relatively simple to compute the frequency response even for fairly complicated systems. Therefore, the frequency response method has many advantages in the practical application to automatic control systems. The frequency response of a transfer function $F(p)$ can be either computed by varying ω from 0 to ∞ in $F(j\omega)$ or found by actual measurements.

4.2. VARIOUS REPRESENTATIONS OF FREQUENCY RESPONSES

As stated above, the frequency response of a transfer function $F(s)$ is the curve of $F(j\omega)$ as ω varies from 0 to ∞. Here, $F(j\omega)$ is the complex-valued function obtained by substituting $j\omega$ for s in $F(s)$. Hence, the value of $F(j\omega)$ can be represented by a vector on the complex plane. Since the vector value of $F(j\omega)$ varies as ω varies, the frequency response will be represented by the vector locus. This representation method is called the vector locus method, and the diagram consisting of the vector locus is called a Nyquist diagram. The image of the vector locus on the logarithmic plane is called a logarithmic vector locus or gain-phase diagram. This diagram is the vector locus obtained by plotting the logarithm of $|F(j\omega)|$ (or a value proportional to it) on the vertical axis and $\angle F(j\omega)$ on the horizontal axis (or vice versa). In particular, the logarithmic vector locus obtained by plotting $20 \log |F(j\omega)|$ [dB] against $\angle F(j\omega)$ [degrees] is widely used. Sometimes, it is more convenient to use a logarithmic scale for the vertical axis so that the magnitude of $|F(j\omega)|$, rather than $20 \log |F(j\omega)|$, will appear on the diagram.

Since the vector value consists of the magnitude $|F(j\omega)|$ and the phase angle $\angle F(j\omega)$, a frequency response can be represented by a set of two separate curves: one is the curve obtained by plotting $|F(j\omega)|$ against ω and the other is the curve obtained by plotting $\angle F(j\omega)$ against ω. In particular, if we use a logarithmic scale for the ω-axis, the curve obtained by plotting $20 \log |F(j\omega)|$ (which is the magnitude of the frequency response expressed in decibels) against ω and the curve obtained by plotting the phase angle $\angle F(j\omega)$ against ω together constitute what is called a Bode diagram.

4.3. VECTOR LOCI (NYQUIST DIAGRAMS)

With the vector locus method, the locus of the magnitude of the frequency response, with varying ω, and the locus of the phase angle can be combined into a single curve on the plane with either a rectangular coordinate system (where the horizontal axis is the real axis and the vertical axis is the imaginary axis) or a polar coordinate system.

As an example, let us find the vector locus of the transfer function

$$F(s) = K(1+sT) \tag{4.10}$$

$$F(j\omega) = K(1+j\omega T) \tag{4.11}$$

If we plot the locus of $F(j\omega)$ for positive values of ω, we obtain a half-line as shown in Fig. 4.5. The vector locus in Fig. 4.5 is the locus with K = 2 and T = 0.5 [sec].

Consider the transfer function $F(s)$ given by

$$F(s)=\frac{K}{1+sT} \tag{4.12}$$

The frequency response $F(j\omega)$ of this transfer function is

$$F(j\omega)=\frac{K}{1+j\omega T} \tag{4.13}$$

Plotting the vector locus of $F(j\omega)$ as ω varies from 0 to ∞, we obtain the semicircle shown in Fig. 4.6. Figure 4.6 shows the vector locus for K = 2 and T = 0.5 [sec]. There are other transfer functions with semicircular vector loci besides the transfer function given by equation (4.12). The transfer functions

$$\frac{sT_2}{1+sT}, \qquad \frac{1+sT_2}{1+sT_1}$$

are such.

Except for certain special cases, the vector loci of the frequency responses of transfer functions become complicated when the

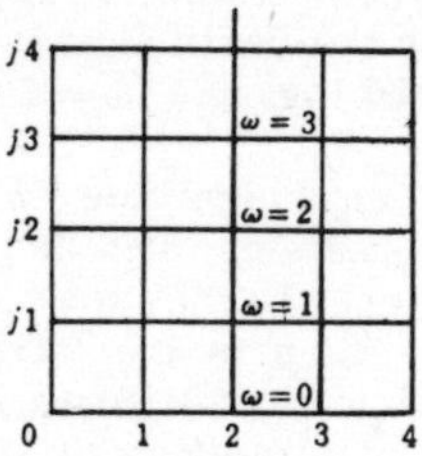

Fig. 4.5 A vector locus determined by the frequency response $F(j\omega)$ given in equation (4.11)

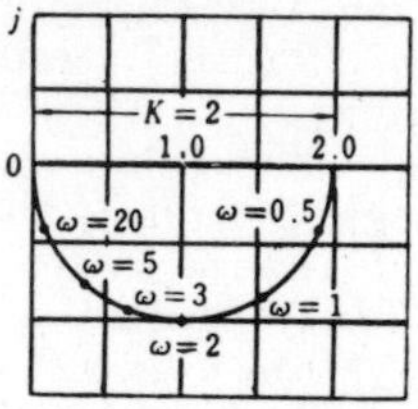

Fig. 4.6 A vector locus determined by the frequency response $F(j\omega)$ given in equation (4.13)

degree of the denominator of the transfer function exceeds 1. For example, consider the transfer function

$$F(s)=\frac{K}{s(1+sT_1)(1+sT_2)} \tag{4.14}$$

where K = 5, T_1 = 0.6 [sec], and T_2 = 0.1 [sec]. The frequency response of this transfer function is

$$F(j\omega)=\frac{5}{j\omega(1+0.6\,j\omega)(1+0.1\,j\omega)} \tag{4.15}$$

If we set ω = 0 in this equation, we have

$$F(j0)=\frac{5}{j0(1+j0)(1+j0)}=\infty\underline{/-90^\circ} \tag{4.16}$$

Thus, the vector locus begins at $-j\infty$ which corresponds to $\omega = 0$. For $\omega = 2$, we have

$$F(j2) = \frac{5}{j2(1+j1.2)(1+j0.2)} \tag{4.17}$$

$$= \frac{5/0^\circ}{2 \times 1.56 \times 1.02 \, /90^\circ + 50.2^\circ + 11.3^\circ} \tag{4.18}$$

$$= 1.57/-151.5^\circ \tag{4.19}$$

Computing the values of $F(j\omega)$ for $\omega = 1, 3, 5$, we obtain the numerical values shown in Table 4.1. If we plot the vector locus from Table 4.1, we obtain the curve shown in Fig. 4.7. In many cases, automatic control systems have vector loci such that their magnitudes decrease to 0 and their phase lags increase at $\omega = \infty$, as shown in Fig. 4.7. In particular, most of the open loop transfer functions of servomechanisms have such loci.

TABLE 4.1
CALCULATED VALUES OF A FREQUENCY RESPONSE

ω	$\lvert F(j\omega) \rvert$	$/F(j\omega)$
0	∞	-90°
1	4.28	-126.9°
2	1.57	-151.5°
3	0.775	-167.7°
5	0.283	-188.2°

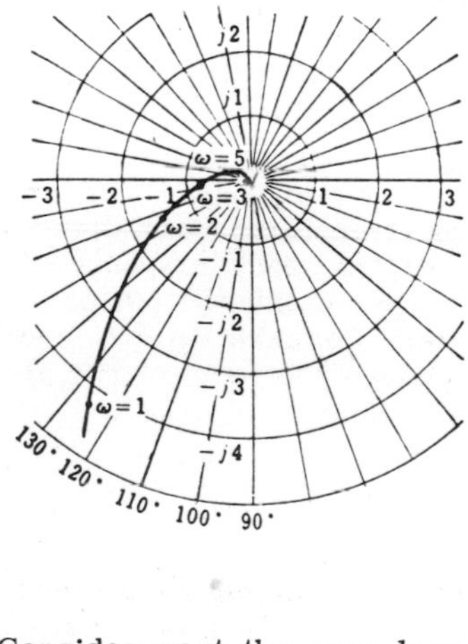

Fig. 4.7 Vector locus of the frequency response given by equation (4.15)

Consider next the open-loop transfer function of the automatic control system shown in Fig. 4.8. Let us construct the vector locus of the frequency response when the reference input signal $R(j\omega)$ and the controlled variable $C(j\omega)$ are regarded as the input and the output signals, respectively. Denoting this frequency response by $F_o(j\omega)$, we have

$$F_o(j\omega) = \frac{F(j\omega)}{1+F(j\omega)} \tag{4.20}$$

$$= \frac{5}{j\omega(1+0.6\,j\omega)(1+0.1\,j\omega)+5} \tag{4.21}$$

Plotting the vector locus of this frequency response, we obtain a curve issuing from the point $1 + j\,0$, which corresponds to $\omega = 0$, as shown in Fig. 4.9. Comparing this vector locus and the one in 4.7, we note that the two curves differ considerably for small values of ω but they have much the same shape for large values of ω.

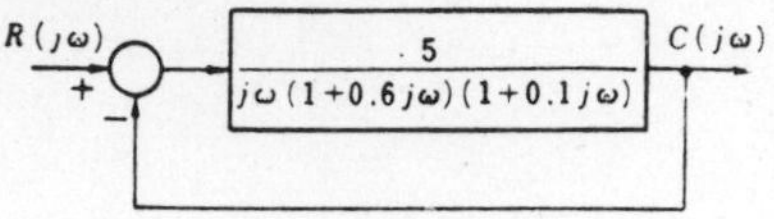

Fig. 4.8

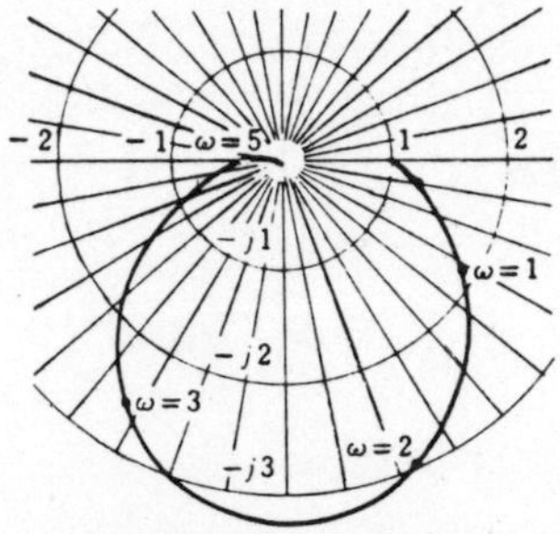

Fig. 4.9 Vector locus of the frequency response given by equation (4.21)

Beside these vector loci, inverse vector loci of transfer functions are often used to express the frequency responses of transfer functions. The inverse vector locus of a transfer function is defined as the vector locus determined by the frequency response of the reciprocal of the given transfer function. An inverse vector locus is also called an inverse Nyquist diagram. For example, the inverse vector locus of the transfer function (4.14) is the vector locus of the reciprocal of the frequency response (4.15)

$$\frac{1}{F(j\omega)} = \frac{1}{5}\,j\omega(1+0.6j\omega)(1+0.1\,j\omega) \tag{4.22}$$

If we plot the vector locus of this expression, we obtain the inverse vector locus shown in Fig. 4.10. Calculations for plotting this inverse vector locus are simpler than the calculations using equation (4.15) for plotting the vector locus. Moreover, for a system containing a feedback path, such as the one shown in Fig. 4.8, the reciprocal of the frequency response is

$$\frac{1}{F_o(j\omega)}=\frac{1+F(j\omega)}{F(j\omega)}=\frac{1}{F(j\omega)}+1$$

from equation (4.20). Hence, the calculations for plotting the inverse locus are even more simplified. As shown in Fig. 4.11, the inverse vector locus of the frequency response (4.21) is the translation of the inverse vector locus (shown in Fig. 4.10) of the frequency response (4.15) by -1 + j 0.

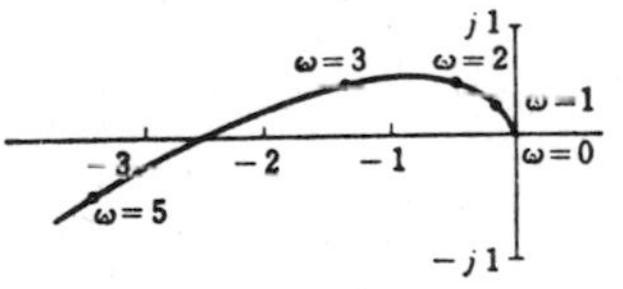

Fig. 4.10 The inverse vector locus of the frequency response give by equation(4.15)

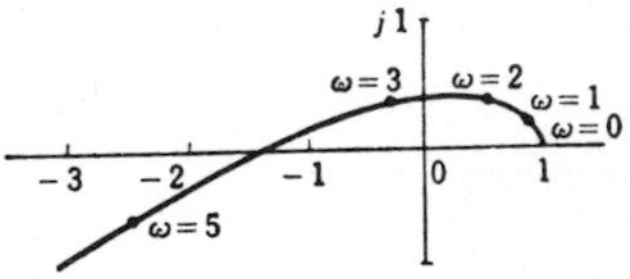

Fig. 4.11 The inverse vector locus of the frequency response given by equation (4.21)

4.4. LOGARITHMIC VECTOR LOCI

A frequency response $F(j\omega)$ can also be represented in the following manner. Writing $F(j\omega)$ in the form

$$F(j\omega)=A\epsilon^{j\phi} \qquad (4.23)$$
$$A=|F(j\omega)|,\ \phi=\underline{/F(j\omega)}$$

where $A=|F(j\omega)|$ and $\phi=\angle F(j\omega)$, and taking the natural logarithm of both sides, we get

$$\ln F(j\omega)=\ln A+j\phi$$

Hence, $\ln F(j\omega)$ can be again represented as a vector quantity. That is, if we plot $\ln A$ on the real axis and the phase angle ϕ on the imaginary, axis, then $\ln F(j\omega)$ will be expressed by a vector on the complex plane. In actual applications, it is convenient to plot 20 log A instead of $\ln A$ and to express the phase angle in degrees. A vector locus plotted in this manner on the complex plane is called a logarithmic vector locus or a gain-phase diagram. We may also use a logarithmic scale for the real axis, in which case we can simply write A instead of $\ln A$ or 20 $\log A$. This is sometimes a more convenient procedure. Figure 4.12 shows the logarithmic vector locus of the frequency response (4.15) plotted on the plane in this manner.

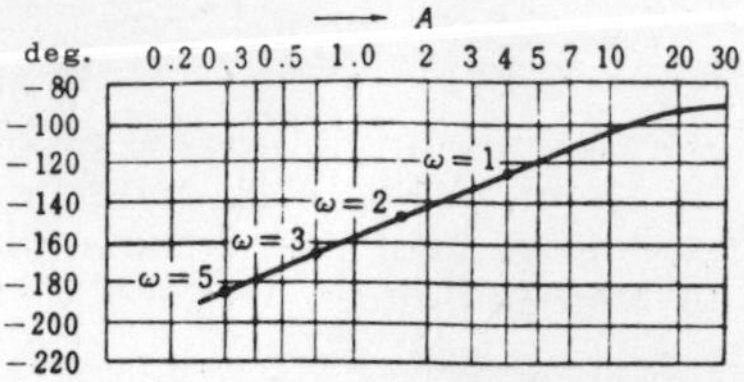

Fig. 4.12 The logarithmic vector locus of the frequency response given by equation (4.15)

The logarithmic vector locus method has some advantages. The values read from a logarithmic vector locus will have only a certain fixed reading error. (That is, the reading error will not depend on the value.) Multiplication or division of vectors is reduced to addition or subtraction on the logarithmic plane. Moreover, with the more common automatic control systems, the logarithmic vector loci of open-loop transfer functions have relatively simple forms, as shown in Fig. 4.12, and can be easily constructed.

4.5. THE BODE DIAGRAM

The magnitude of the vector representing the frequency response of the transfer function is called the gain of the transfer function. The curve obtained by plotting the gain expressed in decibels against the frequency ω (as measured on the horizontal axis with a logarithmic scale) is called the gain characteristic curve; the curve obtained by plotting the phase angle expressed in degrees against the frequency ω with the same logarithmic scale is called the phase characteristic curve. These two curves are said to form a Bode diagram.

For example, consider the frequency response

$$F(j\omega)=\frac{K}{1+j\omega T} \tag{4.24}$$

If we denote by G $[dB]$ the gain of the frequency response, then

$$G=20\log|F(j\omega)| \tag{4.25}$$

$$=20\log K-20\log\sqrt{1+\omega^2T^2} \tag{4.26}$$

$$=20\log K-10\log(1+\omega^2T^2) \tag{4.27}$$

If we denote the phase angle by ϕ, we have

$$\phi=-\tan^{-1}\omega T \tag{4.28}$$

Before plotting these curves, let us find the curve of the second term $-10\log(1+\omega^2T^2)$ in equation (4.27). If ω is sufficiently small, this term is almost equal to 0 $[dB]$. On the other hand, if ω is sufficiently large (so that the 1 can be ignored), this term is almost equal to

$$-20\log\omega T=-20\log\omega-20\log T \tag{4.29}$$

Here, $-20\log T$ is a constant, and the only variable quantity depending on ω is $20\log\omega$. Therefore, if we plot the graph of equation (4.29) on a plane where the horizontal axis denotes 20 log ω the graph will be a line with angle of inclination -45°. In Fig. 4.13, the lines (a) and (b) are the asymptotes of the curve of equation (4.29) as $\omega \to 0$ and as $\omega \to \infty$ respectively. The two asymptotes intersect at the value of ω for which the expression (4.29) is 0. This value of ω is

$$\omega = \frac{1}{T} = \omega_s \tag{4.30}$$

and this angular frequency ω_s is called the break frequency or the corner frequency. In general, the break frequency is equal to the reciprocal of the time constant.

Figure 4.13 shows the gain curve with $\omega_s = 1.0$ [rad/sec] that is, the gain curve of the frequency response (4.24) with $T = 1$ [sec]. The observed slope of the line (b) in the diagram varies according to the length of the unit used for the ω-axis. However, the slope of the line (b) is 20 [dB/decade], so that the height of the line decreases by 20 [dB] for every tenfold increase in ω. If we compute the value of the second term on the right side of equation (4.27) at the break frequency $\omega_s = 1/T$, we obtain

$$-10 \log (1+1) \fallingdotseq -3 \text{ [dB]} \tag{4.31}$$

Using this value and the two asymptotes, we can sketch the curve of the second term in the expression (4.27), that is, the Bode diagram for the amplitude of $1/(1 + j\omega t)$. This is curve (c) in Fig. 4.13. Consequently, the Bode diagram (the gain characteristic curve) of the expression (4.27) will be obtained by translating curve (c) upward by 20 log K [dB]. This is the curve (c′) in Fig. 4.13.

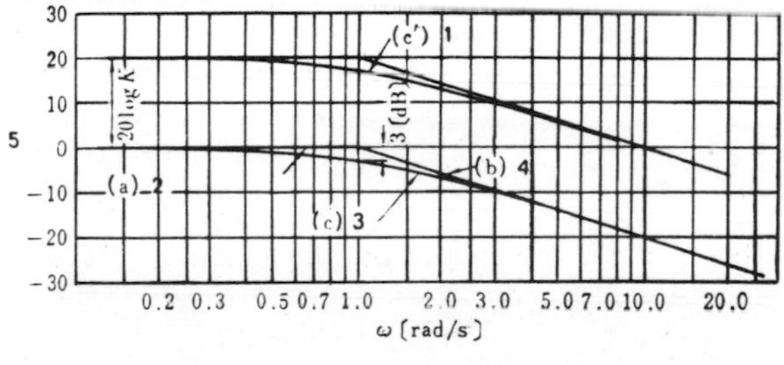

1 - *curve of equation* (4.27); 2 - *asymptote as* $\omega \to 0$
3 - *curve of* - 10 *log* $(1 + \omega^2 T^2)$; 4 - *asymptote as* $\omega \to \infty$; 5 - *gain* [dB]

Fig. 4.13 Bode diagram (gain characteristic curve) of $K/(1 + j\omega t)$, where $K = 10$ and $T = 1$ [sec]

Suppose that we approximate the gain characteristic curve by these asymptotes. If we plot the difference between the exact value of the gain and the approximate value against ω / ω_s, we obtain the curve shown in Fig. 4.14. Using this curve, we can easily find the exact value of the gain corresponding to a value of ω if the approximation consisting of the two asymptotes is given.

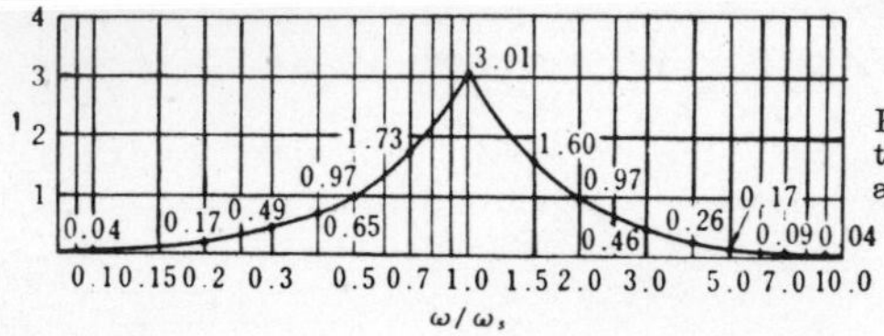

Fig. 4.14 Difference between the exact value of the gain and the approximate value in the Bode diagram of $K/(1 + j\omega t)$

If we denote by ϕ the phase angle of the frequency response (4.24), then ϕ is

$$\phi = -\tan^{-1}\omega T \tag{4.32}$$

as mentioned before. If we use the break frequency ω_s defined by equation (4.30), the phase angle will be

$$\phi = -\tan^{-1}\frac{\omega}{\omega_s} \tag{4.33}$$

Let us examine the shape of the ϕ - curve plotted on the plane with the natural logarithm of ω plotted on the horizontal axis.

Let X be a horizontal coordinate on this plane. Then

$$X = \ln\omega \tag{4.34}$$

or

$$\omega = \epsilon^X \tag{4.35}$$

Substituting this expression into equation (4.33), we obtain

$$\phi = -\tan^{-1}\left(\frac{\epsilon^X}{\omega_s}\right) \tag{4.36}$$

and hence

$$\tan(-\phi) = \frac{\epsilon^X}{\omega_s} \tag{4.37}$$

If we take the natural logarithm of both sides of this equation, we obtain

$$\ln(-\tan\phi) = X - \ln\omega_s \tag{4.38}$$

This equation represents the phase characteristic curve in the Bode diagram. As shown in Fig. 4.15, $\phi \to 0°$ as $\omega \to 0$ (that is, as $X \to -\infty$), and $\phi \to -\pi/2$ (= -90°) as $\omega \to \infty$ (that is, as $X \to \infty$).

For $X = \ln\,\omega_s$ (that is, for $\omega = 1/T = \omega_s$), where ω_s is the break frequency, $\phi = -\pi/4$ (= -45°). The phase characteristic curve is symmetric with respect to the point ($\ln\,\omega_s$, $-\pi/4$). The reason for this is as follows. Move the origin to the point ($\ln\,\omega_s$, $-\pi/4$) by a translation of axes. If we denote by ϕ_0 and X_0 the coordinates in the new coordinate system, we have

$$\phi_0 = \phi + \frac{\pi}{4},\quad X_0 = X - \ln\omega_s \tag{4.39}$$

or

$$\phi=\phi_0-\frac{\pi}{4}, \quad X=X_0+\ln \omega_s \tag{4.40}$$

If we substitute this relation into equation (4.38), we obtain

$$\ln \tan\left(\frac{\pi}{4}-\phi_0\right)=X_0 \tag{4.41}$$

If we replace ϕ_0 with $-\phi_0$, the left-hand side of this equation becomes

$$\ln \tan\left(\frac{\pi}{4}+\phi_0\right)=\ln \cot\left(\frac{\pi}{4}-\phi_0\right) \tag{4.42}$$

$$=-\ln \tan\left(\frac{\pi}{4}-\phi_0\right) \tag{4.43}$$

$$=-X_0 \tag{4.44}$$

which is equal to the expression obtained by substituting $-X_0$ for X_0 in the right-hand side of equation (4.41). Therefore, the Bode

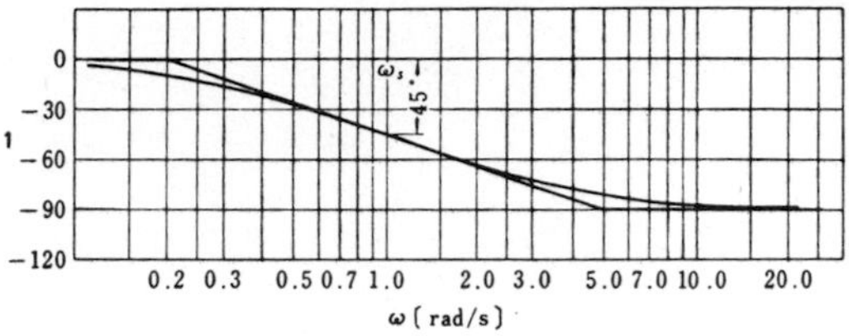

1 - *phase angle (degrees)*

Fig. 4.15 The Bode diagram (phase characteristic curve $K/(1+j\omega T)$ in the case of $T=1$

diagram (the phase characteristic curve) defined by equation (4.32) is symmetric with respect to the point ($\ln \omega_s$, $-\pi/4$), where $X=\ln \omega_s$ and $\omega_s=1/T$, as desired.

In order to find the slope of the phase characteristic curve at the symmetric point ($\ln \omega_n$, $-\pi/4$), we differentiate both sides of equation (4.41) with respect to X_0 and obtain

$$\frac{1}{\tan\left(\frac{\pi}{4}-\phi_0\right)} \frac{d \tan\left(\frac{\pi}{4}-\phi_0\right)}{d\phi_0} \frac{d\phi_0}{dX_0}=1 \tag{4.45}$$

$$\frac{-1}{\tan\left(\frac{\pi}{4}-\phi_0\right)} \sec^2\left(\frac{\pi}{4}-\phi_0\right)\frac{d\phi_0}{dX_0}=1 \tag{4.46}$$

Solving for $d\phi_0 / dX_0$, we get

$$\frac{d\varphi_0}{dX_0}=-\tan\left(\frac{\pi}{4}-\phi_0\right)\cos^2\left(\frac{\pi}{4}-\phi_0\right) \tag{4.47}$$

$$=-\sin\left(\frac{\pi}{4}-\phi_0\right)\cos\left(\frac{\pi}{4}-\phi_0\right) \tag{4.48}$$

$$=-\frac{1}{2}\sin\left(\frac{\pi}{2}-2\phi_0\right) \tag{4.49}$$

Thus, the value of the derivative $d\phi_0/dX_0$ at $\phi_0 = 0$, which is equivalent to $\phi = -\pi/4$, is

$$\left|\frac{d\phi_0}{dX_0}\right|_{\phi_0=0}=-\frac{1}{2} \tag{4.50}$$

This means that, if we use the scale determined by the natural logarithm of ω for the horizontal axis and the radian scale for the vertical axis (ϕ-axis), then the slope of the phase characteristic curve for $\phi = -\pi/4$ or equivalently for $\omega = 1/T = \omega_s$ is -1/2.

Figure 4.15 shows (1) an approximation of the phase characteristic curve by the tangent line at the point ($\ln \omega_s$, $-\pi/4$), (2) the asymptote to the curve as $\omega \to 0$, and (3) the asymptote as $\omega \to \infty$ (here, $T = 1$ and $\omega_s = 1$). Let us find the intersecting points of these three lines. The equation of the tangent line at the point ($1/T$, $-\pi/4$) is

$$\phi_0=-\frac{1}{2}X_0 \tag{4.51}$$

Therefore, if $\phi_0 = -\pi/4$, that is, if $\phi = -\pi/2$, then

$$X_0=\frac{\pi}{2} \tag{4.52}$$

By use of equation (4.39), equation (4.52) can be expressed in terms of X:

$$X=\frac{\pi}{2}+\ln\omega_s \tag{4.53}$$

If we substitute equation (4.34) into this equation, we obtain

$$\ln\omega=\frac{\pi}{2}+\ln\omega_s \tag{4.54}$$

Therefore,

$$\omega=\epsilon^{\frac{\pi}{2}}\omega_s \tag{4.55}$$

$$=4.81\,\omega_s\doteqdot 5\,\omega_s \tag{4.56}$$

Similarly, if $\phi_2 = \pi/4$, that is, if $\phi = 0$, then

$$\omega=\epsilon^{-\frac{\pi}{2}}\omega_s \tag{4.57}$$

$$=\frac{\omega_s}{4.81} \tag{4.58}$$

$$\doteqdot\frac{\omega_s}{5} \tag{4.59}$$

Therefore, we can divide the phase characteristic curve of the frequency response (4.24) into three parts defined respectively on frequency range less than $\omega_s/5$, between $\omega_s/5$ and $5\omega_s$, and larger than $5\omega_s$. These three parts can be approximated by lines, as shown in Fig. 4.15. Figure 4.16 shows the curve obtained by plotting the difference between the exact and approximate values of the phase angle against ω / ω_s. Using this curve, we can easily find the exact value of the phase angle corresponding to a value of ω when we need to.

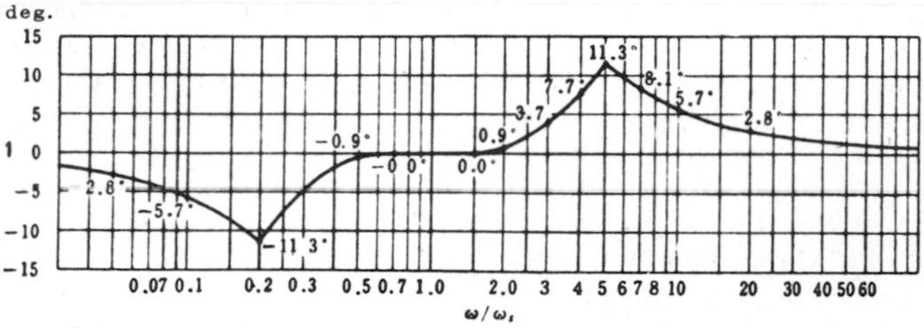

1 - *difference value (degrees)*

Fig. 4.16 The difference between the exact and approximate values of the phase angle in the Bode diagram of $K/(1 + j\omega T)$

Using the above results, let us construct the Bode diagram of the frequency response of the transfer function given by equation (4.14). The frequency response of this transfer function is

$$F(j\omega)=\frac{K}{j\omega(1+j\omega T_1)(1+j\omega T_2)} \tag{4.60}$$

First, we find the gain characteristic curve. From equation (4.60), the magnitude $|F(j\omega)|$ of the frequency response $F(j\omega)$ is

$$|F(j\omega)|=\frac{K}{\omega\sqrt{1+\omega^2 T_1^2}\ \sqrt{1+\omega^2 T_2^2}} \tag{4.61}$$

Then, the gain G can be computed by taking the common logarithm of equation (4.61) as follows:

$$G=20\log|F(j\omega)| \tag{4.62}$$

$$=20\log K-20\log\omega-10\log(1+\omega^2T_1^2)-10\log(1+\omega^2T_2^2) \tag{4.63}$$

Therefore, if we construct the gain characteristic curve for each term in equation (4.63), the Bode diagram with respect to the gain G (the gain characteristic curve of G) is obtained by superposing the gain characteristic curves of the different terms.

The first term in equation (4.63) has a constant value independent of ω, and hence the gain characteristic curve is the horizontal line (a) shown in Fig. 4.17. The gain characteristic curve of the second term, -20 log ω, is a line of slope -20 [dB/decade] as ω increases (the line (b) in Fig. 4.17). The third term, $-\log(1+\omega^2T_1{}^2)$, and the fourth term, $-10\log(1+\omega^2T_2{}^2)$, both have the same form as the second term, $-10\log(1+\omega^2T^2)$ of equation (4.27). Thus, if we replace T by T_1 or T_2 in the second term of equation (4.27), we shall obtain the third or the fourth term of equation (4.63), respectively. Therefore, from what was said above, we see that the gain characteristic curve of the third term is approximated by a horizontal line passing through a point with ordinate 0 [dB] and a line of slope -20 [dB/decade] which intersects the horizontal line at $\omega_{s1} = 1/T_1$. Also, the gain characteristic of the fourth term is approximated by a horizontal line with ordinate 0 [dB] and a line of slope -20 [dB/decade] which intersects this horizontal line at $\omega_{s2} = 1/T_2$. These approximations are the curves (c) and (d) shown in Fig. 4.17. If we superimpose these approximations (a), (b), (c), and (d), each of which is the exact gain characteristic curve or the approximation of the gain characteristic curve of a term in equation (4.63), we obtain curve (e) in Fig. 4.17, which is the approximation of the gain characteristic curve of G. From this approximate curve, we can easily sketch the gain characteristic curve, as illustrated by curve (f) in Fig. 4.17. If we need to know the exact value of the gain for a certain value of ω, we can also use 4.14 for this purpose. The curves in Fig. 4.17 were plotted under the assumption that $K = 10$ [sec^{-1}] $T_1 = 0.5$ [sec], $T = 0.1$ [sec] in equation (4.60).

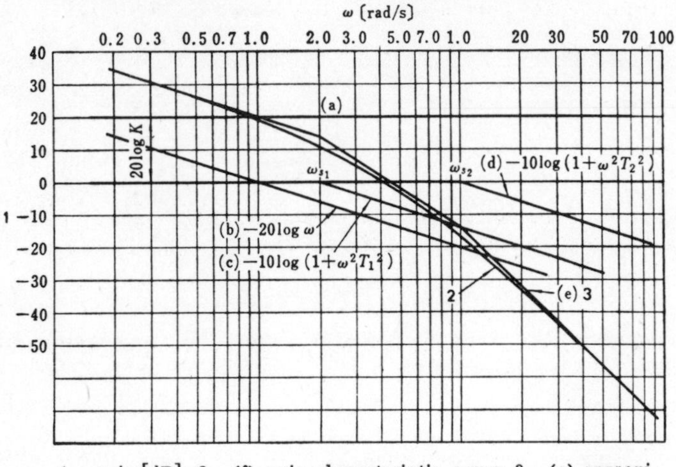

1 - *gain* [dB]; 2 - (f) *gain characteristic curve*; 3 - (e) *approximate gain characteristic curve*

Fig. 4.17 Bode diagram (gain characteristic curve) of frequency response $K/j\omega(1 + j\omega T_1)(1 + j\omega T_2)$ (where $K = 10$ [sec^{-1}], $T_1 = 0{\cdot}5$ [sec], and $T_2 = 0{\cdot}1$ [sec]) and a method of constructing the Bode diagram

Let ϕ be the phase angle of the frequency response (4.60). Then,

$$\begin{aligned}\phi &= \underline{/F(j\omega)} \\ &= -90° - \tan^{-1}\omega T_1 - \tan^{-1}\omega T_2\end{aligned} \tag{4.64}$$

This expression for ϕ indicates that the phase characteristic curve of the frequency response (4.60) can also be obtained by superimposing the phase characteristic curves of the elements constituting the frequency response (4.60). Fig. 4.18 illustrates graphically the procedure for constructing the phase characteristic curve in the case that $T_1 = 0.5$ [sec] and $T_2 = 0.1$ [sec]. More specifically, curve (a) in Fig. 4.18 is the phase characteristic curve of the first term in equation (4.64), and curves (b) and (c) are the approximations of the phase characteristic curves of the second and the third terms, respectively. Superimposing curves (a), (b), and (c), we obtain the curve (d), which is the approximation of the phase characteristic curve of ϕ. From this approximation, we can also sketch the phase characteristic curve that is, curve (e) in Fig. 4.18. If we need to know the exact value of the phase angle for a certain value of ω, we can use the curve in Fig. 4.16.

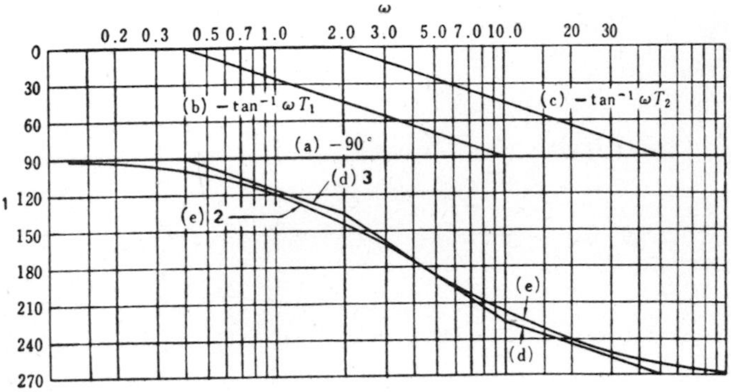

1 - *phase angle (degrees)*; 2 - *phase characteristic curve* 3 - *approximation of phase characteristic curve*

Fig. 4.18 The Bode diagram (phase characteristic curve) of the frequency response $K/j\omega\,(1 + j\omega T_1)\,(1 + j\omega T_2)$ (where $T_1 = 0{\cdot}5$ [sec] and $T_2 = 0{\cdot}1$ [sec]) and the method for constructing the Bode diagram

As shown in equation (2.243), most open-loop transfer functions of automatic control systems are the products of first-order transfer functions of the form $(1 + sT)$ or $1/(1 + sT)$. If the time constant in each factor of an open-loop transfer function is a real number, then the Bode diagram of the overall transfer function can be easily constructed by using the method discussed above. However, some transfer functions have complex-valued time constants when factored into first-order transfer functions. For example, consider the transfer function defined by

$$F(s) = \frac{\omega_n^2}{s^2 + 2\zeta\omega_n s + \omega_n^2} \tag{4.65}$$

$$= \frac{1}{\left(\frac{s}{\omega_n}\right)^2 + 2\zeta\frac{s}{\omega_n} + 1} \tag{4.66}$$

If $\zeta \geq 1$, the two poles of this transfer function are both real numbers, and hence the transfer function is the product of two first-order transfer functions with real-valued time constants. Therefore, the Bode diagram of this transfer function can be easily constructed. On the other hand, if $\zeta < 1$, then the two poles of the transfer function are complex conjugate numbers, and the frequency response is then of a different type from the examples we have been discussing. Let us investigate this frequency response. If we set $s = j\omega$ in equation (4.66), we obtain the frequency response

$$F(j\omega)=\frac{1}{1-\left(\frac{\omega}{\omega_n}\right)^2+2j\zeta\frac{\omega}{\omega_n}} \tag{4.67}$$

Therefore, the gain G can be computed as follows:

$$G=-20\log\sqrt{\left[1-\left(\frac{\omega}{\omega_n}\right)^2\right]^2+\left(2\zeta\frac{\omega}{\omega_n}\right)^2} \tag{4.68}$$

$$=-10\log\left\{\left[1-\left(\frac{\omega}{\omega_n}\right)^2\right]^2+\left(2\zeta\frac{\omega}{\omega_n}\right)^2\right\} \tag{4.69}$$

If ω is sufficiently small (so that ω/ω_n can be neglected), then

$$G=-10\log 1=0[\mathrm{dB}] \tag{4.70}$$

For a large value of ω (so that the 1 can be neglected in comparison with ω/ω_n),

$$G=-10\log\left(\frac{\omega}{\omega_n}\right)^4 \tag{4.71}$$

$$=-40\log\frac{\omega}{\omega_n} \tag{4.72}$$

That is, the asymptote of the gain characteristic curve for $\omega >> \omega_n$ is a line such that the value of the ordinate (gain) of a point on the line decreases in proportion to $\log(\omega/\omega_n)$. In the Bode diagram, the asymptote is a line with slope -40 [dB/decade] and intersects the horizontal axis (0 dB) at $\omega = \omega_n$. Fig. 4.19 shows the Bode diagrams (the gain characteristic curves) for various values of ζ. It should be noted that resonance occurs for $\zeta < 1/\sqrt{2}$.

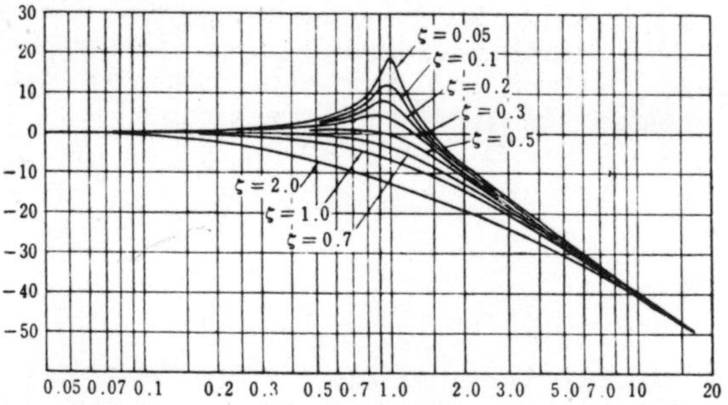

1 - *gain* [dB]

Fig. 4.19 The Bode diagram (gain characteristic curve) of $1/[1-(\omega/\omega_n)^2+2j\zeta\omega/\omega_n]$

Let ϕ be the phase angle of the frequency response (4.67). Then,

$$\phi = -\tan^{-1}\frac{2\zeta\frac{\omega}{\omega_n}}{1-\left(\frac{\omega}{\omega_n}\right)^2} \tag{4.73}$$

The phase angle is $\phi = -\pi/2$ at $\omega = \omega_n$, and the phase characteristic curve is symmetric with respect to the point $(\omega_n, -\pi/2)$. In order to find the slope of the phase characteristic curve, we compute $d\phi/d\ln\omega$:

$$\frac{d\phi}{d\ln\omega} = \frac{d\phi}{d\omega}\cdot\frac{d\omega}{d\ln\omega} \tag{4.74}$$

$$= -\frac{\dfrac{2\zeta\frac{1}{\omega_n}\left(1-\left(\frac{\omega}{\omega_n}\right)^2\right)-2\zeta\frac{\omega}{\omega_n}\left(-2\frac{\omega}{\omega_n^2}\right)}{\left(1-\left(\frac{\omega}{\omega_n}\right)^2\right)^2}}{1+\left[\dfrac{2\zeta\frac{\omega}{\omega_n}}{1-\left(\frac{\omega}{\omega_n}\right)^2}\right]^2}\cdot\omega \tag{4.75}$$

$$= -\frac{\frac{2\zeta}{\omega_n}\left[1-\left(\frac{\omega}{\omega_n}\right)^2\right]+4\zeta\frac{\omega^2}{\omega_n^3}}{\left(1-\left(\frac{\omega}{\omega_n}\right)^2\right)^2+4\zeta^2\left(\frac{\omega}{\omega_n}\right)^2}\cdot\omega \tag{4.76}$$

The slope of the phase characteristic curve at $\omega = \omega_n$ is

$$\left|\frac{d\phi}{d\ln\omega}\right|_{\omega=\omega_n} = \left|-\frac{4\zeta\left(\frac{\omega}{\omega_n}\right)^3}{4\zeta^2\left(\frac{\omega}{\omega_n}\right)^2}\right|_{\omega=\omega_n} \tag{4.77}$$

$$= -\frac{1}{\zeta} \tag{4.78}$$

Therefore, the phase characteristic curve of equation (4.73) is approximated, as shown in Fig. 4.20, by three lines: (1) the tangent to the characteristic curve at the point $(\omega_n, -90°)$, with slope $-1/\zeta$, (2) the line $\phi = 0$, and (3) the line $\phi = -180°$. If we denote by ω_1 and ω_2 the abscissas of the points at which the line with slope $-1/\zeta$ intersects the 0° and -180° lines respectively, we have the following relation:

$$\frac{-\frac{\pi}{2}}{\log\omega_1-\log\omega_n} = -\frac{1}{\zeta} \tag{4.79}$$

which can be written

$$\frac{\pi}{2}\zeta = \log\frac{\omega_1}{\omega_n} \tag{4.80}$$

Therefore,

$$\omega_1 = \omega_n e^{\frac{\pi}{2}\zeta} \tag{4.81}$$

$$= \omega_n(4.81)^{\zeta} \tag{4.82}$$

and

$$\omega_2 = \omega_n/(4.81)^{\zeta} \tag{4.83}$$

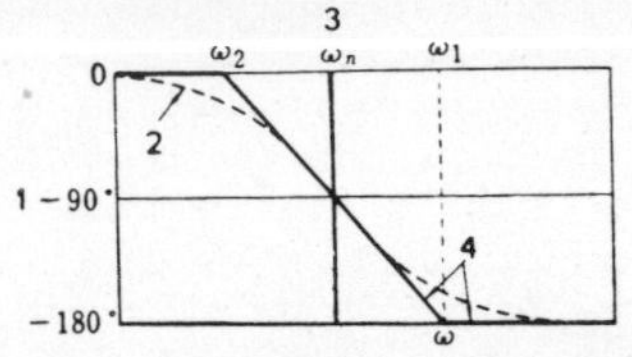

1 - *phase angle*; 2 - *phase characteristic* 3 - *angular frequency (on logarithmic scale)*; 4 - *approximation curve*

Fig. 4.20 Approximation of the phase characteristic curve of the frequency response $[1 - (\omega/\omega_n)^2 + 2j\zeta\omega/\omega_n]^{-1}$

Figure 4.21 shows the phase characteristic curves of the transfer function (4.65) plotted for various values of ζ.

As can be seen clearly from the above, the Bode diagrams are fairly easy to construct even for certain complicated systems, that is, an approximate form of the frequency response can be easily found by means of the Bode diagram even for a complicated system. Moreover, with a little more computation, we can get an accurate form of the frequency response. For these reasons, Bode diagrams are often used for actual analysis and synthesis of automatic control systems.

On the other hand, the Bode diagram method requires two characteristic curves. This is a disadvantage of the method. However, there is a close relation between the gain and phase characteristic curves, so that sometimes separate computations are not required for plotting them. For example, if we are given the ω values corresponding to the break points of the approximation of the gain characteristic curve and the slope of the line segment between the break points, the phase characteristic curve shown in Fig. 4.18 can be constructed from the given values. Thus 'The phase angle of a system with an arbitrary frequency can be found from the slope of the gain characteristic of the system at every frequency between $-\infty$ and ∞.'

This statement is known as Bode's theorem. It should be noted

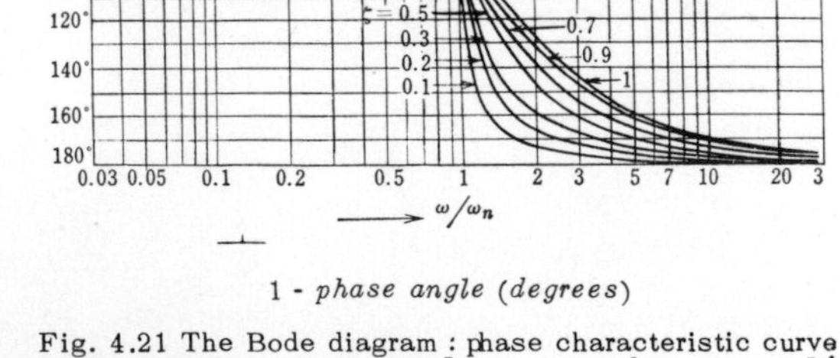

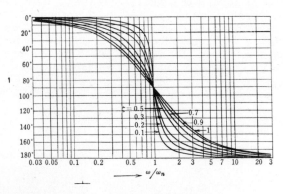

1 - *phase angle (degrees)*

Fig. 4.21 The Bode diagram : phase characteristic curve of the frequency response $[1 - (\omega/\omega_n)^2 + 2j\zeta\omega/\omega_n]^{-1}$

that it holds only for a minimum-phase-shift network. A minimum-phase-shift network is the network with the minimum phase shift among those networks with the same gain characteristics. Most of the network elements of automatic control systems are minimum-phase-shift networks. However, distributed constant networks or networks that generate oscillations by themselves (networks whose transfer functions have poles lying on the right half-plane of the root plane) are not minimum-phase-shift networks. Therefore, Bode's theorem does not hold for them. In general, the frequency responses of automatic control systems can be expressed only by the gain characteristics of the system. This property is often used (among other purposes) to measure the performance of an automatic control system.

4.6. STABILITY AND INSTABILITY

As the first step in evaluating the transient performance of an automatic control system, we shall study a method of determining the stability of the automatic control system.

An automatic control system is said to be stable if the transient phenomenon attenuates as time passes and the response of the system finally maintains a certain constant value. It is said to be unstable if the transient phenomenon either increases or maintains a constant value as time passes and the response of the system never maintains a constant value. Therefore, the problem of determining the stability or the instability of an automatic control system reduces to seeing whether the transient phenomenon attenuates or not.

As discussed in Section 3.3, we need to solve the characteristic equation of an automatic control system in order to evaluate the transient phenomena. If we denote the characteristic roots by r_1, r_2, r_3,... the transient error component $e(t)$ of the error response of the automatic control system is given by

$$e(t) = A_1\epsilon^{r_1 t} + A_2\epsilon^{r_2 t} + A_3\epsilon^{r_3 t} + \cdots\cdots \tag{4.84}$$

This equation shows that the real parts of all the characteristic roots must be negative for the transient phenomenon to attenuate. If any of the characteristic roots have positive real parts, the terms in equation (4.84) corresponding to these characteristic roots will become infinitely great with increasing time, so that the system is unstable. Therefore, to determine the stability or instability of an automatic control system, it is sufficient to see whether the real parts of all the characteristic roots are negative or not. This may be expressed more specifically in geometrical terms. Suppose that we plot all the characteristic roots on the complex plane, as shown in Fig. 4.22. This complex plane is called the root plane. An automatic control system is stable if none of the characteristic roots lie to the right of the imaginary axis on the root plane. If any characteristic root lies to the right of the imaginary axis, the automatic control system is unstable.

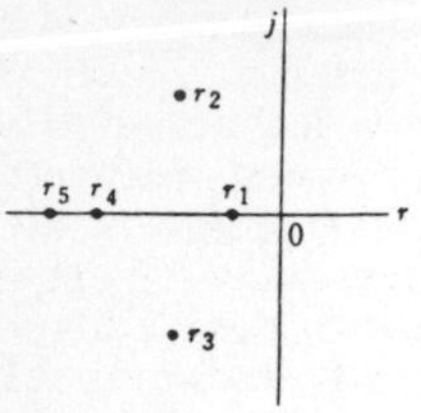

Fig. 4.22 Root configuration on the root plane

If all the characteristic roots are found, the transient response of an automatic control system can be exactly calculated. Consequently, there is no need to determine the stability or instability of the system. However, calculation of the characteristic roots is quite laborious for a complicated automatic control system. Indeed, the importance of the methods in use for determining the stability of a system lies in the fact that the stability can be determined by use of these methods without actually computing all the characteristic roots.

4.7. NYQUIST'S STABILITY CRITERION

There are several methods for determining stability of an automatic control system. We shall discuss here only Nyquist's stability criterion, which is the most widely applied method.

In general, an open-loop transfer function $F(s)$ of an automatic control system has the following form:

$$F(s)=\frac{K(1+sT_a)(1+sT_b)\cdots}{(1+sT_1)(1+sT_2)(1+sT_3)\cdots} \tag{4.85}$$

This expression can be written

$$F(s)=\frac{A(s-z_1)(s-z_2)(s-z_3)\cdots}{(s-p_1)(s-p_2)(s-p_3)\cdots\cdots} \tag{4.86}$$

The values p_1, p_2, p_3, ... of s for which the value of $F(s)$ is infinite are called the poles of $F(s)$. The values z_1, z_2, ... of s for which the value of $F(s)$ is 0 are called the zeros of $F(s)$.

If an open-loop transfer function is given in the form (4.86), the characteristic equation is

$$1+F(s)=1+\frac{A(s-z_1)(s-z_2)\cdots}{(s-p_1)(s-p_2)(s-p_3)\cdots} \tag{4.87}$$

$$=\frac{(s-p_1)(s-p_2)(s-p_3)\cdots+A(s-z_1)(s-z_2)\cdots}{(s-p_1)(s-p_2)(s-p_3)\cdots\cdots} \tag{4.88}$$

$$=0$$

If we can factorise the numerator of this expression, we can easily solve the characteristic equation. However, the factorisation is generally quite difficult. If we assume the numerator factorised, expression (4.88) can be written

$$1+F(s)=\frac{B(s-r_1)(s-r_2)(s-r_3)\cdots\cdots}{(s-p_1)(s-p_2)(s-p_3)\cdots\cdots} \tag{4.89}$$

Here, B is a constant, and p_1, p_2, p_3, ... are the poles of $F(s)$, which are known values. The complex numbers r_1, r_2, r_3, ... are the characteristic roots, as yet undetermined. To determine the stability of the system, it is not necessary to compute the characteristic roots; it is sufficient to see whether the real parts of all the characteristic roots are negative or not.

To determine the signs of the real parts of all characteristic roots, we make the following observation. Suppose that we plotted the poles p_1, p_2, p_3, ... and the characteristic roots on the root plane and obtained Fig. 4.23. If we give a value to the variable s and plot this value on the root plane, then the factors in the numerator and denominator of the expression (4.89) will be represented (as shown in Fig. 4.23) by the vectors $\overrightarrow{r_1 s}$, $\overrightarrow{r_2 s}$, ... (each of which originates at a root and ends at s) and the vectors $\overrightarrow{p_1 s}$, $\overrightarrow{p_2 s}$, $\overrightarrow{p_3 s}$, ... (each of which originates at a pole and ends at s) respectively. Equation (4.89) can then be expressed in terms of these vectors as follows:

$$1+F(s)=\frac{B\times\overrightarrow{r_1 s}\times\overrightarrow{r_2 s}\times\cdots\times\overrightarrow{r_n s}\times\overrightarrow{r_m s}\times\cdots}{\overrightarrow{p_1 s}\times\overrightarrow{p_2 s}\times\overrightarrow{p_3 s}\times\cdots} \tag{4.90}$$

Let us now investigate how the phase angle of $1 + F(s)$ given by equation (4.89) varies when s varies continuously along the circle around r_n as shown in Fig. 4.23. If we denote the phase angle by $\underline{/1 + F(s)}$, we get from equation (4.90)

$$\underline{/1+F(s)}=\underline{/\overrightarrow{r_1 s}}+\underline{/\overrightarrow{r_2 s}}+\cdots+\underline{/\overrightarrow{r_n s}}+\underline{/\overrightarrow{r_m s}}+\cdots-\underline{/\overrightarrow{p_1 s}}-\underline{/\overrightarrow{p_2 s}}-\underline{/\overrightarrow{p_3 s}}-\cdots \tag{4.91}$$

As can be seen from Fig. 4.23, the variation of each of the phase angles (such as $\underline{/p_1 s}$, $\underline{/p_2 s}$, ...) sum to 0 when s goes around the circle once. However, the phase angle $\underline{/r_n s}$ of the vector $r_n s$ varies through 360° in the clockwise direction. Therefore, in equation (4.91), only the term $\underline{/r_n s}$ varies through 360° in the clockwise direction and no other term varies. Consequently, the phase angle $\underline{/1 + F(s)}$ varies through 360° in the clockwise direction when s goes around the circle once.

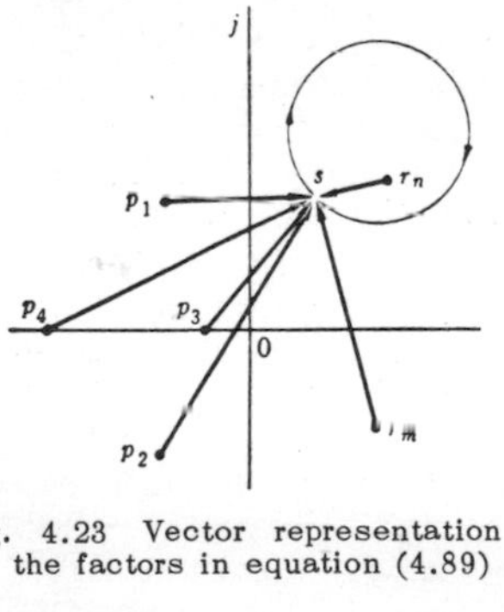

Fig. 4.23 Vector representation of the factors in equation (4.89)

As another example, consider a closed curve enclosing two roots r_n and r_m, as shown in Fig. 4.24. As s goes around the closed curve once, each of the two vectors $\underline{/ r_n s}$ and $\underline{/ r_m s}$ is rotated 360° in the clockwise direction and every other vector remains with phase angle unchanged. Therefore, the phase angle $\underline{/1 + F(s)}$ varies by 720° = 360° × 2 in the clockwise direction when s traces out the closed curve once.

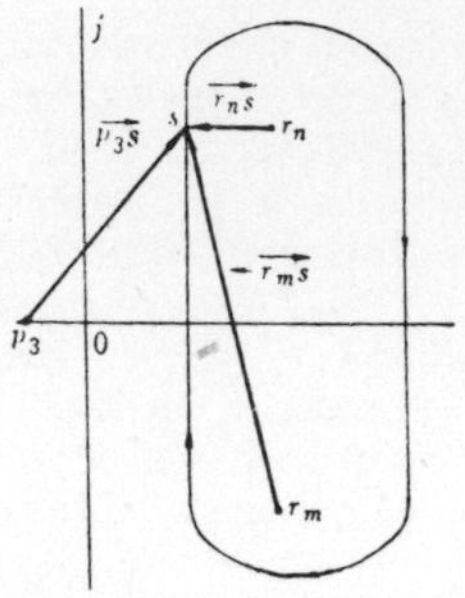

Fig. 4.24

The above results may be generalised as follows. Consider a closed curve on the root plane. If there are R characteristic roots enclosed by the closed curve, then the phase angle $\underline{/1 + F(s)}$ of $1 + F(s)$ given by equation (4.89) or (4.90), varies by $R \times 360°$ when s goes around the closed curve once. Conversely, if the phase angle $\underline{/1 + F(s)}$ of $1 + F(s)$ varies by $360° \times R$ when s goes around a closed curve once, then there are exactly R characteristic roots inside the closed curve.

Now, consider a closed curve enclosing a pole. If s goes around this closed curve once, it is clear from equation (4.91) that the phase angle $\underline{/1 + F(s)}$ varies by -360°. That is, the vector $1 + F(s)$ makes -1 revolution.

Suppose that the vector $1 + F(s)$ make N revolutions when s goes around a closed curve once. Let P denote the number of poles enclosed by the curve and let R denote the number of characteristic roots enclosed by it. Then,

$$N = R - P \tag{4.92}$$

Now, extend the closed curve to be traced by s so that the entire right half-plane will be enclosed, as shown in Fig. 4.25. Then, the number of revolutions N of the vector $1 + F(s)$ is equal to the number of characteristic roots R lying in the right half-plane minus the number of poles P lying in the right half-plane. Since the poles are given from the beginning, the number of poles P lying in the right half-plane is known. Therefore, we can easily find the number of characteristic roots R lying in the right half-plane. It is clear that the system is stable if and only if $R = 0$.

The closed curve enclosing the entire right half-plane is constructed as follows: Set $s = j\omega$ and let ω vary from $\omega = -\infty$ to $\omega = +\infty$. Then s varies from $-j\infty$ to $+j\infty$. And let s vary from $+j\infty$ to $-j\infty$ along the semicircle of infinite radius as shown in Fig. 4.25. Then, the closed curve traced out by s which varies in the above manner is the desired closed curve. One may suspect that the function $1+F(j\omega)$ might be discontinuous at $\omega = +\infty$ and $\omega = -\infty$. However, almost without exception, the values of $F(j\omega)$ at $\omega = +\infty$ and $\omega = -\infty$ are equal to 0 for automatic control systems. Consequently, the values of $1+F(j\omega)$ at $\omega = +\infty$ and $\omega = -\infty$ are equal to 1, so that $1+F(j\omega)$ is not discontinuous at $\omega = +\infty$ and $\omega = -\infty$.

When s varies along the aforementioned closed curve, the corresponding number of revolutions of the vector $1+F(s)$ will be found from the locus of $1+F(j\omega)$ obtained by varying ω from $-\infty$ to $+\infty$, which is the vector locus of $1+F(j\omega)$. It can also be found from the vector locus $F(j\omega)$ Specifically, we count the number of revolutions of the vector $F(j\omega)$, temporarily regarding $-1+j0$ as the origin, when ω varies from $-\infty$ to $+\infty$, as shown in Fig. 4.26. Then, the number of revolutions of $F(j\omega)$ is equal to that of $1+F(j\omega)$. As mentioned previously, the locus of $F(j\omega)$, when ω varies from zero to $+\infty$, is the vector locus of the frequency response of the open-loop transfer function. Fortunately, the locus of $F(j\omega)$, when ω varies from $-\infty$ to 0, is always symmetric to the above locus about the real axis, as shown in Fig. 4.26. Therefore, we can

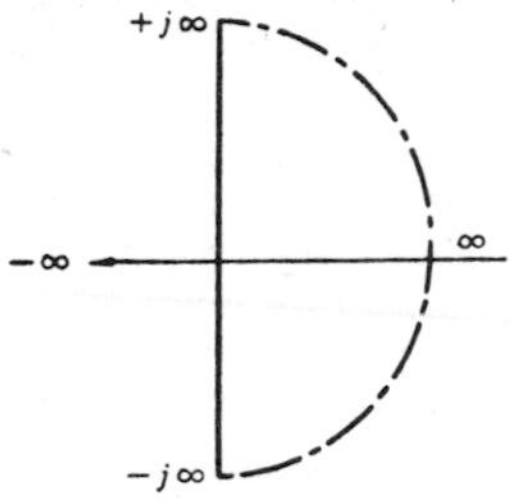

Fig. 4.25 Domain to be investigated for the existence of the characteristic roots lying in it

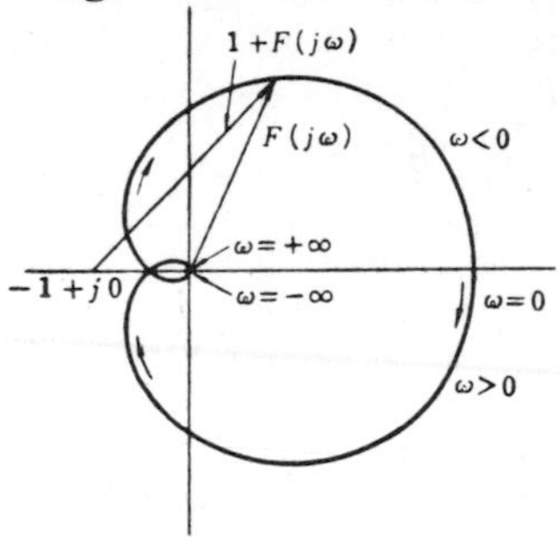

Fig. 4.26 Graphical illustration of the method of determining stability from the vector locus of the frequency response of an open-loop transfer function

determine the stability of an automatic control system if the vector locus of the frequency response of the open-loop transfer function is known.

4.8 PROCEDURE FOR DETERMINING STABILITY

The procedure for determining the stability of an automatic control system, based on the principle discussed in the previous section, is as follows:

1. Construct the vector locus of the frequency response of the given open-loop transfer function.
2. Construct the curve symmetric to the vector locus about the

real axis and form a closed curve from this curve and the vector locus.

3. Draw a vector originating at the point $-1 + j0$ and ending on the closed curve, and count the number of revolutions N of this vector when the end point of the vector goes around the closed curve. Here we take the clockwise direction as positive.

4. Find the number of poles P of the open-loop transfer function which will be lying in the right half-plane of the root plane.

5. Find the number of characteristic roots R lying in the right half-plane from the equation

$$R=N+P$$

6. If $R = 0$, then the automatic control system is stable. If $R \geq 1$, then the automatic control system is unstable.

Let us use this procedure to determine the stability of the automatic control system whose open-loop transfer function is

$$F(s)=\frac{40}{(1+0.6\,s)(1+0.5\,s)(1+0.1\,s)} \tag{4.93}$$

1. We construct the vector locus of the transfer function $F(s)$ When ω changes from 0 to ∞, we obtain the solid curve shown in Fig. 4.27. This figure shows a five-times enlargement of the locus near the origin.

2. The locus of the frequency response for $\omega = -\infty$ to 0 is constructed by drawing a curve symmetric to the above vector locus about the real axis. This locus is the broken curve in Fig. 4.27.

3. We consider a vector originating at the point $-1 + j0$ and ending on the closed curve formed by the solid curve and the broken curve. Counting the number of revolutions N made by this vector when its end point goes around the closed curve in the direction of increasing ω, we obtain

$$N=2 \tag{4.94}$$

4. It is clear from equation (4.93) that the number P of poles of the transfer function $F(s)$ lying in the right half-plane is 0. That is,

$$P=0 \tag{4.95}$$

5. Therefore, the number of characteristic roots R lying in the right half-plane is

$$R=N+P=2\neq 0 \tag{4.96}$$

6. This equation shows that there are two characteristic roots lying in the right half-plane. Therefore, we conclude that the given system is unstable.

Let us now consider the case in which the open-loop transfer function has the following form:

$$F(s)=\frac{K}{s^n(1+sT_1)(1+sT_2)\cdots} \tag{4.97}$$

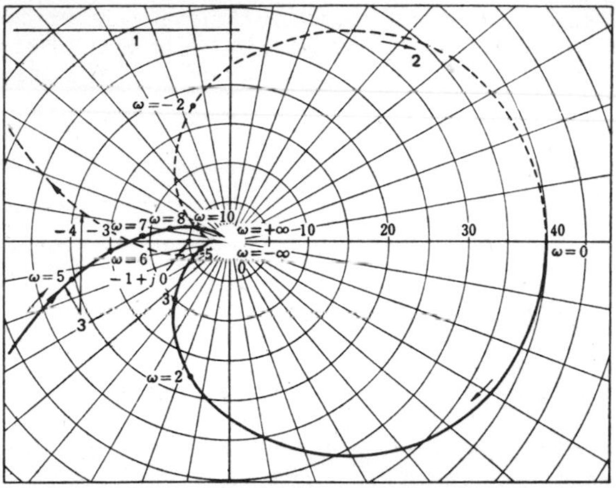

1 - *locus of the frequency response of* 40/1(1 + 0.6s)(1 + 0.5s) (1 + 0.1s); 2 - *direction of increasing* ω; 3 - *Five-times enlargement of the locus near the origin*

Fig. 4.27 Determination of stability by Nyquist's stability criterion

Since $F(j\omega) = \infty$ at $s = 0$, the vector locus of this transfer function does not form a closed curve. For example, consider the open-loop transfer function

$$F(s) = \frac{K}{s(1+sT_1)(1+sT_2)} \tag{4.98}$$

The vector locus of this transfer function is the solid curve shown in Fig. 4.28. If ω approaches 0 from the negative side, $F(j\omega)$ tends to $j\infty$, whereas if ω approaches 0 from the positive side, $F(j\omega)$ tends to $-j\infty$. Therefore, $F(j\omega)$ is discontinuous at $\omega = 0$.

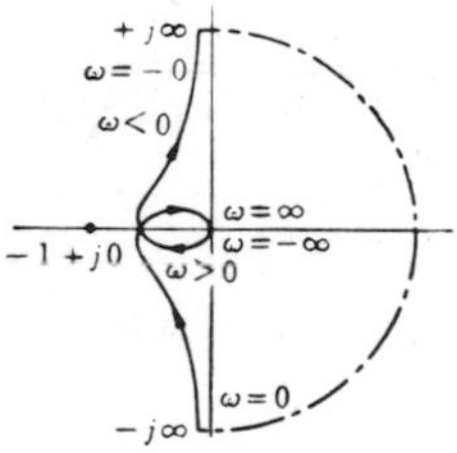

Fig. 4.28 The vector locus of the open-loop transfer function of an integral control system

Consequently, the stability of this system cannot be determined by Nyquist's stability criterion without a modification. To eliminate the discontinuity of $F(j\omega)$ at $\omega = 0$, we modify the closed curve along which $s = j\omega$ is to vary. Specifically, instead of having the closed curve pass through the origin, we let it pass very close to the origin but to the right of it, as shown in Fig. 2.29. For this modified closed curve, the locus of $F(j\omega)$ forms a closed curve consisting of the solid and broken curves shown in Fig. 4.28. When s goes around the modified closed curve, we must assume that the origin is contained in the domain (the right half-plane) to be investigated for the existence of the characteristic roots and that

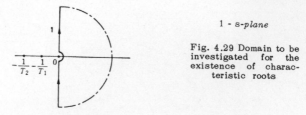

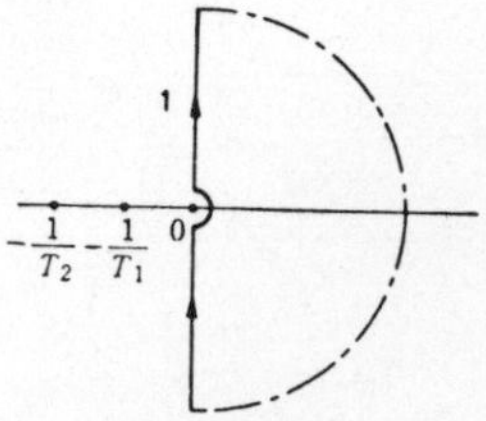

Fig. 4.29 Domain to be investigated for the existence of characteristic roots

there are n poles at the origin (n is the exponent of s in equation 4.97).

To illustrate the determination of stability in the case in which some poles of the open-loop transfer function lie in the right half-plane, consider the open-loop transfer function $F(s)$ given by

$$F(s)=\frac{-5(1+0.3s)}{(1+s)(1-0.2s)} \tag{4.99}$$

This transfer function can be written

$$F(s)=\frac{\frac{5\times0.3}{0.2}(s+1/0.3)}{(s+1)(s-1/0.2)}=\frac{7.5(s+10/3)}{(s+1)(s-5)} \tag{4.100}$$

This expression shows that $p_1 = -1$ and $p_2 = 5$ are the poles. Since the pole $p_2 = 5$ lies in the right half-plane, the number of poles P lying in the right half-plane is $P = 1$. Constructing the vector locus, we obtain the closed curve shown in Fig. 4.30. If we count the number of revolutions of the vector (which originates at the point $1+j0$ and ends on the closed curve) for the closed curve, we have 1 revolution in the counterclockwise direction. That is,

$$N=-1 \tag{4.101}$$

Therefore, the number of characteristic roots R lying in the right half-plane is

$$R=N+P=-1+1=0 \tag{4.102}$$

Since $R = 0$, this automatic control system is stable.

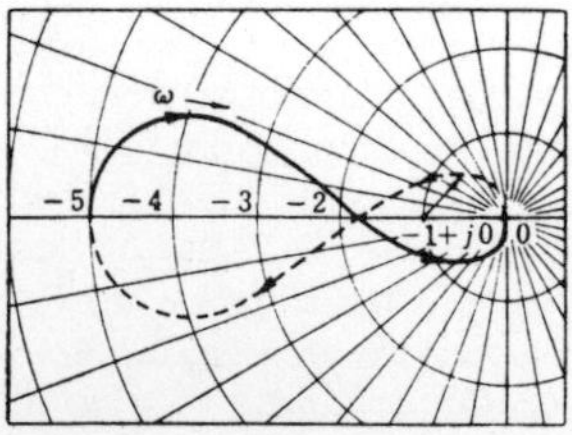

Fig. 4.30 An example of the determination of stability by Nyquist's stability criterion (where some poles lie in the right half-plane)

Unlike the transfer function (4.99) the open-loop transfer functions of automatic control systems in use rarely have poles lying in the right half-plane. In most cases, their vector loci are relatively simple curves, as shown in Fig. 4.31 and Fig. 4.32. Then, the procedure for determining stability is simplified even more. We need not plot the complete vector locus but only that part in the vicinity of the point $-1 + j0$ for $\omega > 0$. Moreover, we can determine that the system is stable if the point $-1 + j0$ is located to the left of the vector locus when a point moves along the vector

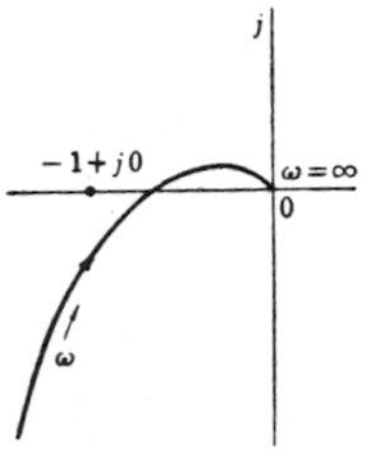

Fig. 4.31 Simplified method of determing the stability of the usual type of automatic control system (stable case)

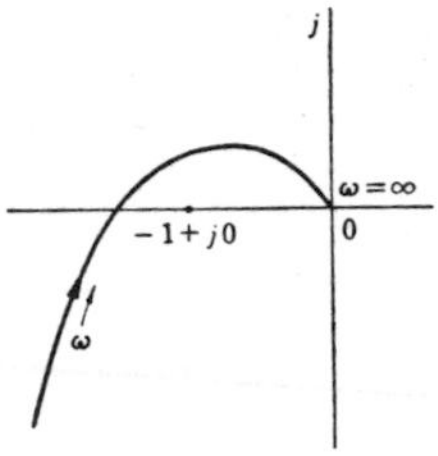

Fig. 4.32 Simplified method of determing the stability of the usual type of automatic control system (unstable case)

locus in the direction of increasing ω, as shown in Fig. 4.31. If the point $-1 + j0$ is located to the right of the vector locus, as shown in Fig. 4.32, then the system is unstable.

The same simplified procedure is applicable for determining the stability from the logarithmic vector locus. We then need to use the point (0 [dB], -180°) instead of the point $-1 + j0$, as shown in Fig. 4.33.

There is another modified method of determining stability. Draw a unit circle on the complex plane with centre at the origin and

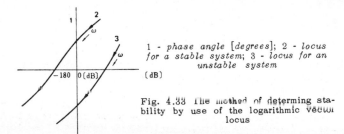

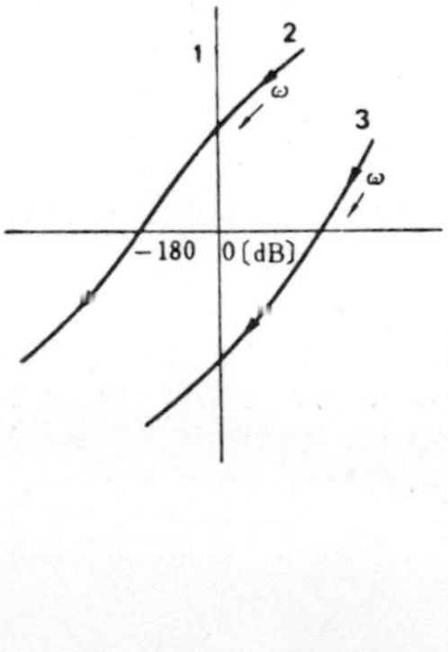

1 - *phase angle* [*degrees*]; 2 - *locus for a stable system*; 3 - *locus for an unstable system*

(dB)

Fig. 4.33 The method of determing stability by use of the logarithmic vector locus

observe the intersection of this unit circle and the vector locus. If the intersecting point is in the third quadrant of the complex plane, we conclude that the system is stable; if it is in the second quadrant, we conclude that the system is unstable (see Fig. 4.34).

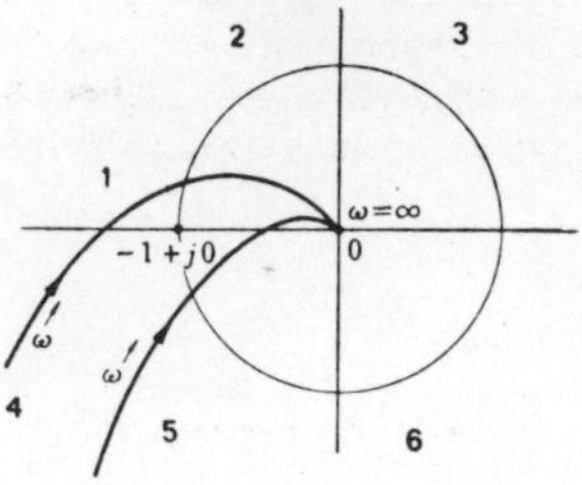

1 - *locus for an unstable system*; 2 - *second quadrant*; 3 - *first quadrant*; 4 - *locus for a stable system*; 5 - *third quadrant* 6 - *fourth quadrant*

Fig. 4.34 The method of determing stability from the intersection of the unit circle and the vector locus

We can also determine stability from the Bode diagram. The unit circle in Fig. 4.34 corresponds to the 0 [*dB*] line (i.e., the horizontal axis) on the Bode diagram. The cross-over angular frequency is defined to be the angular frequency at which the gain characteristic curve crosses the 0 [*dB*] line (the horizontal axis), as shown in Fig. 4.35, and is denoted by ω_c. Therefore, we may conclude that the system is stable if the phase angle at the cross-over frequency is less than -180° in the Bode diagram and that it is unstable if the phase angle is more than -180°.

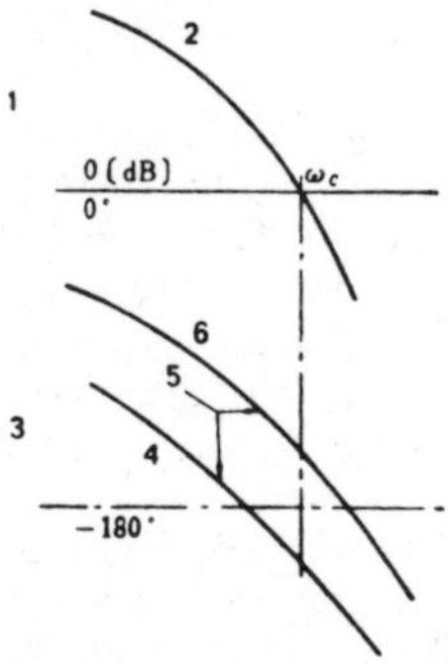

1 - *gain*; 2 - *gain characteristic curve* 3 - *phase angle*; 4 - *unstable case* 5 - *phase characteristic curves* 6 - *stable case*

Fig. 4.35 Determination of stability by use of Bode diagrams

4.9. EVALUATION OF TRANSIENT RESPONSE FROM THE RESONANCE VALUE

Usable automatic control systems must be stable, and their transient responses or error responses must attenuate sufficiently fast.

The transient response or the error response of a higher-order automatic control system can be approximated by those of a suitable second-order system. Thus, we find a second-order system whose frequency response is approximately equal to that of the higher-order system, and we compute the transient response or the error response of the second-order system by using equation (3.78), equation (3.75), or Fig. 3.10. Then, the transient response and the error response of this second-order system can be used as approximations of those responses of the higher-order system.

Thus, we find the frequency response of the second-order system whose block diagram is shown in Fig. 3.9 (b). If we set $s = j\omega$ in Fig. 3.9 (b), we obtain the block diagram shown in Fig. 4.36. Accordingly, the frequency response $A(j\omega) = C(j\omega)/R(j\omega)$ is computed as follows:

$$A(j\omega) = \frac{C(j\omega)}{R(j\omega)} = \frac{K/j\omega(1+j\omega T)}{1+K/j\omega(1+j\omega T)} \tag{4.103}$$

$$= \frac{K}{j\omega(1+j\omega T)+K} \tag{4.104}$$

If we rewrite this equation by using the specific angular frequency ω_n and the damping ratio ζ, defined by equation (3.51), we have

$$A(j\omega) = \frac{\dfrac{\omega_n}{2\zeta}}{j\omega\left(1+j\dfrac{1}{2\zeta}\dfrac{\omega}{\omega_n}\right)+\dfrac{\omega_n}{2\zeta}} = \frac{1}{1-\left(\dfrac{\omega}{\omega_n}\right)^2+j2\zeta\dfrac{\omega}{\omega_n}} \tag{4.105}$$

To simplify this expression further, we set

$$\Omega = \frac{\omega}{\omega_n} \tag{4.106}$$

The number Ω is the ratio of the angular frequency of a signal to the specific angular frequency. It is called the relative angular frequency, the normalised angular frequency, or the nondimensional angular frequency. Equation (4.105) can now be written in the form

$$A(j\omega) = \frac{1}{1-\Omega^2+j2\zeta\Omega} \tag{4.107}$$

As we know, the frequency response $A(j\omega)$ can be expressed as a vector quantity. Denoting the magnitude of the vector by $M(\Omega)$, we get

$$M(\Omega) = |A(j\omega)| = \frac{1}{\sqrt{(1-\Omega^2)^2+4\zeta^2\Omega^2}} \tag{4.108}$$

Denoting the phase angle by $\Phi(j\omega)$, we get

$$\Phi(j\omega) = \underline{/A(j\omega)} = -\tan^{-1}\frac{2\zeta\Omega}{1-\Omega^2} \tag{4.109}$$

However, to evaluate the transient response, we need only consider the magnitude characteristics (the gain characteristics).

If we plot $M(\Omega)$ against Ω, we obtain the curves shown in Fig. 4.37. These curves are determined by the values of ζ. As can be seen from Fig. 4.37, the value of $M(\Omega)$ is always 1 independently of the value of ζ for angular frequencies lower by a certain value than the resonant angular frequency. (The resonant angular frequency will be defined later.) It is always 0 independently of the value of ζ for angular frequencies that exceed the resonant angular frequency by a certain value. This shows that the value of $M(\Omega)$ differs primarily according to the value of ζ only for angular frequencies in the vicinity of the resonant angular frequency. Therefore, if the values of $M(\Omega)$ for angular frequencies in the vicinity of the resonant angular frequency ($\Omega \doteqdot 1$) are known in the frequency response curve, the corresponding values of ζ can be found, and hence the transient response can be evaluated. To obtain a simple relation between $M(\Omega)$ and ζ, we compute the maximum value of $M(\Omega)$, that is, the value of $M(\Omega)$ at the resonant angular frequency. We first set up the equation

$$\frac{dM(\Omega)}{d\Omega}=0 \qquad (4.110)$$

If we compute from this equation the relative angular frequency Ω_r at which $M(\Omega)$ has a maximum value, we obtain

$$\Omega_r=\sqrt{1-2\zeta^2} \qquad (4.111)$$

It should be noted that $M(\Omega)$ has a maximum value only if $\zeta<-1/\sqrt{2}$. From the definition of relative angular frequency,

$$\Omega_r=\frac{\omega_r}{\omega_n} \qquad (4.112)$$

where ω_n is the specific angular frequency and ω_r is the resonant angular frequency. In fact, the resonant angular frequency is defined by equation (4.112). If we substitute Ω_r given by equation (4.111) into equation (4.108), we obtain the maximum value of $M(\Omega)$. Denoting the maximum value by M_p, we have

$$M_p=\frac{1}{2\zeta\sqrt{1-\zeta^2}} \qquad (4.113)$$

From this equation, ζ can be expressed in terms of M_p.

$$\zeta=\sqrt{\frac{1}{2}\left(1-\sqrt{1-\frac{1}{M_p^2}}\right)} \qquad (4.114)$$

The maximum value M_p is called the resonant value. The above discussion shows that the resonant value M_p is determined by the damping ratio ζ; that is, M_p is determined by the transient response.

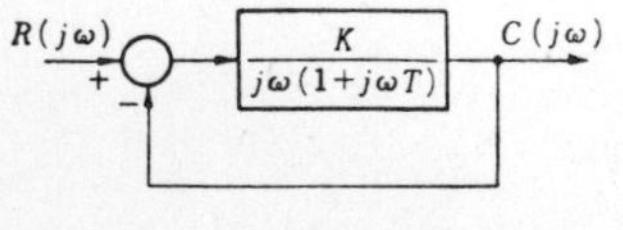

Fig. 4.36 A block diagram for determing the frequency response of a standard second-order system

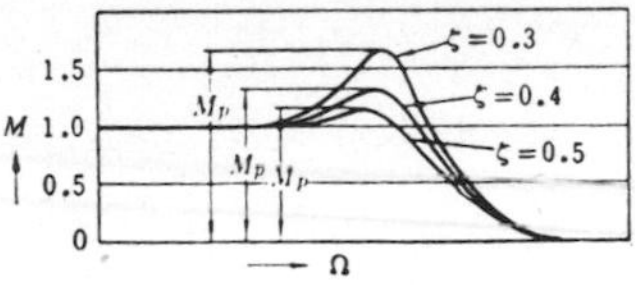

Fig. 4.37 The frequency response of a standard second-order system

From what was said in Section 3.5, in the case of a higher-order system $M(\Omega)$ is in general 1 for $\Omega \ll 1$ and approximately 0 for $\Omega \gg 1$; it is approximately equal to the resonant value of a second-order system even for $\Omega \doteq 1$. Therefore, if we find a second-order system whose resonant value and resonant angular frequency are approximately equal to those of the higher-order system, the transient response of the higher-order system can be approximated by that of the second-order system. Then the resonant angular frequency ω_r of the higher-order system is approximately equal to the specific angular frequency ω_n of the second-order system. Consequently, the resonant value M_p of the higher-order system can also be used to represent the wave form of the transient response of the higher-order system, and the resonant angular frequency ω_r can be used to represent the rapidity of the transient response if ω_r is known.

4.10. AMPLITUDE LOCUS AND PHASE LOCUS

The resonant value M_p can be found from the curve of the closed-loop frequency response. For example, if an automatic control system whose block diagram is the one shown in Fig. 4.38 is given, construct the frequency response curve of the closed-loop transfer function, which is a transfer function whose input is the reference input R (s) and whose output is the controlled variable C (s). Then, the maximum value of the frequency response curve is precisely the resonant value M_p and the maximum value can easily be read from the frequency response curve. However, in general, it is rather laborious to construct the closed-loop frequency response of a system. Moreover, the frequency response of an open-loop transfer function is used for the actual design of systems or for the

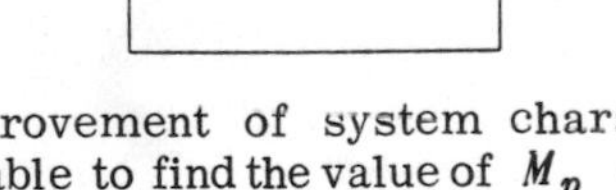

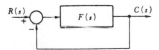

Fig. 4.38 Block diagram of an automatic control system

improvement of system characteristics. Consequently, it is desirable to find the value of M_p directly from the frequency response of an open-loop transfer function.

Denoting by $A(s)$ the closed-loop transfer function of the block diagram in Fig. 4.38, we have

$$A(s) = \frac{C(s)}{R(s)} = \frac{F(s)}{1+F(s)} \tag{4.115}$$

Accordingly, the closed-loop frequency response is

$$A(j\omega)=\frac{F(j\omega)}{1+F(j\omega)}=M\underline{/\Phi} \tag{4.116}$$

where $F(j\omega)$ is the frequency response of the open loop transfer function. As mentioned previously, $F(j\omega)$ is a complex-valued function and $F(j\omega)$ can be represented by a vector on the complex plane. Let **OP** be the vector representing $F(j\omega)$, as shown in Fig. 4.39. Then, the vector **QP**, originating at the point $-1+j0$ and ending at the point P, represents the denominator $1+F(j\omega)$ of the expression (4.116). Therefore, the magnitude of the vector $C(j\omega)/R(j\omega)$ which is the closed-loop frequency response, is equal to $|OP|/|QP|$ where $|OP|$ and $|QP|$ are the magnitudes of the vectors **OP** and **QP**, respectively. When the ratio $|OP|/|QP|$ is constant, the locus P is a circle, the so-called Apollonius circle. Fig. 4.40 shows such loci plotted for several values of the ratio $|OP|/|QP|$. Since $M(\Omega)=|A(j\omega)|=|C(j\omega)|/|R(j\omega)|=|OP|/|QP|$, these circles are the images of the lines defined by $M(\Omega)=$ constant. We shall call these circles M-circles.

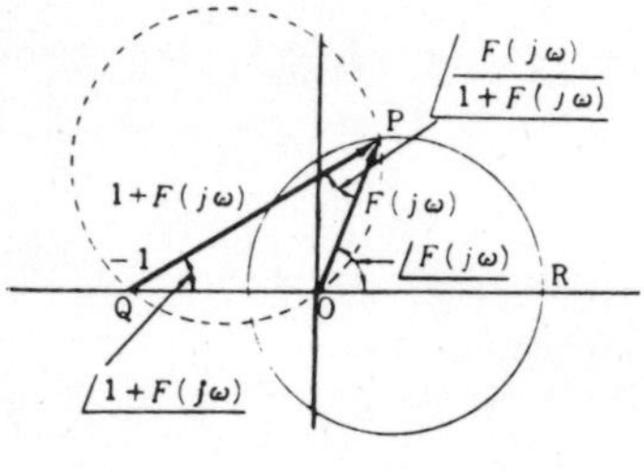

Fig. 4.39 Properties of the closed-loop frequency response in vector representation

Let us find the relation between M ($M=M(\Omega)$) and the radius and centre of the M-circles. For this purpose, we represent the end point P of the vectors in rectangular coordinates as shown in Fig. 4.41. Then, the magnitudes of the numerator and the denominator of the expression (4.116) are $(X^2+Y^2)^{1/2}$ and $[(X+1)^2+Y^2]^{1/2}$ respectively. Therefore,

$$M=\frac{\sqrt{X^2+Y^2}}{\sqrt{(X+1)^2+Y^2}} \tag{4.117}$$

$$M^2=\frac{X^2+Y^2}{(X+1)^2+Y^2} \tag{4.118}$$

These equations are the equations of the M-circles, and they can be written

$$X^2+Y^2+2X\frac{M^2}{M^2-1}=-\frac{M^2}{M^2-1} \tag{4.119}$$

or

$$\left(X+\frac{M^2}{M^2-1}\right)^2+Y^2=\left(\frac{M}{M^2-1}\right)^2 \tag{4.120}$$

Therefore, the coordinates of the centres of the M-circles are

$$X=-\frac{M^2}{M^2-1},\quad Y=0 \tag{4.121}$$

and the radius R is

$$R = \frac{M}{M^2 - 1} \tag{4.122}$$

If we denote by Φ the phase angle of $A(j\omega)$, it is clear from equation (4.116) that Φ is equal to $\underline{/F(j\omega)} - \underline{/1 + F(j\omega)}$. In Fig. 4.39, this phase angle difference may be expressed by $\underline{/POR}$ -

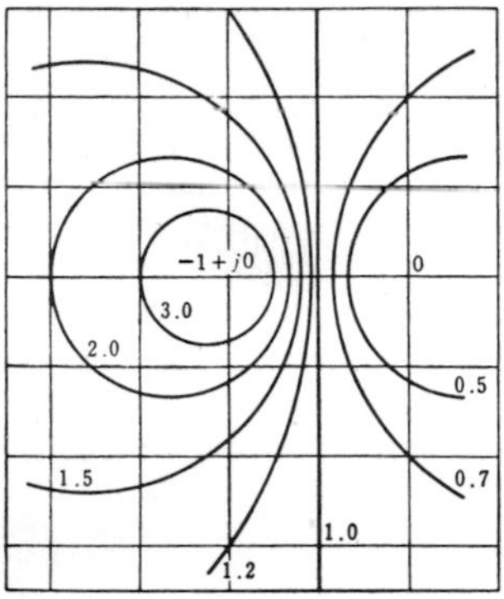

Fig. 4.40 The M-circles of a closed-loop frequency response

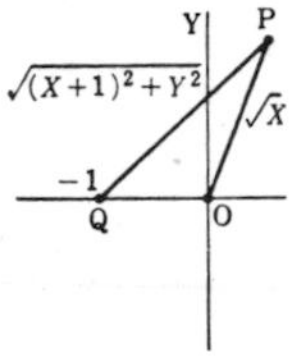

Fig. 4.41 Rectangular coordinate representation of a point on a M-circle

$\underline{/PQR}$, where $\underline{/POR}$ and $\underline{/PQR}$ are the phase angles of the vectors OP and QP, respectively, and $\underline{/POR}$ - $\underline{/PQR}$ is equal to $\underline{/QPO}$. Consequently, Φ is equal to $\underline{/QPO}$. When $\underline{/QPO}$ is constant, the locus of the point P is clearly a circle. Fig. 4.42 shows a family of such circles for various values of Φ. These circles are the images of the lines defined by Φ = constant. Thus, we shall call them Φ-circles.

Figure 4.43 shows the M-circles and Φ-circles plotted together on the complex plane. If we plot these circles on the plane on which the locus of the frequency response of the open-loop transfer function is plotted, the value $M\underline{/\Phi}$ of the closed-loop frequency response for an arbitrary angular frequency can be read directly from the diagram. However, for design of an automatic control system or for certain other purposes, it is not necessary to know the $M\underline{/\Phi}$ value of the closed-loop frequency response for all angular frequencies; it is sufficient to know the resonant value M_p. In fact, the value of M_p is often part of the specifications accompanying an order for a design and the problem is one of improving the design after a manufactured automatic control system fails to have the specified value of M_p. If this is the purpose, we only need to

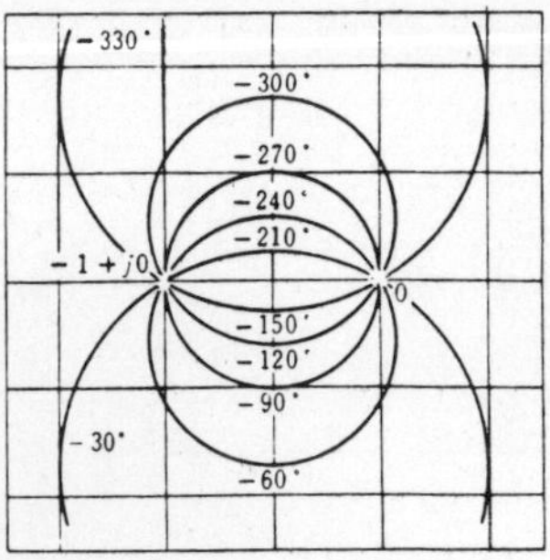

Fig. 4.42 ϕ-circles of a closed-loop frequency response

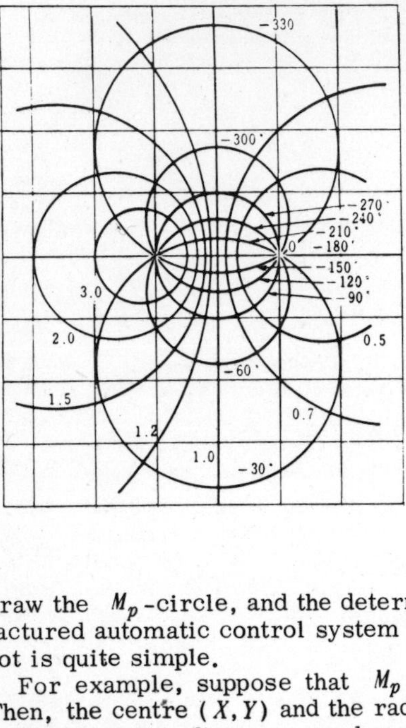

Fig. 4.43 M-circles and ϕ-circles of a closed-loop frequency response plotted together on the complex plane

draw the M_p-circle, and the determination as to whether the manufactured automatic control system has the specified value of M_p or not is quite simple.

For example, suppose that $M_p = 1.5$ is given in a specification. Then, the centre (X, Y) and the radius R of the M_p-circle plotted in the Nyquist diagram can be computed from equations (4.121) and (4.122) as follows:

centre: $$X = -\frac{(1.5)^2}{(1.5)^2 - 1} = -1.8, \quad Y = 0$$

radius: $$R = \frac{1.5}{(1.5)^2 - 1} = 1.2$$

Therefore, the M_p-circle plotted in the Nyquist diagram is the circle (a) shown in Fig. 4.44.

If the vector locus of the frequency response of the open loop transfer function of the manufactured automatic control system is curve (b), which intersects the M_p-circle as shown in Fig. 4.44, the resonant value M_p of the system is larger than the specified value 1.5. Accordingly, the characteristics of the system have to be improved so that the system will meet the specified resonant value.

If the vector locus of the open-loop transfer function of the system is curve (c) outside the M_p-circle, the resonant value M_p of the system is less than the specified value. This indicates that the manufactured system has more damping in its response than it should under the given specification.

If the vector locus of the open-loop transfer function is the curve (d) which is tangent to the M_p-circle ($M_p = 1.5$), as shown in Fig. 4.44, then the resonant value of the system is exactly equal to the specified value.

We have been discussing M-loci (M-circles) and Φ-loci (Φ-circles) on the Nyquist diagram. If we wish to use logarithmic vector loci for analysis or design of automatic control systems, we need to construct M-loci (the images of the lines defined by M = constant) and Φ-loci (the images of the lines defined by Φ = constant) plotted on the logarithmic plane. Fig. 4.45 shows these M-loci and Φ-loci on the logarithmic plane. The solid curves are the M-loci expressed in dB, and the dashed curves are the Φ-loci expressed in degrees. If we plot the logarithmic vector locus of an open-loop transfer function together with the M-locus and the Φ-locus on the logarithmic plane, the resonant value M_p and the resonant angular frequency ω_r can easily be read from the diagram as in the case of a Nyquist diagram.

We have been discussing the method of finding the resonant value M_p of a closed-loop frequency response and the method of finding a closed-loop frequency from the vector locus of the frequency response of the open-loop transfer function. As mentioned in Section 4.3, the use of inverse vector loci provides an even simpler method of finding these values. The reciprocal of a closed-loop frequency response is given by

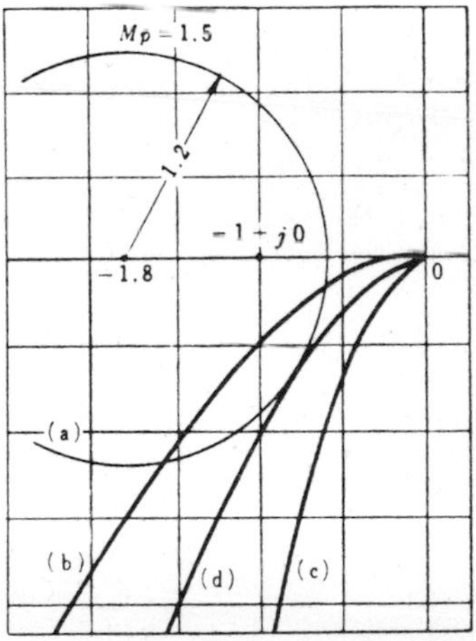

Fig. 4.44 Examination of the resonant value M_p of an automatic control system

$$\frac{R(j\omega)}{C(j\omega)} = \frac{1+F(j\omega)}{F(j\omega)} = \frac{1}{F(j\omega)} + 1 \tag{4.123}$$

Therefore, if we plot the vector locus of the reciprocal of the frequency response of the open-loop transfer function, the reciprocal of the closed-loop frequency response can be found immediately by reading the diagram resulting from the translation of the vector locus by $-1 + j0$. The M-locus and Φ-loci in this case are families of concentric circles with centres at the point $-1 + j0$ and families of rays originating at the point $-1 + j0$, as shown in Fig. 4.46. It should be noted that it is not actually necessary to plot the M-locus

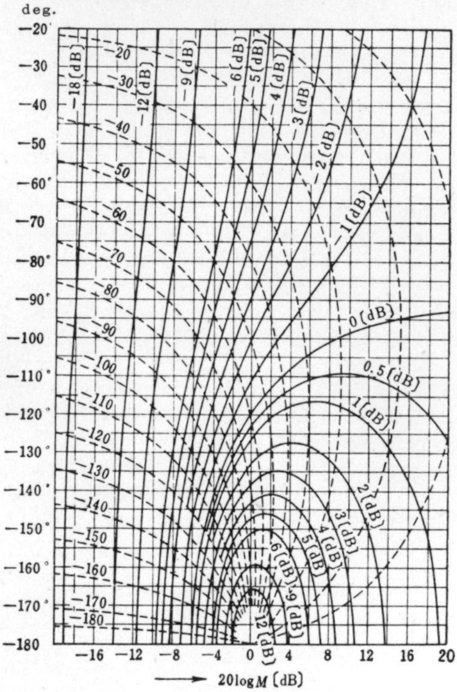

Fig. 4.45 $M - \phi$ diagram (also known as a Nicols chart)

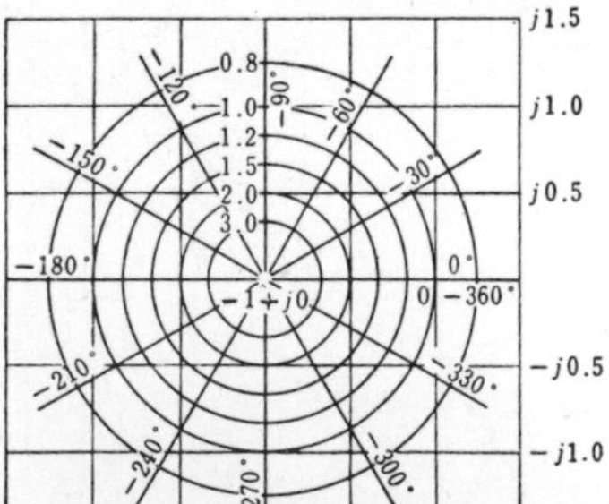

Fig. 4.46 M loci and ϕ loci for the inverse vector locus method

and the Φ-locus on the diagram sheet to evaluate M_p or ω_r as in the previous case. As shown here, the inverse vector locus method is often more convenient than the vector locus method. In particular, the inverse vector locus method is preferable for a multiloop automatic control system.

4.11. PHASE MARGIN

As shown in the preceding section, from the vector locus of the frequency response of an open-loop transfer function, we can find a resonant value M_p or can judge whether an automatic control system has a specified value of M_p; consequently, we can evaluate a transient response approximately. This method, however, requires us to construct the vector locus of the frequency response. In general, the Bode diagram of an automatic control system can be more easily constructed than the vector locus of the frequency response. Therefore, it will be convenient if we can evaluate the transient response from the Bode diagram.

In general, the vector locus of the open-loop transfer function of an automatic control system is such that the phase angle lags and the magnitude attenuates at a constant rate as the frequency increases in the vicinity of the point $-1 + j0$, as shown in Fig. 4.47. Consider an open-loop transfer function with such a frequency response. If we draw a unit circle with centre at the origin as shown in Fig. 4.47, the intersection of the unit circle with the vector locus will be located very close to the point at which the magnitude M of the closed-loop frequency response attains its maximum value M_p. This is easily seen if we compare Figs. 4.47 and 4.44. Consequently, the transient response can be approximately evaluated from the position of the intersection, and the rapidity of the response can also be evaluated from the frequency at the intersection. This point of intersection is called a cross-over point, and the angular frequency for the cross-over point is called the cross-over angular frequency. The position of the intersection (cross-over point) can be found as shown in Fig. 4.47 if we know the phase angle for the point of intersection (measured from the left half of the horizontal axis). This angle is called the phase margin. The unit circle shown in Fig. 4.47 is the locus of a vector whose magnitude is 1; therefore, it corresponds to the horizontal axis zero [dB] line of the Bode diagram. Accordingly, the angular frequency ω_c, at which the gain characteristic curve intersects the zero [dB] line is the cross-over angular frequency, and the phase angle corresponding to the cross-over frequency ω_c (measured from the -180° line) is the phase margin, as shown in Fig. 4.48. Fig. 4.49 shows how the phase margin appears on the logarithmic vector locus.

To get a quantitative relationship between the phase margin and the transient response, we find the phase margin of a standard second-order system with no steady-state error and its relation to the damping ratio ζ. The block diagram of the standard second-order system was given in Fig. 3.9.

The frequency response of the open-loop transfer function of the

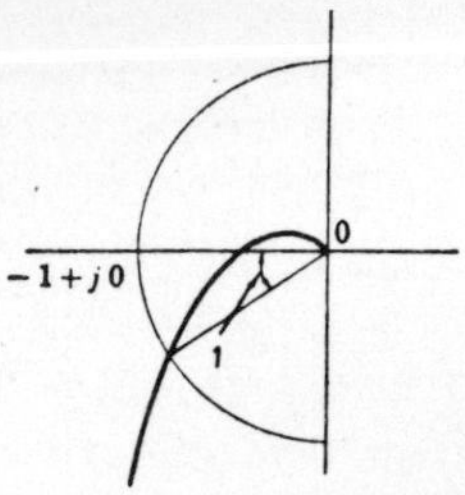

1 - *phase margin*

Fig. 4.47 Definition of phase margin (on Nyquist diagram

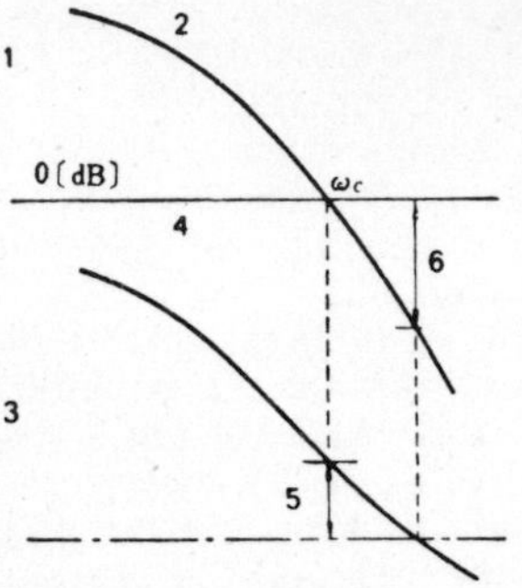

1 - *gain*; 2 - *gain characteristic curve* 3 - *phase angle*; 4 - 0 *degree → angular frequency*; 5 - *phase margin*; 6 - *gain margin*

Fig. 4.48 Phase margin on Bode diagram

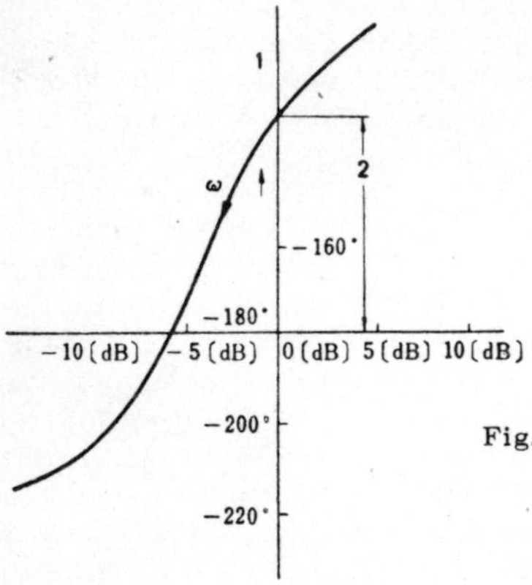

1 - *phase angle*; 2 - *phase margin*

Fig. 4.49 Phase margin logarithmic plane

standard second-order system (see Fig. 3.9) is

$$F(j\omega)=\frac{K}{j\omega(1+j\omega T)} \tag{4.124}$$

If we express this equation in terms of ζ and ω_n by using equation (3.52), we have

$$F(j\omega)=\frac{1}{2\zeta j\frac{\omega}{\omega_n}\left(1+j\frac{1}{2\zeta}\frac{\omega}{\omega_n}\right)} \tag{4.125}$$

where ω_n is the specific angular frequency of the closed-loop system and ζ is the damping ratio of the closed-loop system. Normalising equation (4.125) by use of the relative angular frequency $\Omega = \omega/\omega_n$, we obtain

$$F(j\omega)=\frac{1}{2\zeta j\Omega\left(1+j\frac{\Omega}{2\zeta}\right)} \tag{4.126}$$

Let Ω_c denote the value of Ω for which $F(j\omega)= 1$. Then, from equation (4.126)

$$\Omega_c=\sqrt{\sqrt{4\zeta^4+1}-2\zeta^2} \tag{4.127}$$

The phase angle for $\Omega = \Omega_c$ is $-90° - \tan^{-1} \Omega_c/2\zeta$. Therefore,

$$\phi_m=180°-90°-\tan^{-1}\frac{\Omega_c}{2\zeta} \tag{4.128}$$

$$=90°-\tan^{-1}\sqrt{\frac{1}{4}\sqrt{4+1/\zeta^4}-\frac{1}{2}} \tag{4.129}$$

Figure 6.1 shows a graph of this function.

As a result of equation (4.129), we can also evaluate the transient response by use of the phase margin. However, this method is good only when the vector locus is sufficiently simple in the vicinity of the point $-1 + j0$. This fact may also be stated in terms of the Bode diagram. If the Bode diagram is such that the gain characteristic curve attenuates in inverse proportion to the angular frequency in the vicinity of the cross-over angular frequency, then the transient response can be evaluated in terms of the phase margin. Otherwise, the method is not effective and we need other methods for an accurate evaluation of the transient response.

4.12. EVALUATION OF THE TRANSIENT RESPONSE BY COMPLEX FREQUENCY LOCUS

If the frequency response of an automatic control system is given, we can determine the stability of the system from the frequency response as described earlier. For design or analysis of an automatic control system, determination of the stability is not sufficient; we need to know the approximate form of the transient response. In connection with this evaluation of the transient response, a suitable extension of the vector locus method used for the determination of stability provides a simple method for determining whether an automatic control system has a desired transient response or not.

Recall the method used to determine the number of characteristic roots lying in a certain domain of the root plane for a given automatic control system whose open-loop transfer function is $F(s)$. As explained in Section 4.7, we take a curve enclosing the domain to be examined for the existence of characteristic roots, and we let s go around the closed curve. Then, the number of characteristic roots lying in the domain is determined by the number of revolutions made by the vector $1 + F(s)$ when s goes around the closed curve once. To determine the stability, we examine the entire right half-plane for the existence of characteristic roots, as shown in Fig. 4.25. If we extend this domain suitably, we can determine the approximate form of the transient response.

The general form of the transient response of an automatic control system is

$$e(t)=(A_1\epsilon^{r_1t}+A_2\epsilon^{r_2t}+A_3\epsilon^{r_3t}+\cdots\cdots)\ U(t) \tag{4.130}$$

as shown in equation (4.84). The numbers r_1, r_2, r_3, ... are the characteristic roots; in general, they are complex. We write them in the form

$$r_1=-\alpha_1+j\omega_1,\quad r_2=-\alpha_2+j\omega_2,\quad r_3=-\alpha_3+j\omega_3,\cdots\cdots\cdots\cdots \tag{4.131}$$

Here the real numbers α_1, α_2, α_3, ... are the damping factors of the characteristic roots, and they are all positive real numbers for a stable automatic control system.

Let α_0 be a real number. Then, by a suitable choice of α_1', α_2', α_3',... we can have

$$\alpha_1=\alpha_0+\alpha_1',\quad \alpha_2=\alpha_0+\alpha_2',\quad \alpha_3=\alpha_0+\alpha_3',\cdots\cdots\cdots\cdots\cdots\cdots\cdots \tag{4.132}$$

Substituting these values into equation (4.130), we get the transient response $e(t)$;

$$\begin{aligned}&=(A_1\epsilon^{-\alpha_0t}\epsilon^{(-\alpha_1'+j\omega_1)t}+A_2\epsilon^{-\alpha_0t}\epsilon^{(-\alpha_2'+j\omega_2)t}+A_3\epsilon^{-\alpha_0t}\epsilon^{(-\alpha_3'+j\omega_3)t}+\cdots)\ U(t)\\&=\epsilon^{-\alpha_0t}(A_1\epsilon^{(-\alpha_1'+j\omega_1)t}+A_2\epsilon^{(-\alpha_2'+j\omega_2)t}+A_3\epsilon^{(-\alpha_3'+j\omega_3)t}+\cdots\cdots)\ U(t)\end{aligned} \tag{4.133}$$

The expression

$$A_1\epsilon^{(-\alpha_1'+j\omega_1)t}+A_2\epsilon^{(-\alpha_2'+j\omega_2)t}+A_3\epsilon^{(-\alpha_3'+j\omega_3)t}+\cdots$$

in this equation represents an attenuation if α_1', α_2', α_3', ... all are positive and a divergence if any of them are negative. Accordingly, the error response $e(t)$ attenuates more rapidly than does the wave $A\epsilon^{-\alpha_0 t}$ (where A is a constant) if α_1', α_2', α_3'... are all positive but more slowly if any of them are negative. Therefore, in order to determine whether a transient response attenuates more rapidly or more slowly than does a given wave $A\epsilon^{-\alpha_0 t}$, it is sufficient to find out whether each attenuation exponent α_1 (for $i = 1, 2, 3$...) is larger than the fixed value α_0 or any α_1 is smaller than α_0. This is equivalent to seeing whether there exists a characteristic root to the right of the vertical line $\alpha_0 = 0$ (the line obtained by shifting the imaginary axis to the left by a distance α_0, as shown in Fig. 4.50). We set

$$s=-\alpha_0+j\omega \tag{4.134}$$

and substitute this expression into the open-loop transfer function $F(s)$. Then, the existence of characteristic roots to the right of the vertical line $\alpha_0 = 0$ can be determined by the number of revolutions made by the vector $F(-\alpha_0 + j\omega)$ as ω varies from $-\infty$ to $+\infty$. It is clear that the locus of $F(-\alpha_0 + j\omega)$ is somewhat different from the locus of $F(j\omega)$. For example, compare the loci of $F(-\alpha_0 + j\omega)$ and $F(j\omega)$ in Fig. 4.51, when the given open loop transfer function is

$$F(s)=\frac{1}{1+sT} \tag{4.135}$$

It can be seen from Fig. 4.51 that the loci of $F(j\omega)$ and $F(-\alpha_0 + j\omega)$ are similar but that their magnitudes are different. Note that $F(-\alpha_0 + j\omega)$ is obtained by substituting a complex number $-\alpha_0 + j\omega$ (instead of a pure imaginary number $j\omega$) into the open-loop transfer function $F(s)$. Thus, the locus of $F(-\alpha_0 + j\omega)$ is called a complex frequency locus. As can be seen from what has been said, the procedure for evaluating the rapidity of response is the same as that for determining the stability except that the complex frequency locus of $F(-\alpha_0 + j\omega)$ is used instead of the vector locus of the frequency response $F(j\omega)$.

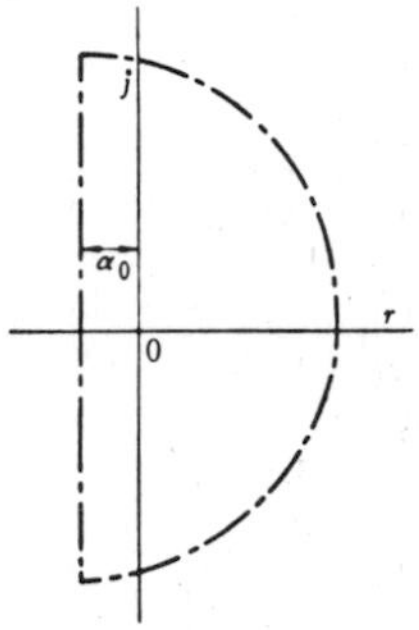

Fig. 4.50 Domain to be examined for existence of characteristic roots as a means of evaluating the rapidity of response

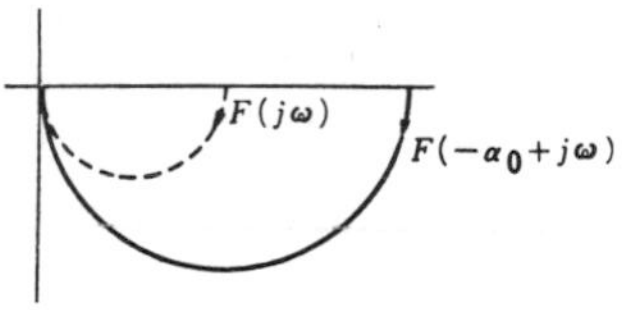

Fig. 4.51 Difference between the vector locus and the complex frequency locus of the transfer function $1/(1 + sT)$

As an example, we consider the case in which there are no poles in the domain to be examined (that is, $P = 0$). If the point $-1 + j0$ is located to the left of the locus of $F(-\alpha_0 + j\omega)$ as we look in the direction of increasing ω (cf. curve (a) in Fig. 4.52), then the transient error response attenuates more rapidly than does the wave $A\epsilon^{-\alpha_0 t}$. On the other hand, if the point $-1 + j0$ is located to the right of the locus of $F(-\alpha_0 + j\omega)$, as with curve (c), then the transient response attenuates more slowly than does the wave $A\epsilon^{-\alpha_0 t}$.

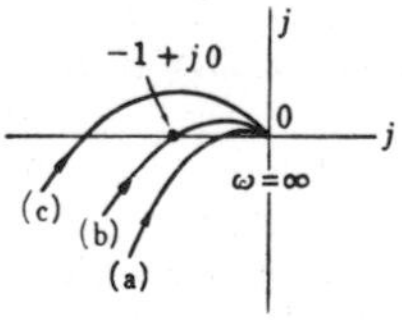

Fig. 4.52 Determination of stability

We have just discussed a method of investigating whether the attenuation of a transient error response is equal to a specified value. We shall now discuss a method of examining whether a wave form of a transient error response is better or worse than a specified form.

Suppose that the characteristic root r_n has the value

$$r_n = -\alpha_n + j\omega_n \tag{4.136}$$

for an arbitrary component wave $A_n\epsilon^{r_n t}$ of the transient error response (4.130). Then, the ratio of α_n to ω_n is, as mentioned before, the damping coefficient. We denote it by γ_n :

$$\gamma_n = \frac{\alpha_n}{\omega_n} \tag{4.137}$$

The damping coefficient γ_n is, of course, a constant characterising the form of the component wave $A_n\epsilon^{r_n t}$. If we denote by γ_0 the damping coefficient of a specified wave form, the set of all characteristic roots with damping coefficient γ_0 constitutes two half-lines intersecting the imaginary axis at the origin at an angle $\tan^{-1}\gamma_0$. Then, a characteristic root with damping coefficient smaller than γ_0 is located to the right of the two half-lines, whereas a characteristic root with damping coefficient larger than γ_0 is located to the left of the two half-lines. Therefore, we can determine whether the form of a transient error response is better or worse than the specified wave form by examining the existence of the characteristic roots in the domain to the right of the two half-lines. If we set $s = (-\gamma_0\omega + j\omega)$ and substitute this expression into $F(s)$, we obtain $F(-\gamma_0\omega + j\omega)$. Then, the existence of the characteristic roots in the domain can be examined by using the complex frequency locus of $F(-\gamma_0\omega + j\omega)$.

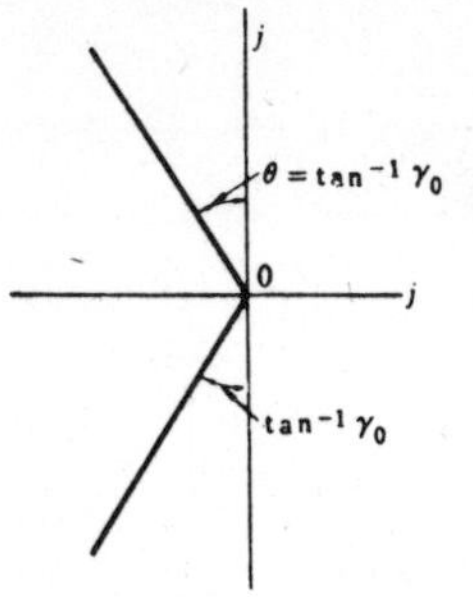

Fig. 4.53 A domain for examination of stability

This complex frequency locus method for the evaluation of a transient response can be extended to the logarithmic vector locus method and the inverse vector locus method. In particular, if the open-loop transfer function has no zero in the domain to be examined for characteristic roots, the complex frequency locus method can be reduced to a simpler procedure, as in the case of the determination of stability. It should be noted, however, that the domain to be examined for characteristic roots is generally larger with the complex frequency method than with the vector locus method. Consequently, there are often poles of the open-loop transfer function in the domain even for automatic control systems of the usual type.

EXERCISE PROBLEMS

1. Figures (a), (b), and (c) show compensating networks used for series compensation. For each network, construct the vector locus accurately, and give angular frequencies to the corresponding curves.

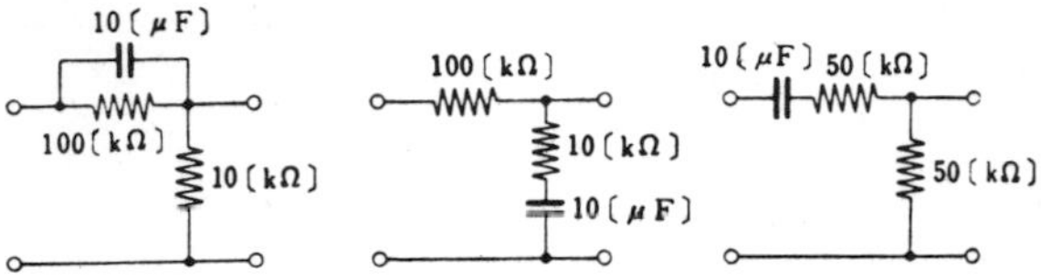

(a) (b) (c)

2. Construct the vector locus of the frequency response for each of the following transfer functions:

(i) $\dfrac{10}{(1+2s)(1+3s)}$ (ii) $\dfrac{10(1+3s)}{(1+4s)(1+2s)}$

(iii) $\dfrac{10(1+2s)}{s^2(1+0.5s)}$ (iv) $\dfrac{10}{s^2+0.5s+1}$

3. Sketch the Bode diagram of each of the following transfer functions:

(i) $\dfrac{3(1+0.2s)}{s(1+s)}$

(ii) $\dfrac{10(1+2s)(1+0.5s)}{s(1+5s)(1+s)(1+0.2s)}$

(iii) ϵ^{-3s}

(iv) $\dfrac{\epsilon^{-0.2s}}{1+0.5s}$

4. The diagram bolow shows an approximation of a gain characteristic curve in a certain Bode diagram. Sketch the phase characteristic curve, assuming the system does not contain a dead time or a negative time constant.

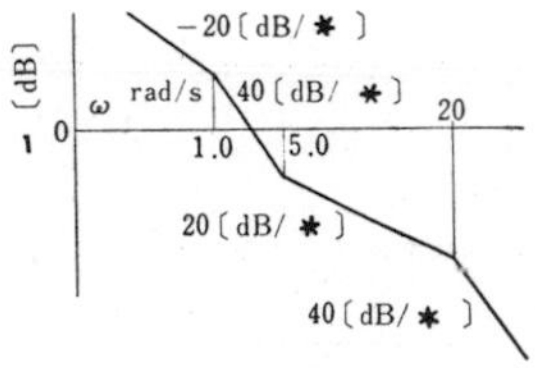

1 - gain

* degrees.

5. An ultra-low-frequency oscillator was connected to the input terminals of an electrical element of the automatic control system shown below, and the frequency response of the electrical element was measured. The numerical values of the frequency response are listed in the accompanying table. Find the transfer function of this electrical element, assuming that the input and the output signals were shown by an oscillograph test to be distortion-free sinusoidal waves.

f[c/s]	E_i[V]	E_o[V]
0.1	4.50	42.5
0.5	4.51	40.3
1.0	4.51	37.9
2.0	4.55	32.3
4.0	4.60	19.3
6.0	10.0	28.2
10.0	10.1	17.9
20	10.1	7.17
40	10.2	2.02
60	10.2	0.99
100	10.1	0.36

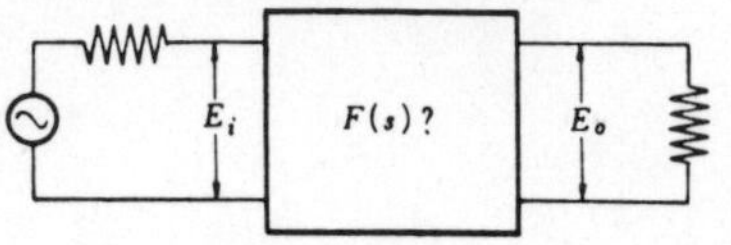

6. Construct the Nyquist diagram of an automatic control system whose open-loop transfer function is

$$\frac{2(1+s)}{s^2(1+0.2\,s)}$$

and determine the stability of the system. If the system is stable, find an approximate value of the resonant value M_p.

7. Construct the Nyquist diagram of an automatic control system whose open-loop transfer function is

$$F(s)=\frac{20(s+5)}{(s-1)(s+2)}$$

and determine the stability.

8. Find the phase margin of an automatic control system whose open-loop transfer function is

$$F(s)=\frac{2}{s(1+2\,s)(1+0.5\,s)(1+0.1\,s)}$$

By what fraction should the gain constant be reduced to have the phase margin $\phi_m = 45°$?

9. Consider an automatic control system whose open-loop transfer function is

$$\frac{k}{s(1+0.5\,s)(1+0.1\,s)}$$

Find the range of values of k for which the damping coefficient γ (ratio of real part to imaginary part) of every characteristic root exceeds 0.5.

5

Characteristic Roots of Automatic Control Systems

5.1 DISTRIBUTION OF CHARACTERISTIC ROOTS AND TRANSIENT RESPONSE

As stated above, to evaluate a transient performance, we need to solve the characteristic equation to find the characteristic roots and to find the magnitude of the wave determined by each characteristic root. The number of characteristic roots is equal to the degree of the characteristic equation. Since the characteristic roots are complex numbers, they can be represented by points on the complex plane, as shown in Fig. 5.1. The diagram showing the distribution of characteristic roots is called the root configuration, and the complex plane in this case is called the root plane.

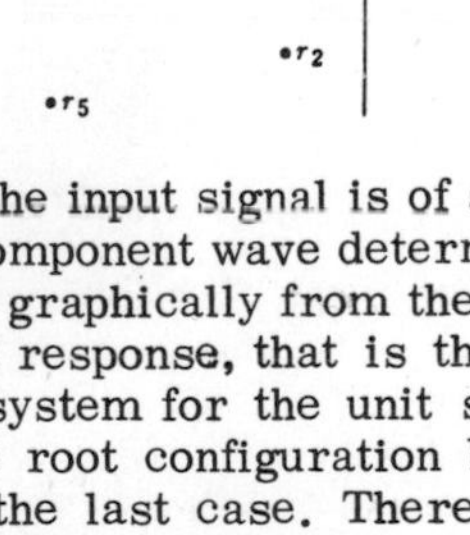

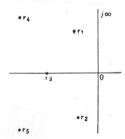

Fig. 5.1 An example of root configuration

When the input signal is of a particular wave form, the magnitude of the component wave determined by each characteristic root can be found graphically from the root configuration. In particular, the transient response, that is the transient reaction of an automatic control system for the unit step input signal, can easily be found from the root configuration by a graphical computation. We shall discuss the last case. There are some technical problems in the actual construction of a root configuration, which we shall discuss in detail later. Here, we assume that a root configuration has already been constructed.

As shown in Section 2.9, the open-loop transfer function of an automatic control system in general can be expressed by

$$F(s)=\frac{K_0(1+sT_1')(1+sT_2')\cdots(1+sT_m')}{s(1+sT_1)(1+sT_2)(1+sT_3)\cdots(1+sT_l)} \tag{5.1}$$

This equation is the representation of the open-loop transfer function in terms of time constants. It was convenient for the calculation of the frequency response. However, to deal with the root configuration, it is convenient to use the representation of the open-loop transfer function in terms of poles and zeros. If we express the open loop transfer function (5.1) in terms of poles and zeros, we have

$$F(s)=\frac{K(s-z_1)(s-z_2)\cdots(s-z_m)}{(s-p_0)(s-p_1)(s-p_2)\cdots(s-p_l)} \tag{5.2}$$

where the values of K, of the poles p_0, p_1, p_2, ..., p_l, and of the zeros z_1, z_2, ..., z_m are as follows:

$$K=K_0\frac{T_1'T_2'T_3'\cdots T_m'}{T_1T_2T_3\cdots T_l} \tag{5.3}$$

$$p_0=0,\ p_1=-\frac{1}{T_1},\ p_2=-\frac{1}{T_2},\cdots\cdots,p_l=-\frac{1}{T_l} \tag{5.4}$$

$$z_1=-\frac{1}{T_1'},\ z_2=-\frac{1}{T_2'},\cdots\cdots,z_m=-\frac{1}{T_m'} \tag{5.5}$$

If we use this representation, an open-loop transfer function with three poles but no zero can be expressed as

$$F(s)=\frac{K}{(s-p_1)(s-p_2)(s-p_3)} \tag{5.6}$$

For simplicity, we shall discuss the output signal of an automatic control system whose open-loop transfer function is given by equation (5.6) when the unit step signal is used as the input signal (see Fig. 5.2). If we denote by $C(s)$ the s-representation of the output signal, then

$$C(s)=\frac{F(s)}{1+F(s)}\cdot\frac{1}{s} \tag{5.7}$$

$$=\frac{\dfrac{K}{(s-p_1)(s-p_2)(s-p_3)}}{1+\dfrac{K}{(s-p_1)(s-p_2)(s-p_3)}}\cdot\frac{1}{s}$$

$$=\frac{K}{(s-p_1)(s-p_2)(s-p_3)+K}\cdot\frac{1}{s} \tag{5.8}$$

$$=\frac{K}{s(s-r_1)(s-r_2)(s-r_3)} \tag{5.9}$$

where r_1, r_2, and r_3 are the roots of the characteristic equation

$$(s-p_1)(s-p_2)(s-p_3)+K=0 \tag{5.10}$$

of this system. Plotting these characteristic roots on the root plane, we obtain, for example, the root configuration shown in Fig. 5.3.

Now, equation (5.9) can be expanded into partial fractions as follows:

$$C(s)=\frac{A_0}{s}+\frac{A_1}{s-r_1}+\frac{A_2}{s-r_2}+\frac{A_3}{s-r_3} \tag{5.11}$$

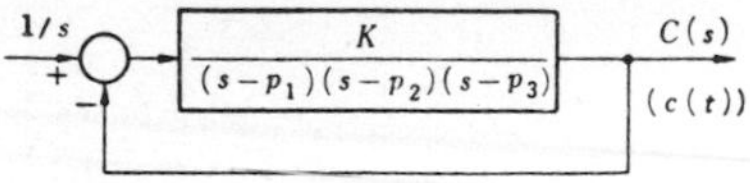

Fig. 5.2 Block diagram of an automatic control system whose open-loop transfer function is given by equation (5.6)

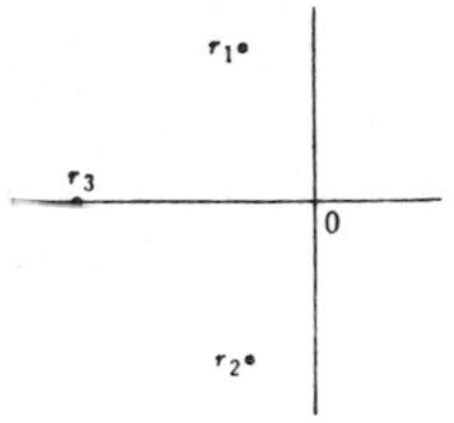

Fig. 5.3 Root configuration of the system shown in Fig. 5.2

From formula (2.99)

$$\left.\begin{aligned}
A_0 &= |C(s)s|_{s=0} = \frac{K}{(-r_1)(-r_2)(-r_3)}\\
A_1 &= |C(s)(s-r_1)|_{s=r_1} = \frac{K}{r_1(r_1-r_2)(r_1-r_3)}\\
A_2 &= |C(s)(s-r_2)|_{s=r_2} = \frac{K}{r_2(r_2-r_1)(r_2-r_3)}\\
A_3 &= |C(s)(s-r_3)|_{s=r_3} = \frac{K}{r_3(r_3-r_1)(r_3-r_2)}
\end{aligned}\right\} \tag{5.12}$$

If we apply the inverse Laplace transformation to equation (5.11) we obtain the t-representation $c(t)$ of the transient response:

$$c(t) = \mathcal{L}^{-1}C(s) = (A_0 + A_1\epsilon^{r_1 t} + A_2\epsilon^{r_2 t} + A_3\epsilon^{r_3 t})\,U(t) \tag{5.13}$$

Here, $A_0 U(t)$ is the steady-state term, and $A_1\epsilon^{r_1 t}$, $A_2\epsilon^{r_2 t}$, and $A_3\epsilon^{r_3 t}$ are the transient terms. Dividing both sides of equation (5.13) by A_0, we get

$$\frac{c(t)}{A_0} = \left(1 + \frac{A_1}{A_0}\epsilon^{r_1 t} + \frac{A_2}{A_0}\epsilon^{r_2 t} + \frac{A_3}{A_0}\epsilon^{r_3 t}\right) U(t) \tag{5.14}$$

The constant A_0 in this equation is 1 for an integral control system; it is approximately 1 for many proportional control systems. Thus, we may assume that $c(t)/A_0$ is approximately equal to $c(t)$. Consequently, if we set

$$B_1 = -\frac{A_1}{A_0}, \quad B_2 = -\frac{A_2}{A_0}, \quad B_3 = -\frac{A_3}{A_0} \tag{5.15}$$

equation (5.13) can be written

$$c(t) \doteqdot c(t)/A_0 = (1 - B_1\epsilon^{r_1 t} - B_2\epsilon^{r_2 t} - B_3\epsilon^{r_3 t})\,U(t) \tag{5.16}$$

The expression $B_1\epsilon^{r_1 t} + B_2\epsilon^{r_2 t} + B_3\epsilon^{r_3 t}$ is a representation of the transient error in terms of its ratio to the steady state term. The coefficients B_1, B_2, and B_3 are computed, by substituting (5.12) into equation (5.15):

$$B_1 = -\frac{A_1}{A_0} = \frac{-r_2}{r_1-r_2}\cdot\frac{-r_3}{r_1-r_3} \tag{5.17}$$

$$B_2 = -\frac{A_2}{A_0} = \frac{-r_1}{r_2 - r_1} \cdot \frac{-r_3}{r_2 - r_3} \tag{5.18}$$

$$B_3 = -\frac{A_3}{A_0} = \frac{-r_1}{r_3 - r_1} \cdot \frac{-r_2}{r_3 - r_2} \tag{5.19}$$

These values of the coefficients B_1, B_2, and B_3 can easily be found graphically by vector computation on the root plane. For example, the numbers $-r_2/(r_1/r_2)$ and $-r_3/(r_1 - r_3)$ can be separately computed by using a simple graphical vector computation. Hence, B_1 can also be found graphically as the product of the two vectors. Fig. 5.4 (a) shows the graphical computations for obtaining the value of B_1. The vector $-r_2/(r_1 - r_2)$ is found by dividing the vector R_{20} by the vector R_{21}. It is clear that the length of the quotient vector is the ratio of the length of the vector R_{20} to the length of the vector R_{21} and that the phase angle of the quotient vector is θ_2, which is the angle formed by the two vectors R_{20} and R_{21}, as shown in Fig. 5.4 (a). The vector $-r_3/(r_1 - r_3)$ can also be found by a similar computation : the length of $-r_3/(r_1 - r_3)$ is found to be the ratio of the length of the vector R_{30} to the length of the vector R_{31} ; the phase angle is θ_3, as shown in Fig. 5.4 (a). If we express the vector B_1 in the form

$$B_1 = B\epsilon^{j\phi} \tag{5.20}$$

we get

$$B = \left|\frac{R_{20}}{R_{21}}\right| \times \left|\frac{R_{30}}{R_{31}}\right| \tag{5.21}$$

$$\phi = \theta_2 + \theta_3 \tag{5.22}$$

With these relations, the vector B_1 can now be computed graphically from the two vectors already computed.

Similarly, the vector B_2 is found by graphical computation, as shown in Fig. 5.4 (b). As shown clearly in Fig. 5.4, since r_1 and r_2 are conjugate roots, B_1 and B_2 are complex conjugate numbers, and hence the length of the vector B_2 is equal to B, which is the length of the vector B_1, and the phase angle of B_2 is equal to $-\phi = -(\theta_2 + \theta_3)$ which is the phase angle of the vector B_1 with a minus sign. Consequently, for a pair of complex conjugate characteristic roots, it suffices to compute the length and the phase angle of the vector corresponding to one of them. That is, for a pair of complex conjugate characteristic roots

$$r_1 = -\alpha + j\omega, \qquad r_2 = -\alpha - j\omega$$

the corresponding two vectors B_1 and B_2 are

$$B_1 = B\epsilon^{j\phi}, \qquad B_2 = B\epsilon^{-j\phi}$$

Therefore, if we superimpose these two component waves, we obtain

$$\begin{aligned} B_1\epsilon^{r_1 t} + B_2\epsilon^{r_2 t} &= B\epsilon^{j\phi}\epsilon^{(-\alpha+j\omega)t} + B\epsilon^{-j\phi}\epsilon^{(-\alpha-j\omega)t} \\ &= B\epsilon^{-\alpha t}\{\epsilon^{j(\omega t+\phi)} + \epsilon^{-j(\omega t+\phi)}\} \\ &= 2B\epsilon^{-\alpha t}\cos(\omega t+\phi) \end{aligned} \tag{5.23}$$

The coefficient $2B$ can then be expressed as

$$2B = 2\left|\frac{R_{20}}{R_{21}}\right| \cdot \left|\frac{R_{30}}{R_{31}}\right| = \left|\frac{R_{20}}{R_{21}/2}\right| \cdot \left|\frac{R_{30}}{R_{31}}\right| \tag{5.24}$$

and hence it can be found by using $R_{21}/2$ instead of R_{21} in the graphical computations of B_1 and B_2, as shown in Fig. 5.4 (a). The phase angle ϕ is clearly equal to $\theta_2 + \theta_3$. Moreover, $-\alpha$ and ω are respectively the real and the imaginary coordinates of a characteristic root. Therefore, the wave form (5.23) can easily be found by a graphical computation based on the root configuration.

For the real characteristic root r_3, the coefficient B_3 of the corresponding component wave always has phase angle 0. The length is immediately computed from the root configuration. The above example indicates how to find the wave form of a transient response from the root configuration. Let us now apply this method to the case in which a given open-loop transfer function has a zero. Consider an automatic control system whose transfer function is

$$F(s) = \frac{K(s-z_1)}{(s-p_1)(s-p_2)(s-p_3)} \tag{5.25}$$

where z_1 is the pole. The block diagram of this system is shown in Fig. 5.5. The s-representation $C(s)$ of the transient response will then be computed as follows:

$$C(s) = \frac{\dfrac{K(s-z_1)}{(s-p_1)(s-p_2)(s-p_3)}}{1+\dfrac{K(s-z_1)}{(s-p_1)(s-p_2)(s-p_3)}} \cdot \frac{1}{s} \tag{5.26}$$

$$= \frac{K(s-z_1)}{(s-p_1)(s-p_2)(s-p_3)+K(s-z_1)} \cdot \frac{1}{s} \tag{5.27}$$

Since the characteristic equation of tho system is of degree 3, we have three characteristic roots. If we denote them by r_1, r_2, and r_3, equation (5.27) can be written

$$C(s) = \frac{K(s-z_1)}{s(s-r_1)(s-r_2)(s-r_3)} \tag{5.28}$$

Therefore, the t-representation $c(t)$ of the transient response is

$$c(t) = (A_0 + A_1\epsilon^{r_1 t} + A_2\epsilon^{r_2 t} + A_3\epsilon^{r_3 t})\, U(t) \tag{5.29}$$

where the coefficients A_0, A_1, A_2, and A_3 are as follows:

$$\left.\begin{aligned} A_0 &= \frac{K(-z_1)}{(-r_1)(-r_2)(-r_3)} \\ A_1 &= \frac{K(r_1-z_1)}{r_1(r_1-r_2)(r_1-r_3)} \\ A_2 &= \frac{K(r_2-z_1)}{r_2(r_2-r_1)(r_2-r_3)} \\ A_3 &= \frac{K(r_3-z_1)}{r_3(r_3-r_1)(r_3-r_2)} \end{aligned}\right\} \tag{5.30}$$

If we express equation (5.29) in the same manner as equation (5.16) the coefficients B_1, B_2, and B_3 are as follows:

$$\left.\begin{aligned} B_1 &= -\frac{A_1}{A_0} = \frac{r_1 - z_1}{-z_1} \cdot \frac{-r_2}{r_1 - r_2} \cdot \frac{-r_3}{r_1 - r_3} \\ B_2 &= -\frac{A_2}{A_0} = \frac{r_2 - z_1}{-z_1} \cdot \frac{-r_1}{r_2 - r_1} \cdot \frac{-r_3}{r_2 - r_3} \\ B_3 &= -\frac{A_3}{A_0} = \frac{r_3 - z_1}{-z_1} \cdot \frac{-r_1}{r_3 - r_1} \cdot \frac{-r_2}{r_3 - r_2} \end{aligned}\right\} \qquad (5.31)$$

In order to compute B_1, B_2, and B_3 graphically from the root configuration, we need to plot the zeros as well as the roots on the root plane. Fig. 5.6 (a) shows the graphical computations of B_1 and B_2 from the roots r_1, r_2, and r_3 and the zero z_1 plotted on the root plane. As shown in Fig. 5.6 (a), B_1 is found by multiplying $(r_1 - z_1)/(-z_1)$, which would be the value of B_1 in the absence of the zero z_1 by z_{11}/z_{10}. It is clear that B_2 is the complex conjugate of B_1.

Figure 5.6. (b) shows the graphical computation of B_3, which is the coefficient of the component wave form which corresponds to the real characteristic root. In this case, the value of B_3 is obtained by multiplying z_{13}/z_{10} by the number that would be the value of B_3 in the absence of the zero z_1. It should be noted that z_{13}/z_{10} is a negative real number or equivalently a real number with phase angle 180°.

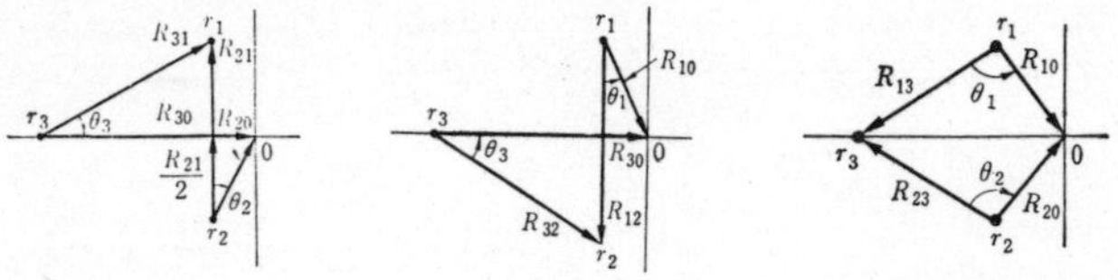

computation of B_1 *computation of B_2* *computation of B_3*

Fig. 5.4 Computations of the coefficients in the wave form of the transient response of the automatic system shown in Fig. 5·2

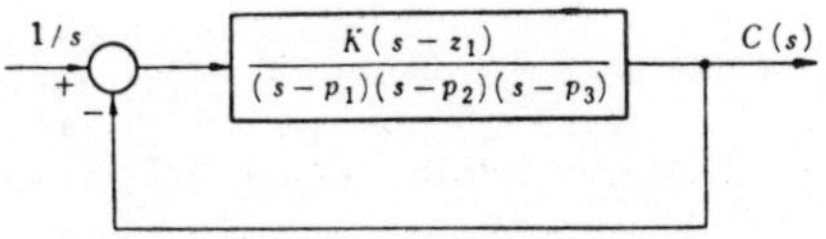

Fig. 5.5 An automatic control system whose transfer function is given by equation (5·25)

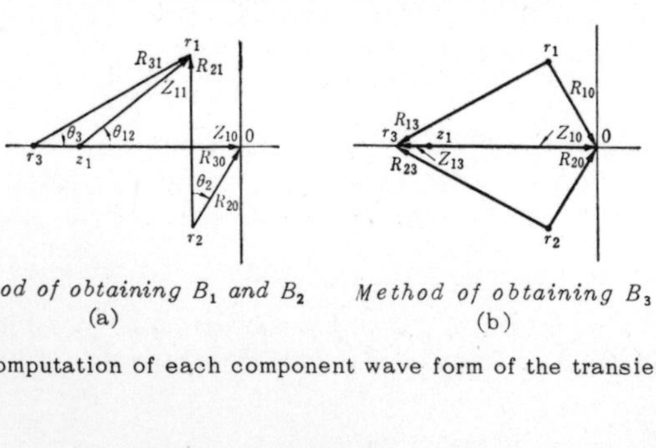

Method of obtaining B_1 and B_2 (a) *Method of obtaining B_3* (b)

Fig. 5.6 Computation of each component wave form of the transient response

We have given simple examples illustrating the method of finding the wave form of a transient response from a root configuration. This method is applicable to the case in which a given open-loop transfer function has more zeros or more poles than in these examples.

5.2. APPROXIMATION BY SECOND-ORDER SYSTEMS AND THE RESIDUE AT DOMINANT ROOTS*

As discussed in the preceding chapter, a transient response is a superposition of several wave forms. Namely, a wave form corresponding to a pair of complex conjugate characteristic roots is $2B\epsilon^{-at}\cos(\omega t \quad \phi)_{,}$ a wave form corresponding to a real characteristic root is $B\epsilon^{-\omega t}$; and a transient response is a superposition of these wave forms. The contribution of each component wave form to the transient response varies greatly according to the values of the coefficient B and the damping factor α. To be more specific, the properties of the values of B and α may be stated as follows:

1. Suppose that one of two characteristic roots is quite close to the origin of the root plane and that the other is far away from it. Then, the coefficient B of the wave form corresponding to the former characteristic root is large, and the coefficient B' of the wave form corresponding to the latter is small.
2. If several characteristic roots are located close to each other, the coefficients of the wave forms corresponding to the characteristic roots are large.
3. If a characteristic root is located near a zero of the open-loop transfer function, the coefficient corresponding to the characteristic root is small.
4. Consider two wave forms such that the damping factor of one wave form is larger than the damping factor of the other. Then, the wave form with the smaller damping factor contributes more to the transient response than the other wave form does except immediately after the transient response begins (that is, except for $t \doteqdot 0$).

We can see from these properties that if characteristic roots are distributed on the root plane without being dense in any region, and if one characteristic root is located closer to both the origin and the imaginary axis, then the component wave form corresponding to this characteristic root makes the dominant contribution to the transient response; that is, the component wave form almost completely determines the transient response. As mentioned before, this characteristic root is called the dominant root. Thus, if a higher-order system has a dominant root, the transient response of the given higher-order system can be approximated by the component wave form corresponding to the dominant root. In fact, the

*The subjects discussed in Section 5.2 and 5.3 are necessary for designing an automatic control system by the root configuration method, discussed in Chapter VIII. When the reader gets to Chapter VIII, therefore he is advised to re-read these sections to assist him.

transient response of a well designed automatic control system can be well approximated in most cases by such a component wave form. The corresponding dominant root is a complex number. Therefore, we shall analyse such an approximation of a transient response.

Consider a higher-order automatic control system whose characteristic roots are r_0, r_0^*, r_1, r_2, r_3, ..., and suppose that r_0 and r_0^* are complex conjugate roots such that

$$\left.\begin{aligned} r_0 &= -\alpha_0 + j\omega_0 \\ r_0^* &= -\alpha_0 - j\omega_0 \end{aligned}\right\} \tag{5.32}$$

Then, the transient response $c(t)$ will be

$$c(t) = 1 - \boldsymbol{B}_0\epsilon^{r_0 t} - \boldsymbol{B}_0^*\epsilon^{r_0^* t} - \boldsymbol{B}_1\epsilon^{r_1 t} - \boldsymbol{B}_2\epsilon^{r_2 t} - \boldsymbol{B}_3\epsilon^{r_3 t} - \cdots \tag{5.33}$$

$$= 1 - 2\,B_0\epsilon^{-\alpha_0 t}\cos(\omega_0 t - \phi_0) - \boldsymbol{B}_1\epsilon^{r_1 t} - \boldsymbol{B}_2\epsilon^{r_2 t} - \boldsymbol{B}_3\epsilon^{r_3 t} - \cdots \tag{5.34}$$

where B_0 and ϕ_0 are

$$B_0 = |\boldsymbol{B}_0| \tag{5.35}$$

$$\phi_0 = -\underline{/\boldsymbol{B}_0} \tag{5.36}$$

If we denote by $e(t)$ the error response of this system, we have

$$e(t) = 2\,B_0\epsilon^{-\alpha_0 t}\cos(\omega_0 t - \phi_0) + B_1\epsilon^{r_1 t} + B_2\epsilon^{r_2 t} + \cdots \tag{5.37}$$

If we set

$$\left.\begin{aligned} e_t(t) &= 2\,B_0\epsilon^{-\alpha_0 t}\cos(\omega_0 t - \phi_0) \\ e_r(t) &= B_1\epsilon^{r_1 t} + B_2\epsilon^{r_2 t} + B_3\epsilon^{r_3 t} + \cdots \end{aligned}\right\} \tag{5.38}$$

and substitute these values into equation (5.37), then equation (5.37) can be written in the form

$$e(t) = e_t(t) + e_r(t) \tag{5.39}$$

Suppose that $e_r(t)$ is extremely small in comparison to $e_t(t)$ so that $e_r(t)$ is negligible in the interval $t > 0$. Then, the error response $e(t)$ can be approximated by the superposition of the two wave forms corresponding to the complex conjugate roots r_0 and r_0^*. That is, $e(t)$ can be approximated as

$$e(t) \doteqdot e_t(t) = 2\,B_0\epsilon^{-\alpha_0 t}\cos(\omega_0 t - \phi_0) \tag{5.40}$$

If this approximation holds, the pair of complex conjugate roots r_0 and r_0^* given by equation (5.32) is the pair of dominant roots, and the corresponding component wave form $e_t(t)$ is called the dominant component. Conversely, if the approximation (5.40) is valid for a higher-order automatic control system, we may consider that the given higher-order automatic control system has the dominant roots given by equation (5.32).

Let us now investigate the relation that must hold between the error response $e(t)$ and the component wave form $e_t(t)$ corresponding to a pair of complex characteristic roots (which presumably are the dominant roots) for the approximation specified in equation (5.40) to be valid. Suppose that the approximation (5.40) holds. Then, it is clear from equation (5.40) that $e_t(t)$ is determined by the corresponding characteristic roots and the vector value $\mathbf{B}_0 = B_0 \angle \phi_0$. Consequently, in order to find $e_t(t)$, it is sufficient to determine the vector value $\mathbf{B}_0$, that is, the values of B_0 and ϕ_0 for which the approximation (5.40) holds. From equation (2.221), the initial value of the error response $e(t)$ is

$$e(0) = \lim_{s\to\infty} (sE(s)) = \lim_{s\to\infty} \left| \frac{1}{1+F(s)} \cdot \frac{1}{s} \cdot s \right| = 1 \tag{5.41}$$

Therefore, if the approximation (5.40) holds, the initial value $e_t(0)$ of the dominant component $e_t(t)$ is also approximately equal to 1. Thus, we have the relation

$$e_t(0) = 2\,B_0 \cos \phi_0 \doteqdot 1 \tag{5.42}$$

so that

$$B_0 \cos \phi_0 \doteqdot \frac{1}{2} \tag{5.43}$$

In general, the transient response of a higher-order automatic control system has, as shown in Fig. 5.7, a wave form whose amplitude instantaneously attains the value 1 at $t = 0$ and whose slope at $t = 0$ is 0. Let us justify this statement. Since the error response $e(t)$ is discontinuous at $t = 0$, the slope cannot be found by differentiating $e(t)$. Therefore, we shall use a continuous function $e^*(t)$, which is a modification of $e(t)$ by the approach shown in Fig. 2.33 (b) or in equation (2.193), to compute the slope of $e(t)$ at $t = 0$. Then, the slope of $e^*(t)$ is equal to that of $e(t)$, and it is computed as follows:

$$\left| \frac{d}{dt} e^*(t) \right|_{t=0} = \lim_{s\to\infty} \left| s\mathcal{L} \frac{d}{dt} e^*(t) \right| \tag{5.44}$$

If we apply formula (2.198) to this equation, we obtain

$$\left| \frac{d}{dt} e^*(t) \right|_{t=0} = \lim_{s\to\infty} \left| s\,\{s\mathcal{L}e^*(t) - e^*(0)\} \right| \tag{5.45}$$

Since

$$\mathcal{L}e^*(t) = \frac{1}{1+F(s)} \cdot \frac{1}{s} \tag{5.46}$$

and

$$e^*(0) = 1 \tag{5.47}$$

substitution of these values into equation (5.45) yields

$$\left| \frac{d}{dt} e^*(t) \right|_{t=0} = \lim_{s\to\infty} \left| s\left(s \frac{1}{1+F(s)} \cdot \frac{1}{s} - 1\right) \right| \tag{5.48}$$

$$= \lim_{s\to\infty} \left| \frac{-sF(s)}{1+F(s)} \right| \tag{5.49}$$

As shown by equation (5.2), the general form of the transfer function $F(s)$ is

$$F(s) = \frac{K(s-z_1)(s-z_2)(s-z_3)\cdots(s-z_m)}{(s-p_1)(s-p_2)(s-p_3)\cdots(s-p_l)} \tag{5.50}$$

where m and n are the degrees of the numerator and the denominator respectively. Then, the limit of $F(s)$ is

$$\lim_{s\to\infty} F(s) = \lim_{s\to\infty}\left|\frac{Ks^m}{s^l}\right| = \lim_{s\to\infty}\left|Ks^{m-l}\right| \tag{5.51}$$

Therefore, equation (5.49) can be written

$$\left|\frac{d}{dt}e^*(t)\right|_{t=0} = \lim_{s\to\infty}\left|\frac{-Ks^{m-l+1}}{1+Ks^{m-l}}\right| \tag{5.52}$$

If we assume here that $m - l + 1 \leq -1$, that is

$$l - m \geqq 2 \tag{5.53}$$

we finally obtain the relation

$$\left|\frac{d}{dt}e^*(t)\right|_{t=0} = 0 \tag{5.54}$$

Condition (5.53) holds for most automatic control systems. The above discussion shows that the error response of an automatic control system begins with slope 0 if the degree of the denominator of the open loop transfer function exceeds that of the numerator by 2 or more.

We now return to the investigation of the approximation. In order for the approximation (5.40) to be valid, relation (5.54) must also hold approximately for the dominant component $e_t(t)$:

$$\left|\frac{d}{dt}e_t^*(t)\right|_{t=0} = \frac{d}{dt}\left|\{2B_0\epsilon^{-\alpha_0 t}\cos(\omega_0 t - \phi_0)\}\right|_{t=0} \doteqdot 0 \tag{5.55}$$

$$\left|-2B_0\omega_0\epsilon^{-\alpha_0 t}\sin(\omega_0 t - \phi_0) - 2B_0\alpha_0\epsilon^{-\alpha_0 t}\cos(\omega_0 t - \phi_0)\right|_{t=0} \doteqdot 0 \tag{5.56}$$

Therefore,

$$\left|\tan(\omega_0 t - \phi_0)\right|_{t=0} \doteqdot -\frac{\alpha_0}{\omega_0} = -\gamma_0 \tag{5.57}$$

$$\therefore \tan(-\phi_0) \doteqdot -\gamma_0 \tag{5.58}$$

Thus, we finally have the relation

$$\phi_0 \doteqdot \tan^{-1}\gamma_0 \tag{5.59}$$

Consequently, we can assert that for the transient response to be well approximated by the dominant component, relation (5.59) must hold as well as relation (5.43). These two relations are necessary conditions for the transient response to be well approximated by the dominant component. We cannot assert, however, that they are sufficient conditions. Although the error response of a well designed automatic control system can, as we said earlier, be well approximated by the dominant component in most cases, this is not true for all well designed automatic control systems. Even in the case in which component wave forms in a transient response other than the dominant one also make a considerable contribution to the transient response and the dominant component alone is not a good approximation of the transient response, the automatic control system may still be a well-designed one if the other component wave forms contribute to reduce the error in the approximation by the dominant component.

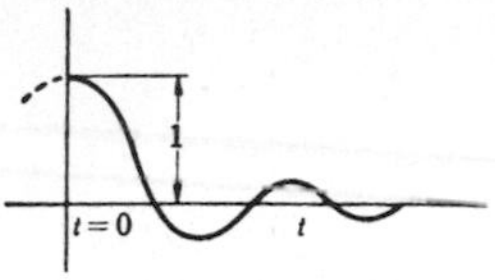

Fig. 5.7 Transient response of a higher-order automatic control system

In this connection, let us examine how the accuracy of the approximation of a transient response by the dominant component is related to the design techniques of automatic control systems. There is a certain value, called the square-error area, by which we can evaluate the quality of a transient response in practice. This value is the integral from 0 to ∞ of the square of the transient error. The square-error area has the advantages that it represents rather faithfully the quality of the transient response as judged from a practical view point and that its value can be easily calculated The value of the square-error area should, of course, be small for an automatic control system.

If the error response of an automatic control system is approximated by the dominant component as shown by equation (5.40), then the square-error area S is, by definition,

$$S=\int_0^{\infty}\{2B_0\epsilon^{-\alpha_1 t}\cos(\omega_0 t-\phi_0)\}^2 dt \tag{5.60}$$

$$=B_0^2\left(\frac{\alpha_0\cos 2\phi_0+\omega_0\sin 2\phi_0}{\alpha_0^2+\omega_0^2}+\frac{1}{\alpha_0}\right) \tag{5.61}$$

Since we assume that the error response is approximated by the dominant component, equation (5.43) also approximately holds:

$$B_0=\frac{1}{2\cos\phi_0} \tag{5.62}$$

Substituting this value of B_0 into equation (5.61), the square-error area S can be computed as follows:

$$S=\frac{1}{4\cos^2\phi_0}\left\{\frac{\alpha_0\cos 2\phi_0+\omega_0\sin 2\phi_0}{\alpha_0^2+\omega_0^2}+\frac{1}{\alpha_0}\right\} \tag{5.63}$$

$$=\frac{1}{4\cos^2\phi_0}\left\{\frac{\alpha_0(\cos^2\phi_0-\sin^2\phi_0)+2\omega_0\sin\phi_0\cos\phi_0}{\alpha_0^2+\omega_0^2}+\frac{1}{\alpha_0}\right\} \tag{5.64}$$

$$=\frac{1}{4(\alpha_0^2+\omega_0^2)}\{\alpha_0(1-\tan^2\phi_0)+2\omega_0\tan\phi_0\}+\frac{1}{4\alpha_0\cos^2\phi_0} \tag{5.65}$$

In order to find the condition for S to be minimum, we differentiate the expression (5.65) with respect to ϕ_0 and equate the derivative to zero:

$$\frac{dS}{d\phi_0}=\frac{1}{4(\alpha_0^2+\omega_0^2)}\left(-\frac{2\alpha_0\tan\phi_0}{\cos^2\phi_0}+\frac{2\omega_0}{\cos^2\phi_0}\right)+\frac{\sin\phi_0}{2\alpha_0\cos^3\phi_0} \tag{5.66}$$

$$=\frac{1}{2\cos^2\phi_0}\left\{\left(\frac{\omega_0-\alpha_0\tan\phi_0}{\alpha_0^2+\omega_0^2}\right)+\frac{\tan\phi_0}{\alpha_0}\right\}=0 \tag{5.67}$$

This equation can be solved for ϕ_0 as follows:

$$\left(\frac{1}{\alpha_0}-\frac{\alpha_0}{\alpha_0^2+\omega_0^2}\right)\tan\phi_0+\frac{\omega_0}{\alpha_0^2+\omega_0^2}=0 \tag{5.68}$$

$$\frac{\omega_0^2}{\alpha_0(\alpha_0^2+\omega_0^2)}\tan\phi_0+\frac{\omega_0}{\alpha_0^2+\omega_0^2}=0 \tag{5.69}$$

$$\frac{\omega_0}{\alpha_0}\tan\phi_0=-1 \tag{5.70}$$

$$\tan\phi_0=-\frac{\alpha_0}{\omega_0}=-\gamma_0 \tag{5.71}$$

Therefore,

$$\phi_0=-\tan^{-1}\gamma_0 \tag{5.72}$$

Thus, for the square-error area to take its minimum value, the phase angle ϕ_0 of the dominant component has to take the value specified by equation (5.72). It should be noted that this condition is not identical with equation (5.59), which is a necessary condition on the phase angle for the error response to be well approximated by the dominant component. In view of this square-error area, high accuracy of approximation of a transient response by the dominant component is not a stringent condition for designing a satisfactory automatic control system. If the phase angle of the dominant component is quite close to the value given by equation (5.72), we may allow some decrease in the accuracy of the approximation by the dominant component. In this sense, in the interval

$$-\tan^{-1}\gamma_0<\phi_0<\tan^{-1}\gamma_0 \tag{5.73}$$

we can consider the approximation of a transient response by the dominant component as maintaining a satisfactory accuracy and the square-error area as being satisfactorily small. From experience, it is known that the ϕ_0 interval (5.73) can even be extended to the interval

$$\boxed{-\tan^{-1}3\gamma_0<\phi_0<\tan^{-1}3\gamma_0} \tag{5.74}$$

In practice, the form of the error response is still satisfactory for ϕ_0 in this interval.

It has been shown that, for an error response to be well approximated by the dominant component, the initial value has to satisfy the relation (5.43); that is,

$$\boxed{B_0\cos\phi_0 \doteqdot \frac{1}{2}} \tag{5.75}$$

and the phase angle ϕ_0 must lie in the interval (5.74). It is clear that we can also allow a certain margin for the initial value $B_0 \cos\phi_0$. There is no standard allowable margin for the initial value. However, again from experience, we know that for any $B_0\cos\phi_0$ in the interval

$$\boxed{\frac{1}{3}<B_0\cos\phi_0<\frac{3}{4}} \tag{5.76}$$

an error response has a satisfactory form in general.

From the interval (5.74) of ϕ_0 -values and the interval (5.76) of ($B_0 \cos \phi_0$) -values, we can determine an interval of allowable values for the residue $\boldsymbol{B}_0 = B_0 \angle \phi_0$ of a dominant component, and we can represent the range by a domain in the complex plane. Therefore, from a practical viewpoint, dominant roots may be defined as follows: a pair of characteristic roots is a pair of dominant roots if the residue vector $\boldsymbol{B}_0 = B_0 \angle \phi_0$ is in the allowable domain. However, in actual computations, to find a dominant root, we use the

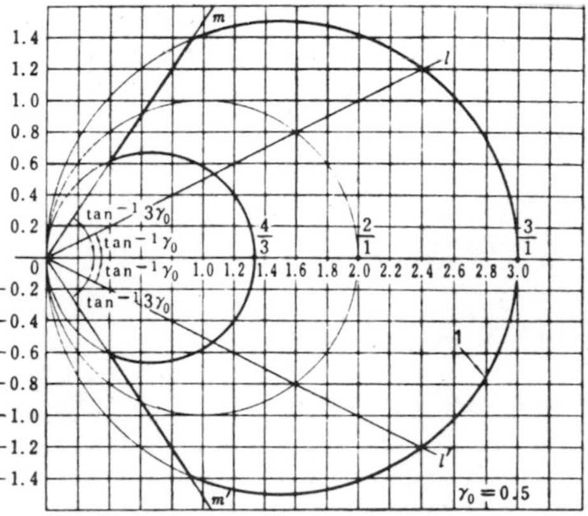

1 - *critical residue*

Fig. 5.8 Critical-residue domain for dominant root

allowable domain for the reciprocal of the residue vector $\boldsymbol{B}_0$ instead of that for $\boldsymbol{B}_0$ itself since this reduces the labour of the calculation. The allowable domain for the reciprocal of a residue vector is called the critical-residue domain for the dominant root. Fig. 5.8 shows a critical-residue domain for the dominant root with $\gamma_0 = 0.5$. By using this diagram, it can be determined whether a given pair of conjugate characteristic roots is a pair of dominant roots. More specifically, for a given pair of conjugate characteristic roots, we first find the reciprocal of the residue at the conjugate characteristic roots, then plot them in the diagram shown in Fig. 5.8. If the plotted characteristic roots are in the critical-residue domain for dominant roots, then we conclude that they are the dominant roots. Otherwise, they are not the dominant roots.

5.3 CALCULATION OF RESIDUES AT DOMINANT ROOTS*

In order to determine the dominancy of given complex conjugate characteristic roots, we need to find the magnitude $B_0 = |\boldsymbol{B}_0|$ of the residue vector $\boldsymbol{B}_0$ of the given characteristic roots and the phase angle $\phi_0 = \angle \boldsymbol{B}_0$. If the root configuration is given, they can easily be found by the graphical computation method discussed in Section 5.1. We recall that it is then necessary to compute all the characteristic roots and to plot them on the root plane in order to

*See footnote to Section 5.2 p.139.

construct the root configuration. However, if we only wish to find the residue of a particular root, we need not compute and plot all the characteristic roots. We can compute the residue of the particular characteristic root when we know the zeros and poles of the transfer function and the particular characteristic root. This method is very useful for the system design to be discussed in Chapter VIII. Therefore, we explain it in detail.

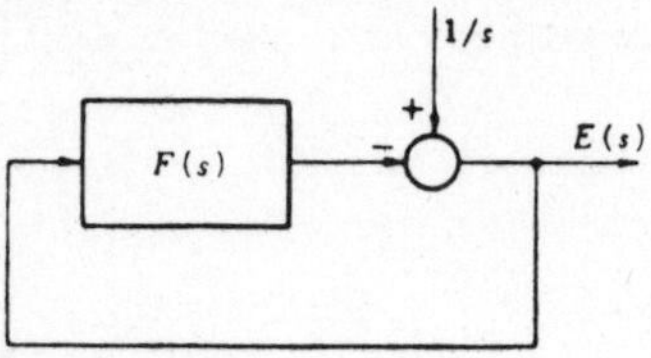

Fig. 5.9

Consider the automatic control system whose block diagram is shown in Fig. 5.9. Then, the s-representation $E(s)$ of the error response is

$$E(s)=\frac{1}{1+F(s)}\cdot\frac{1}{s} \tag{5.77}$$

where $F(s)$ is the open-loop transfer function. Let r_0 be a characteristic root of the given automatic control system. If we denote by B_0 the residue of r_0, then, by formula (2.93),

$$B_0=\left|\frac{1}{\frac{d}{ds}\{(1+F(s))s\}}\right|_{s=r_0} \tag{5.78}$$

This expression can be rewritten as follows:

$$B_0=\left|\frac{1}{1+F(s)+s\frac{dF(s)}{ds}}\right|_{s=r_0} \tag{5.79}$$

$$=\left|\frac{1}{1+F(s)+sF(s)\frac{dF(s)}{F(s)ds}}\right|_{s=r_0} \tag{5.80}$$

$$=\left|\frac{1}{1+F(s)+sF(s)\frac{d}{ds}(\ln F(s))}\right|_{s=r_0} \tag{5.81}$$

On the other hand, we have the relation

$$1+F(r_0)=0 \tag{5.82}$$

or

$$F(r_0)=-1 \tag{5.83}$$

where r_0 is a characteristic root. Substituting equation (5.83) into equation (5.81), we obtain

$$B_0=-\frac{1}{r_0}\frac{1}{\left(\frac{d}{ds}\ln F(s)\right)_{s=r_0}} \tag{5.84}$$

Therefore, the reciprocal $1/B_0$ of the residue B_0 is

$$\frac{1}{B_0} = -r_0 \frac{d}{ds}\left|\ln F(s)\right|_{s=r_0} \tag{5.85}$$

To be more specific, we shall explicitly compute the reciprocal $1/B_0$ of the residue when the open-loop transfer function $F(s)$ takes the following two forms:

$$F(s) = \frac{K(s-z_1)(s-z_2)(s-z_3)\cdots(s-z_m)}{s^n(s-p_1)(s-p_2)(s-p_3)\cdots(s-p_l)} \tag{5.86}$$

and

$$F(s) = \frac{K(1+sT_{z1})(1+sT_{z2})(1+sT_{z3})\cdots(1+sT_{zm})}{s^n(1+sT_{p1})(1+sT_{p2})(1+sT_{p3})\cdots(1+sT_{pl})} \tag{5.87}$$

Let us first compute the reciprocal $1/B$ when $F(s)$ is given by equation (5.86). Taking the logarithms of the two sides of equation (5.86), we obtain

$$\ln F(s) = \ln K + \ln(s-z_1) + \ln(s-z_2) + \ln(s-z_3) + \cdots + \ln(s-z_m)$$
$$-n\ln s - \ln(s-p_1) - \ln(s-p_2) - \ln(s-p_3) - \cdots - \ln(s-p_l) \tag{5.88}$$

If we differentiate this equation with respect to S, we have

$$\frac{d}{ds}\ln F(s) = \frac{1}{s-z_1} + \frac{1}{s-z_2} + \frac{1}{s-z_3} + \cdots + \frac{1}{s-z_m}$$
$$-\frac{n}{s} - \frac{1}{s-p_1} - \frac{1}{s-p_2} - \frac{1}{s-p_3} - \cdots - \frac{1}{s-p_l} \tag{5.89}$$

Substituting this expression for $d \ln F(s)/ds$ into equation (5.85), we get

$$\frac{1}{B_0} = -r_0\left(\frac{1}{r_0-z_1} + \frac{1}{r_0-z_2} + \frac{1}{r_0-z_3} + \cdots + \frac{1}{r_0-z_m} - \frac{n}{r_0} - \frac{1}{r_0-p_1}\right.$$
$$\left.-\frac{1}{r_0-p_2} - \frac{1}{r_0-p_3} - \cdots - \frac{1}{r_0-p_l}\right) \tag{5.90}$$

Thus, if the open-loop transfer function $F(s)$ has the form (5.86), then the reciprocal $1/B_0$ of the residue B_0 is

$$\frac{1}{B_0} = n + r_0\sum_{k=1}^{l}\frac{1}{r_0-p_k} - r_0\sum_{k=1}^{m}\frac{1}{r_0-z_k} \tag{5.91}$$

We now consider the case in which the open-loop transfer function $F(s)$ is given by equation (5.87). Taking the logarithm of equation (5.87) as before, we obtain

$$\ln F(s) = \ln K + \ln(1+sT_{z1}) + \ln(1+sT_{z2}) + \ln(1+sT_{z3}) + \cdots$$
$$+\ln(1+sT_{zm}) - n\ln s - \ln(1+sT_{p1}) - \ln(1+sT_{p2})$$
$$-\ln(1+sT_{p3}) - \cdots - \ln(1+sT_{pl}) \tag{5.92}$$

If we differentiate this equation with respect to S, we get

$$\frac{d}{ds}\ln F(s) = \frac{T_{z1}}{1+sT_{z1}} + \frac{T_{z2}}{1+sT_{z2}} + \frac{T_{z3}}{1+sT_{z3}} + \cdots + \frac{T_{zm}}{1+sT_{zm}}$$
$$-\frac{n}{s} - \frac{T_{p1}}{1+sT_{p1}} - \frac{T_{p2}}{1+sT_{p2}} - \frac{T_{p3}}{1+sT_{p3}} - \cdots - \frac{T_{pl}}{1+sT_{pl}} \tag{5.93}$$

Substituting this expression into equation (5.85), we finally obtain

$$\frac{1}{B_0}=-r_0\left(\frac{T_{z1}}{1+r_0T_{z1}}+\frac{T_{z2}}{1+r_0T_{z2}}+\frac{T_{z3}}{1+r_0T_{z3}}+\cdots+\frac{T_{zm}}{1+r_0T_{zm}}\right.$$
$$\left.-\frac{n}{r_0}-\frac{T_{p1}}{1+r_0T_{p1}}-\frac{T_{p2}}{1+r_0T_{p2}}-\frac{T_{p3}}{1+r_0T_{p3}}-\cdots-\frac{T_{pl}}{1+r_0T_{pl}}\right) \quad (5.94)$$

Therefore, the reciprocal $1/B_0$ in this case is

$$\frac{1}{B_0}=n+l-m+\sum_{k=1}^{m}\frac{1}{1+r_0T_{zk}}-\sum_{k=1}^{l}\frac{1}{1+r_0T_{pk}} \quad (5.95)$$

This equation is the formula for finding the reciprocal of the residue when the open-loop transfer function has the form (5.87). It is clear from equation (5.87) that n is the number of integral elements, l the number of time constants in the numerator of the open-loop transfer function, and m the number of time constants in the numerator.

Thus, we can determine the dominancy of a given characteristic root by plotting this reciprocal $1/B_0$ of the residue B_0 on the diagram of the critical-residue domain for a dominant root such as the one shown in Fig. 5.8.

5.4. ROOT LOCI

As shown in Sections 5.1 and 5.2, a transient response can easily be found if we know the locations of the zeros of the open-loop transfer function and of the characteristic roots. The zeros can usually be found without difficulty. On the other hand, it is not always easy to find the characteristic roots. However, it is relatively simple to find a domain in which the characteristic roots are located and to find the approximate locations of the characteristic roots by a graphical approach. We shall discuss this method in detail. As mentioned above, the characteristic equation of an automatic control system is

$$F(s)=-1 \quad (5.96)$$

where $F(s)$ is the open-loop transfer function. As usual, suppose that $F(s)$ is of the form

$$F(s)=\frac{K(s-z_1)(s-z_2)(s-z_3)\cdots}{(s-p_1)(s-p_2)(s-p_3)\cdots\cdots} \quad (5.97)$$

where z_1, z_2, z_3, ... are the zeros and p_1, p_2, p_3, ... are the poles. Then, the characteristic equation can be written

$$F(s)=\frac{K(s-z_1)(s-z_2)(s-z_3)\cdots}{(s-p_1)(s-p_2)(s-p_3)\cdots\cdots}=-1 \quad (5.98)$$

The characteristic roots can be represented by points on the root plane, as mentioned previously. These points representing the characteristic roots change their locations continuously and draw a number of curves on the root plane as K varies continuously from 0 to ∞ in equation (5.98). The family of these curves is called the root locus.

The characteristic equation (5.98) can be rewritten as the following two equations:

$$\left|\frac{(s-z_1)(s-z_2)(s-z_3)\cdots}{(s-p_1)(s-p_2)(s-p_3)\cdots}\right| = \frac{1}{K} \tag{5.99}$$

$$\angle\frac{(s-z_1)(s-z_2)(s-z_3)\cdots}{(s-p_1)(s-p_2)(s-p_3)\cdots} = (2n+1)\pi \tag{5.100}$$

where $n = 0, \pm 1, \pm 2, \ldots$. Equation (5.99) is the equation for the magnitude, and equation (5.100) is the equation for the phase angle. A complex number s which satisfies these two conditions simultaneously is a characteristic root. Recalling that the root locus is obtained by varying $1/K$ from ∞ to 0, we note that we need not consider both conditions in order to determine the root locus. The root locus is completely determined by the phase angle condition. That is, we may regard equation (5.100) as the equation for the root locus and equation (5.99) as the equation for computing the value of K corresponding to a point on the root locus.

Equation (5.100), which is the equation of the phase angle condition, can also be written

$$\angle s-z_1 + \angle s-z_2 + \angle s-z_3 + \cdots - \angle s-p_1 - \angle s-p_2 - \angle s-p_3 - \cdots = (2n+1)\pi \tag{5.101}$$

or, more briefly,

$$\angle F(s) = (2n+1)\pi \tag{5.102}$$

The zeros z_1, z_2, ... and the poles p_1, p_2,... of the open-loop transfer function can be immediately plotted as shown in Fig. 5.10. The locations of the zeros, the poles, and an arbitrary complex number s, are denoted in the figure by the symbols ○, ● and □ respectively.

For an arbitrary s, the numbers $(s - z_1)$, $(s - z_2)$, $(s - p_1)$, $(s - p_2)$, and $(s - p_3)$ are graphically represented, as shown in Fig. 5.10, by vectors each of which originates at a pole or a zero and ends at the point s. Accordingly, the phase angles $\angle s - z_1$, $\angle s - z_2$, ..., $\angle s - p_1$, $\angle s - p_2$, $\angle s - p_3$, ... are equal to the phase angles θ_{z1}, θ_{z2}, ..., θ_{p1}, θ_{p2}, θ_{p3}, ..., respectively. Therefore, equation (5.101) can be written

$$\theta_{z1} + \theta_{z2} + \cdots - \theta_{p1} - \theta_{p2} - \theta_{p3} - \cdots = (2n+1)\pi \tag{5.103}$$

The locus of a point s satisfying this condition is indeed the root locus.

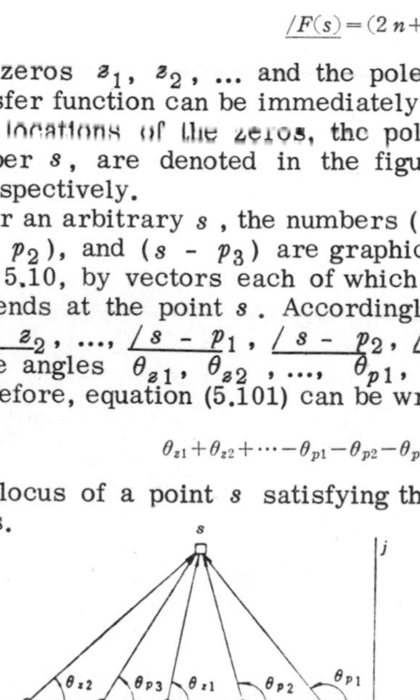

1 - *root plane*

Fig. 5.10

As an example, let us construct the root locus of a simple open loop transfer function. Consider the open loop transfer function

$$F(s)=\frac{K(s-z_1)}{(s-p_1)(s-p_2)} \tag{5.104}$$

where the poles p_1 and p_2 and the zero z_1 are real numbers such that $p_1 > z_1 > p_2$. Then, their locations are as shown in Fig. 5.11. Suppose that s is located on the real axis between p_1 and z_1 as shown in Fig. 5.11 (a). Then, the phase angles of the factors in equation (5.104) are

$$\left.\begin{aligned}\theta_{z1}&=0\\ \theta_{p1}&=\pi\\ \theta_{p2}&=0\end{aligned}\right\} \tag{5.105}$$

as shown in Fig. 5.11 (a). Accordingly, the phase angle condition in this case is

$$\underline{/F(s)}=\theta_{z1}-\theta_{p1}-\theta_{p2}=0-\pi-0=-\pi \tag{5.106}$$

which is the equation obtained by setting n = -1 in the general form (5.103) of the phase angle condition. Therefore, we can conclude that the segment of the real axis between p_1 and z_1 is a part of the root locus. Suppose that s is located on the part of the real axis to the left of the pole p_2, as shown in Fig. 5.11 (b). Then, the phase angles of the factors in equation (5.104) are

$$\left.\begin{aligned}\theta_{z1}&=\pi\\ \theta_{p1}&=\pi\\ \theta_{p2}&=\pi\end{aligned}\right\} \tag{5.107}$$

Accordingly, the equation of the phase angle is

$$\underline{/F(s)}=\theta_{z1}-\theta_{p1}-\theta_{p2}=-\pi \tag{5.108}$$

Therefore, every s located on the part of the real axis to the left of p_2 satisfies the general form of the phase angle condition with n = -1. Consequently, the part of the real axis to the left of the pole p_2 is also a part of the root locus. If s is located on the part of the real axis to the right of the pole p_1 as shown in Fig. 5.11(c), then the phase angles are

$$\theta_{z1}=0,\ \theta_{p1}=0,\ \theta_{p2}=0 \tag{5.109}$$

Accordingly, we have

$$\underline{/F(s)}=\theta_{z1}-\theta_{p1}-\theta_{p2}=0\neq(2n+1)\pi \tag{5.110}$$

that is, any point located to the right of p_1 on the real axis does not satisfy the phase angle condition. Therefore, the part of the real axis to the right of the pole p_1 is not a part of the root locus. If s is in the interval $z_1 < s < p_2$ on the real axis as shown in Fig. 5.11 (d), then the phase angles of the factors are

$$\theta_{z1}=\pi,\ \theta_{p1}=\pi,\ \theta_{p2}=0 \tag{5.111}$$

Accordingly, we again have

$$\underline{/F(s)} = \theta_{z1} - \theta_{p1} - \theta_{p2} = 0 \mp (2n+1)\pi \tag{5.112}$$

and hence the interval $z_1 > s > p_2$ on the real axis is not a part of the root locus. Now, consider a point s in the complex plane not on the real axis, as shown in Fig. 5.11 (e). It is clear from Fig. 5.11 (e) that the angle formed by the vector s - $_1$ and the vector $s - p_2$ is equal to $\theta_{z1} - \theta_{p1}$ and that

$$|(\theta_{p1} - \theta_{z1}) + \theta_{p2}| < \pi \tag{5.113}$$

Consequently, the the phase angle condition does not hold:

$$\underline{/F(s)} = \theta_{z1} - \theta_{p1} - \theta_{p2} \mp (2n+1)\pi \tag{5.114}$$

Summarising these results, we can conclude that the root locus consists of the two intervals shown in Figs. 5.11 (a) and (b) respectively. Fig. 5.12 shows the root locus of the automatic control system whose transfer function is given by equation (5.104). In Fig. 5.12, the heavy line segments represent the root locus.

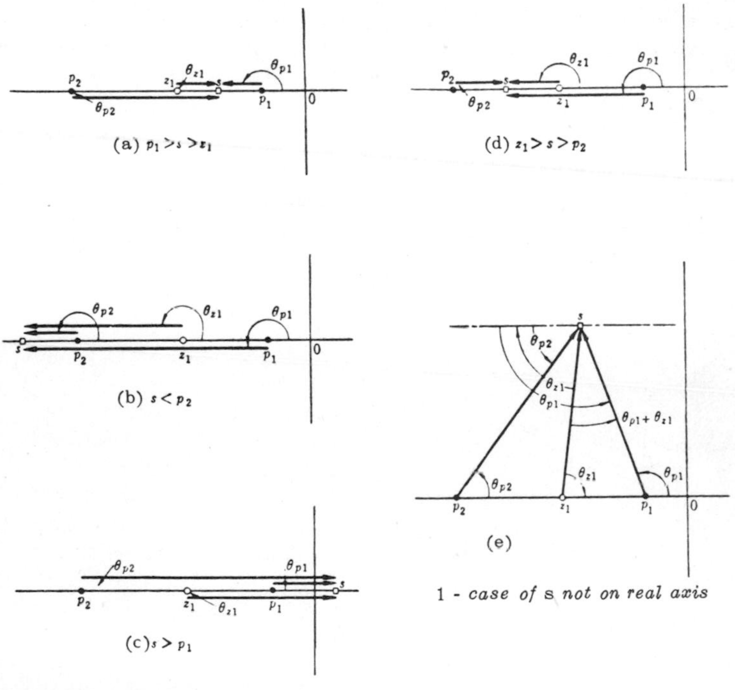

Fig. 5.11 Graphical illustration of phase-angle conditions

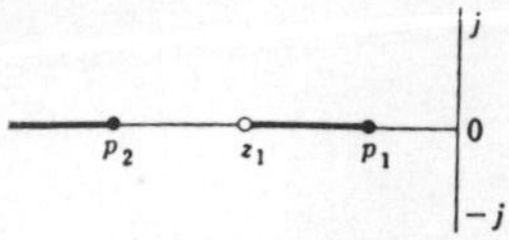

Fig. 5.12 Root locus of an automatic control system whose transfer function has the form (5.104)

Fig. 5.13

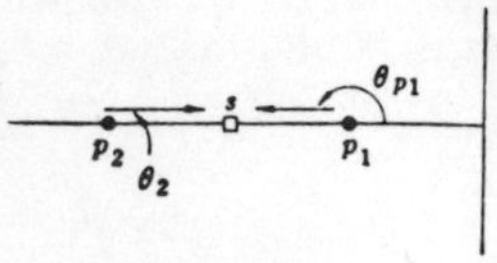

This suggests that a root locus still lies on the real axis even when the open loop transfer function has more poles and more zeros than in the above example, provided the zeros and the poles separate each other on the real axis.

Now, we shall discuss an example of a different type of root locus. Consider a root locus of an automatic control system whose open loop transfer function is given by

$$F(s)=\frac{K}{(s-p_1)(s-p_2)} \tag{5.115}$$

The poles of this open loop transfer function are located as shown in Fig. 5.13. If s is located between the pole p_1 and the pole p_2 on the real axis, then the phase angle $\angle F(s)$ is

$$\angle F(s)=-\theta_{p1}-\theta_{p2}=-\pi-0=-\pi \tag{5.116}$$

Therefore, the phase angle condition holds on the interval $p_1<s<p_2$ and hence the interval is a branch of the root locus. The root locus of this system has another branch. Suppose that s is not on the real axis but is located sufficiently far to the right of the two poles (suppose, for example, that s is located at the point a shown in Fig. 5.14). Then,

$$\theta_{p1}<\frac{\pi}{2}, \quad \theta_{p2}<\frac{\pi}{2} \tag{5.117}$$

and hence,

$$|\theta_{p1}+\theta_{p2}|<\pi \tag{5.118}$$

Consequently,

$$|\angle F(s)|=|(\theta_{p1}+\theta_{p2})|<\pi \tag{5.119}$$

On the other hand, suppose that s is located not on the real axis but far to the left of the two poles (for example, suppose that s is located at the point b shown in Fig. 5.14). Then,

$$\theta'_{p1}>\frac{\pi}{2}, \quad \theta'_{p2}>\frac{\pi}{2} \tag{5.120}$$

and hence we have the inequality

$$\theta'_{p1}+\theta'_{p2}>\pi \tag{5.121}$$

Consequently,

$$|\angle F(s)| = |\theta'_{p1} + \theta'_{p2}| > \pi \tag{5.122}$$

Therefore, in view of the relations (5.119) and (5.122), there exists a point s between a and b such that $\angle F(s) = \pi$. Thus, a branch of the root locus does not lie on the real axis. In fact, such a branch is the perpendicular bisector of the line segment joining the two poles p_1 and p_2. If we take a point s on this bisector, we have

$$\theta_{p1} + \theta_{p2} = \pi \tag{5.123}$$

as shown in Fig. 5.15, and hence

$$\angle F(s) = -(\theta_{p1} + \theta_{p2}) = -\pi \tag{5.124}$$

Therefore, the perpendicular bisector of the line segment joining p_1 and p_2 is a branch of the root locus, as we have mentioned. Fig. 5.16 shows the root locus of the automatic control system whose open-loop transfer function has the form (5.115).

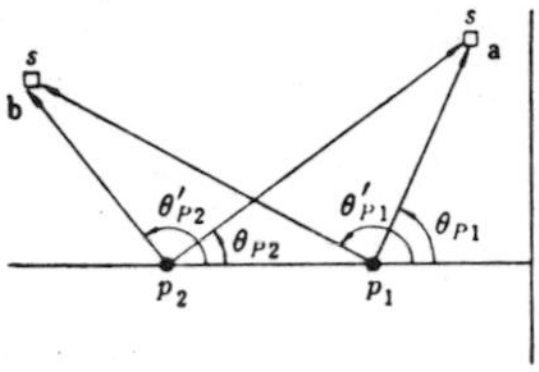

Fig. 5.14 Computation of the phase angle condition for an automatic control system whose open-loop transfer function is given by equation (5.115)

Fig. 5.15

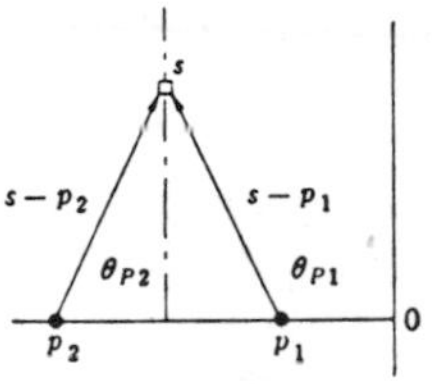

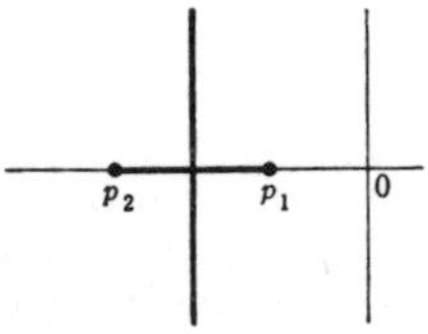

Fig. 5.16 Root locus of the automatic control system whose open-loop transfer function is given by equation (5.115)

As mentioned before, a root locus is the locus of characteristic roots when K varies from 0 to ∞. Therefore, to each point on a root locus there corresponds a value of K between 0 and ∞. Equation (5.99) is a mathematical representation of this correspondence. That is, a value of K corresponding to a certain point s on a root locus can be computed by equation (5.99), as follows:

$$K=\left|\frac{(s-p_1)(s-p_2)(s-p_3)\cdots}{(s-z_1)(s-z_2)(s-z_3)\cdots}\right| \tag{5.125}$$

Here, $(s - p_1)$, $(s - p_2)$, $(s - p_3)$, ..., $(s - z_1)$, $(s - z_2)$, $(s - z_3)$, ... are vectors each of which originates at a pole or zero and ends at the point s. Therefore, the value of K given by equation (5.125) is the ratio of the product of the distances between

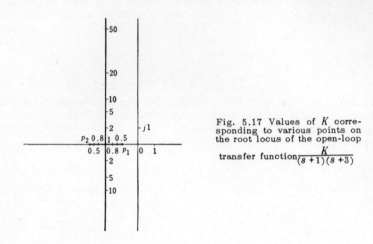

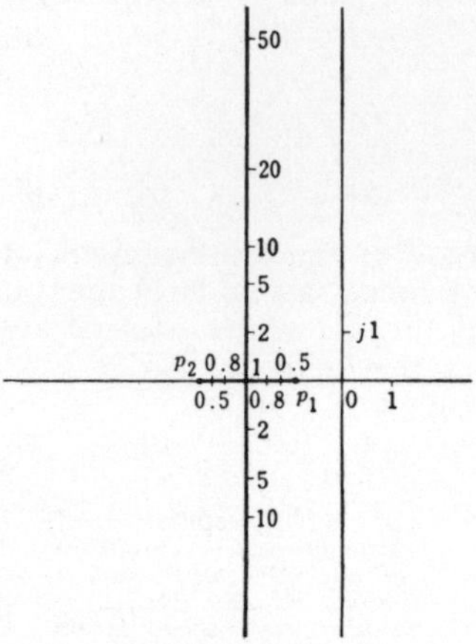

Fig. 5.17 Values of K corresponding to various points on the root locus of the open-loop transfer function $\frac{K}{(s+1)(s+3)}$

s and the poles to the product of the distances between s and the zeros. For example, the value of K corresponding to the point s on the root locus shown in Fig. 5.16 is

$$K=|s-p_1|\times|s-p_2| \tag{5.126}$$

by virtue of equation (5.125). Specifically, it is the product of the distances from s to the poles p_1 and p_2. Figure 5.17 shows the values of K corresponding to various points on the root locus in case in which $p_1 = -1$ and $p_2 = -3$.

5.5. PROPERTIES AND CONSTRUCTION OF ROOT LOCI

We have shown how to construct a root locus for simple automatic control systems. For a complicated automatic control system, the root locus is usually complicated and so is the computation involved in finding it. However, knowledge of the general properties of the root locus reduces the computational labour and hence the chance of error in the construction of the root locus. Therefore, we shall discuss the general properties of root loci.

1. In most cases, an open-loop transfer function of an automatic control system has more poles than zeros. Since the degree of the characteristic root is equal to the number of poles and the number of characteristic roots is equal to the degree of the characteristic

equation, the number of branches of the root locus is equal to the number of poles of the open-loop transfer function.

2. Since a characteristic equation is an algebraic equation with real coefficients, every complex root is conjugate to another complex root. Thus, the root locus is always symmetric with respect to the real axis.

3. Consider the characteristic equation

$$\frac{(s-z_1)(s-z_2)(s-z_3)\cdots(s-z_l)}{(s-p_1)(s-p_2)(s-p_3)\cdots(s-p_m)}=-\frac{1}{K} \tag{5.127}$$

where $m > l$. The characteristic roots of this characteristic equation are precisely the m poles $p_1, p_2, p_3, \ldots, p_m$ of the open loop transfer function when $K = 0$.

4. Consider the characteristic equation (5.127) again. If $K \to \infty$, then l characteristic roots, where l is the number of zeros of the open-loop transfer function, tend to the zeros $z_1, z_2, z_3, \ldots, z_l$, and the remaining $m - l$ characteristic roots tend to ∞.

5. As an immediate consequence of property (4), the root locus for the characteristic equation (5.127) has some branches which extend to ∞. Let us find the asymptotes of these branches. If s is sufficiently large, the relation

$$\frac{(s-z_1)(s-z_2)(s-z_3)\cdots(s-z_l)}{(s-p_1)(s-p_2)(s-p_3)\cdots(s-p_m)} \doteqdot \frac{s^l}{s^m}=s^{l-m} \tag{5.128}$$

holds. Applying the phase angle condition (5.100) to this expression, we obtain

$$\underline{/s^{l-m}}=(2n+1)\pi \tag{5.129}$$

Therefore,

$$\underline{/s}=\frac{2n+1}{l-m}\pi=-\frac{2n+1}{m-l}\pi \tag{5.130}$$

That is, as $K \to \infty$, the angles formed by the real axis and the tangent lines to the branches that extend to ∞ tend to $-(2n + 1)\pi/(m - l)$.

The characteristic equation (5.127) can be written

$$(s-p_1)(s-p_2)(s-p_3)\cdots(s-p_m)+K(s-z_1)(s-z_2)(s-z_3)\cdots (s-z_l)=0 \tag{5.131}$$

If the degree of m of the denominator of the open-loop transfer function exceeds the degree l of the numerator by 2 or more, then equation (5.131) can be rewritten

$$s^m-(p_1+p_2+p_3+\cdots+p_m)s^{m-1}+\cdots\cdots\cdots=0 \tag{5.132}$$

by expanding the left-hand side of equation (5.131). On the other hand, if we denote the m characteristic roots by $r_1, r_2, \ldots, r_m$, then equation (5.131), which is of degree m, can be written

$$s^m-(r_1+r_2+r_3+\cdots+r_m)s^{m-1}+\cdots\cdots\cdots=0 \tag{5.133}$$

Since equations (5.132) and 5.133) are identical, the second terms must also be identical:

$$r_1+r_2+r_3+\cdots+r_m=p_1+p_2+p_3+\cdots+p_m \tag{5.134}$$

If we let K approach ∞ in the characteristic equation (5.127), then l characteristic roots tend to 0 and $m - t$ characteristic roots tend to ∞, as mentioned previously. If we denote these $m - l$ characteristic roots by $r_l + 1$, $r_l + 2$, ..., r_m, then from equation (5.134) we obtain the relation

$$r_{l+1}+r_{l+2}+\cdots+r_m=p_1+p_2+\cdots+p_m-(z_1+z_2+\cdots+z_l)=S \tag{5.135}$$

where

$$S=p_1+p_2+\cdots+p_m-(z_1+z_2+\cdots+z_l) \tag{5.136}$$

Then, equation (5.135) can be written

$$\left(r_{l+1}-\frac{S}{m-l}\right)+\left(r_{l+2}-\frac{S}{m-l}\right)+\cdots+\left(r_m-\frac{S}{m-l}\right)=0 \tag{5.137}$$

This equation shows that if we regard these $m - l$ roots that tend to ∞ as $m - l$ particles each of unit mass, the centre of gravity P_G of the total mass is

$$P_G=\frac{S}{m-l}=\frac{p_1+p_2+\cdots+p_m-(z_1+z_2+\cdots+z_l)}{m-l} \tag{5.138}$$

Therefore, these characteristic roots tend to ∞ in directions parallel to the half-lines radiating from the point P_G with directional angles $-(2n + 1) \ \pi/(m - l)$. That is, the asymptotes of the branches tending to ∞ are the $m - l$ half-lines that radiate from the point P_G, determined by equation (5.138), with directional angles $-(2n + 1) \ \pi/(m - l)$.

6. As is clear from the example in the preceding section, branches of a vector locus lying on the real axis are disjoint pole-to-pole intervals and pole-to-zero intervals.

Besides these general properties, a root locus has certain other useful properties depending on the form of the open-loop transfer function. Let us consider some examples.

Consider the root locus of an automatic control system whose transfer function is

$$F(s)=\frac{K}{(s-p_1)(s-p_2)(s-p_3)} \tag{5.139}$$

The branches of the root locus lying on the real axis consist of the interval between p_1 and p_2 and the half-open interval between p_3 and $-\infty$, as shown in Fig. 5.18. The directional angles of the asymptote lines of the root locus are $-\pi/3$, $-\pi$, and $-5\pi/3$, which are obtained by setting $n = 0$, $n = 1$, and $n = 2$, respectively, in the expression $-(2n + 1) \ \pi/3$. The asymptote lines intersect at a point P_G on the real axis, determined by

$$P_G=\frac{p_1+p_2+p_3}{3} \tag{5.140}$$

Therefore, we may conclude that the shape of the root locus is approximately the pattern consisting of the bold-printed segments and curve shown in Fig. 5.18.

Now we shall find the intersecting point of the locus of a pair of complex characteristic roots and the locus of the real characteristic root. Consider a point s located just above a point thought to be the intersecting point, as shown in Fig. 5.19. Let Δ be the distance from s to the real axis; let l_1, l_2, and l_3 be the distances from s to the poles p_1, p_2, and p_3; and let θ_1, θ_2, and θ_3 be the phase angles of the vectors $s - p_1$, $s - p_2$, and $s - p_3$, as shown in Fig. 5.19. Then,

$$\left.\begin{aligned} \sin(\pi-\theta_1) &= \frac{\Delta}{l_1} \doteqdot \pi-\theta_1 \\ \sin\theta_2 &= \frac{\Delta}{l_2} \doteqdot \theta_2 \\ \sin\theta_3 &= \frac{\Delta}{l_3} \doteqdot \theta_3 \end{aligned}\right\} \tag{5.141}$$

For the point s to lie on the root locus, the phase angle condition

$$\theta_1+\theta_2+\theta_3=\pi \tag{5.142}$$

must be satisfied. That is,

$$\pi-\theta_1=\theta_2+\theta_3 \tag{5.143}$$

Substituting this into equation (5.141), we obtain

$$\frac{\Delta}{l_1}=\frac{\Delta}{l_2}+\frac{\Delta}{l_3} \tag{5.144}$$

and hence

$$\frac{1}{l_1}=\frac{1}{l_2}+\frac{1}{l_3} \tag{5.145}$$

If a point s is extremely close to the real axis, then the phase angle of each vector is either extremely small or extremely close to π; consequently, it is difficult to determine whether the phase angle condition holds for the point s or not. In this case, we can use equation (1.45) to determine whether the point s is on the root locus or not.

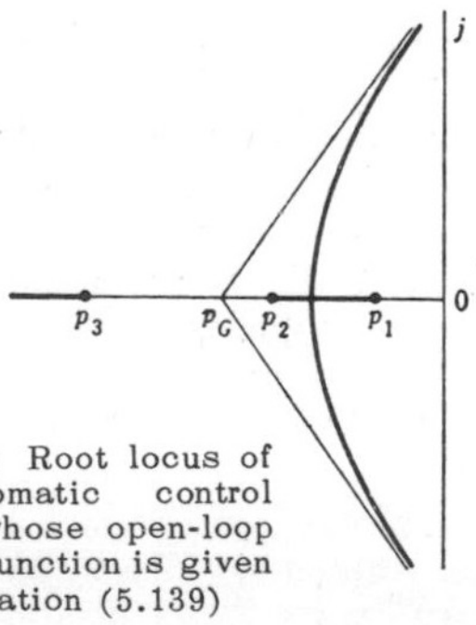

Fig. 5.18 Root locus of an automatic control system whose open-loop transfer function is given by equation (5.139)

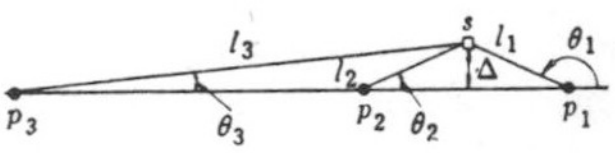

Fig. 5.19 Method of finding a point on the locus of a complex characteristic root near the real axis

Equation (5.145) can be extended to the case in which the open loop transfer function has more poles and more zeros than in the preceding discussion. If we assign positive or negative values suitably to the distances, equation (5.145) may be generalised as follows:

$$\sum_1^n \frac{1}{l_{pn}} + \sum_1^m \frac{1}{l_{zm}} = 0 \tag{5.146}$$

where l_{pn} is the distance from a possible point of intersection of the locus of the real characteristic roots and the locus of a pair of complex characteristic roots to the pole p_n and where l_{zm} is the distance from the possible point of intersection to the zero z_m.

Let us now discuss the root locus of an automatic control system whose open-loop transfer function has a complex-valued pole. Consider the open-loop transfer function

$$F(s) = \frac{K}{(s-p_1)(s-p_1^*)(s-p_2)} \tag{5.147}$$

where p_1 and p_1^* are complex conjugate poles and p_2 is a real-valued pole. From what was said above, we can easily plot the poles, the root locus branches lying on the real axis, and the asymptotes of the root locus (see Fig. 5.20).

Let us see what directions the branches of the root locus take when they leave the complex conjugate characteristic poles. Consider a point s which is extremely close to the complex pole p_1. Then, we have the following relations:

$$\underline{/s-p_2} \doteqdot \underline{/p_1-p_2} = \theta_2 \tag{5.148}$$

$$\underline{/s-p_1^*} \doteqdot \underline{/p_1-p_1^*} = \frac{\pi}{2} \tag{5.149}$$

If s is on the root locus, the phase angle condition

$$\underline{/s-p_1} + \underline{/s-p_1^*} + \underline{/s-p_2} = (2n+1)\pi \tag{5.150}$$

holds, and hence

$$\underline{/s-p_1} = (2n+1)\pi - \frac{\pi}{2} - \theta_2 \tag{5.151}$$

$$= 2n\pi + \frac{\pi}{2} - \theta_2 \tag{5.152}$$

Consequently, if a point s is on the root locus and is extremely close to the pole p_1, the directional angle of the line joining s and p_1 is $2n\pi + \pi/2 - \theta_2$. Therefore, the directional angle of the tangent line of the branch at the pole p_1 is $\pi/2 - \theta_2$. Since a root locus is symmetric with respect to the real axis, the directional angle of the tangent line at the pole p_1^* is found by considering the reflection of the tangent line at p_1 about the real axis. The same approach is applicable to the case in which an open-loop transfer function has more poles or zeros than in the above example.

The approximate shape of the root locus of an automatic control system can be determined fairly easily by using these properties.

Fig. 5.20 Root locus of an automatic control system whose open-loop transfer function has a complex-valued pole

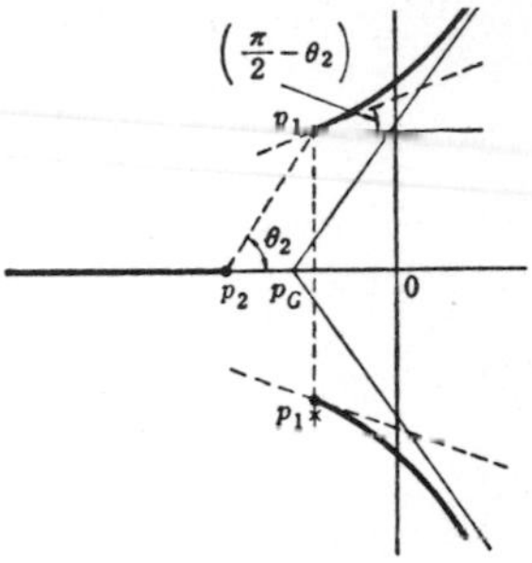

There is an interesting relation between the root locus and an electric line of force. Consider a line of force that exists as a result of placing a unit positive charge of electricity on each pole and a unit negative charge on each zero. Then, the phase loci bear some relation to the electric lines of force satisfying a certain condition. It is in fact possible, using this relationship, to compute the root locus (180-degree phase locus). It is also interesting to note that the gain locus, obtained by letting the value of s vary so that the value of s in equation (5.99) remains constant, bears some relation to the equipotential curves which intersect the lines of force at right angles. Figure 5.21 illustrates this graphically. Figure 5.22 shows the root locus and the corresponding line of force when a zero is added to Fig. 5.21. As shown in Fig. 5.22, the branch a-a' is attracted by a zero if the zero is located close to the branch of the root locus.

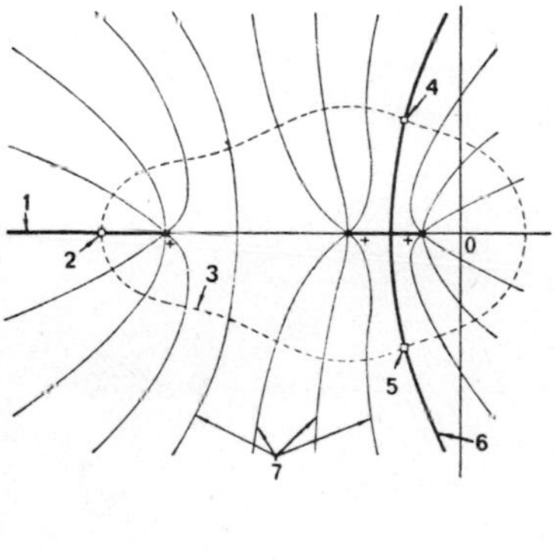

1 - *root locus*; 2 - *characteristic root* 3 - *equipotential line* (K *is constant*) 4 - *characteristic root*; 5 - *characteristic root*; 6 - *root locus*; 7 - *line of force*

Fig. 5.21

1 - *characteristic root*; 2 - *charteristic root*; 3 - *equipotential line* (K *is constant*); 4 - *line of force* 5 - *root locus*

Fig. 5.22

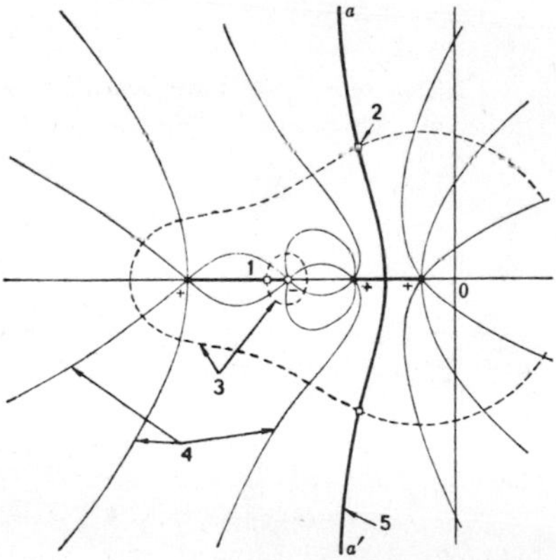

Root locus branches lying on the real axis can be easily and accurately constructed. Root locus branches corresponding to complex characteristic roots require laborious procedures, since we have to pick up the points that satisfy the phase angle condition. However, use of a mechanical angle summator (called a spirule) greatly simplifies these construction procedures.

EXERCISE PROBLEMS

1. The characteristic roots of certain automatic control systems are given as follows:

(i) $r_1=-0.5+j1$, $r_2=-0.5-j1$, $r_3=-3+j0$

(ii) $r_1=-1+j1$, $r_2=-1-j1$, $r_3=-2+j0$, $r_4=-10+j0$

For each of the above groups, plot the characteristic roots on the root plane, and find the transient response by using the root configuration, assuming that the feedback transfer function is 1 in each case.

2. The characteristic roots and a zero of an automatic control system are given as follows:

characteristic roots: $r_1=-0.5+j1$, $r_2=-0.5-j1$, $r_3=-3+j0$

zero: $z_1=-0.7+j0$

Plot them on the root plane, and find the transient response, assuming that the feedback transfer function is 1.

3. Figures (a) and (b) show the block diagrams of two automatic control systems. Find the slope of the response of the controlled variable at $t = 0$ for each automatic control system.

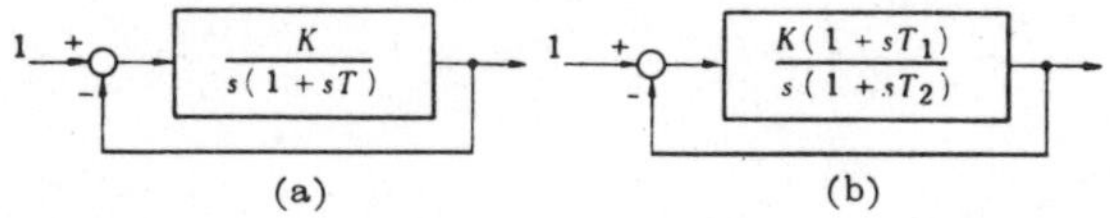

(a) (b)

4. Characteristic roots and zeros of certain open loop transfer functions are given as follows:

(i) $r_1=-1+j3$ $r_2=-1-j3$ $r_3=-2.5+j0.2$ $r_4=-2.5-j0.2$
$z_1=-2+j0$ $z_2=-3+j0$

(ii) $r_1=-1.8+j2.0$ $r_2=-1.8-j2.0$ $r_3=-4+j7$ $r_4=-4-j7$
$z_1=-2+j2.5$ $z_2=-2-j2.5$

Test whether r_1 and r_2 are dominant roots or not for each of the above groups.

5. The open loop transfer function of a certain automatic control system is

$$F(s)=\frac{15(1+0.166\,s)}{s(1+0.25\,s)(1+0.0625\,s)(1+0.0144\,s)}$$

The system has a pair of conjugate characteristic roots

$$r=-5\pm j\,10$$

Examine whether these conjugate characteristic roots are dominant roots or not.

6. An automatic control system whose open-loop transfer function is

$$F(s)=\frac{499(1+0.333\,s)(1+0.228\,s)}{(1+16.6\,s)(1+0.585\,s)(1+0.08\,s)(1+0.0455s)(1+0.03\,s)}$$

has the conjugate characteristic roots

$$r=-16\pm j\,40$$

Examine whether these conjugate characteristic roots are dominant roots or not.

7. Construct the root locus for each of the following open-loop transfer functions:

(i) $\dfrac{K(s+2)(s+4)(s+6)}{(s+1)(s+3)(s+5)(s+7)}$ (iv) $\dfrac{K(s+7)(s+10)}{(s+1)(s+3)(s+5)}$

(ii) $\dfrac{K(1+0.3\,s)}{(1+s)(1+0.5\,s)(1+0.1\,s)}$ (v) $\dfrac{K(1+3\,s)}{s^2(1+0.5\,s)(1+0.1\,s)}$

(iii) $\dfrac{K(s+5)(s+7)}{(s+1)(s+3)}$

8. Certain automatic control systems have the following open-loop transfer functions:

(i) $\dfrac{K}{s(s+3)}$ (iii) $\dfrac{K(1+0.6s)}{s(1+s)(1+0.4\,s)(1+0.1\,s)}$

(ii) $\dfrac{K}{s(s+3)(s+7)}$ (iv) $\dfrac{K(1+4\,s)}{s^2(1+0.5s)}$

For each of these systems, construct the root locus, and determine the value of K so that the damping coefficient $\gamma=\alpha/\omega$ of the characteristic root with the lowest damping coefficient of all the characteristic roots is equal to 0.5.

9. Find the dominant roots of each of the following open-loop transfer functions:

(i) $\dfrac{10}{s(1+0.25\,s)(1+0.05\,s)}$

(ii) $\dfrac{20}{(1+s)(1+0.2s)(1+0.05\,s)}$

Use the root locus to find the response of the automatic control system when the reference input signal is a unit step signal.

10. The open loop transfer function of an automatic control system is

$$F(s)=\frac{2}{s(1+s)(1+0.1\,s)}$$

6

Basic Concepts of Automatic Control System Design

6.1. OUTLINE OF AUTOMATIC CONTROL SYSTEM DESIGN

Thus far, we have been analysing the characteristics of automatic control systems. Specifically, we have discussed various means of evaluating the performance of automatic control systems. However, this analysis itself is not our final purpose, but is an approach to the design of automatic control systems. In this chapter and the following chapters, we shall discuss the methods for designing automatic control systems, using the results of our analysis.

The purpose, controlling method, size and type of system, and desired characteristics vary from one automatic control system to another. Accordingly, the design also varies from one system to another. However, all automatic control systems have certain common properties in their performance mechanisms; hence, there are certain common points in the design methods.

In most cases, the design of an automatic control system can be divided into two stages. The first stage is to determine what structure of the automatic control system to be designed will satisfy the specified performance characteristics and other required conditions, and to find the system constants for obtaining the desired structure. The second stage is to select suitable components and assemble them in an appropriate manner. Here, one must consider manufacturing problems, operating conditions, economic conditions, etc. Finally, blueprints must be drawn for manufacturing the elements and components and for the installation of the automatic control system. The first stage in automatic control system design is called synthesis of the characteristics; the second stage is called the manufacturing design. These two stages are not completely separated from each other. For example, a part of the manufacturing design may sometimes need to be completed at an early stage of the system design. In the synthesis process, one must always consider the question as to whether the elements or components to be used can be easily manufactured. In some cases, the synthesis has to be altered in the manufacturing design process.

Manufacturing design deals mainly with design of elements or components to be used. Therefore, it varies considerably, depending on the conditions imposed on the particular automatic control system that is to be designed. Consequently, it is rather difficult to make a general exposition of the manufacturing design, and fortunately it is not necessary. On the other hand, the synthesis can be discussed from a general point of view although, of course, it too varies somewhat, depending on the type of automatic control system to be designed and the quality required. Therefore, we shall primarily deal with synthesis in this text.

Synthesis can be divided into two parts: steady-state characteristic synthesis and transient characteristic synthesis. The former gives specified steady-state characteristics of the system to be designed, and the latter gives specified transient characteristics. In most cases, the steady-state synthesis is quite simple. Transient characteristic synthesis on the other hand is not always simple, and usually several problems must be solved in order to carry out transient characteristic synthesis.

There are two major methods for the transient characteristic synthesis. They are the frequency response method and the root configuration method. The frequency response method is the oldest approach to the transient characteristic sythesis, and it is still widely used in the design of automatic control systems. This method is convenient for synthesising an approximation of specified transient characteristics. However, synthesis procedure by this method is quite complicated even for a relatively uncomplicated system such as an automatic control system with parallel compensation, and the result of the synthesis is not always satisfactory for such a system. On the other hand, the root configuration method yields an accurate synthesis of transient characteristics. However, because of its newness, it is still not as widely used as the frequency response method. We shall deal primarily with these two methods in the subsequent discussions of synthesis. These two methods each have advantages and disadvantages, the choice as to which to use in a particular case should be determined on the basis of the nature of the transient characteristic specification.

6.2. SPECIFICATION OF CHARACTERISTICS

For synthesis of the characteristics of an automatic control system, a specification of the characteristics is given. This specification is usually written in a form convenient for specifying the operational requests. Accordingly, it may not be written in the most convenient form for synthesis. On the other hand, for the purposes of synthesis, a given specification has a best form in which it can be stated. Therefore, it is necessary to transform a given specification into an equivalent form most suitable for synthesis before starting the latter. Since the transient characteristics are the most complicated of all the characteristics of an automatic control system, it is not always possible to transform specified transient characteristics into a form convenient for synthesis. Thus, what we need to do prior to the synthesis is to transform a given specification into the most convenient form that we can obtain for the synthesis, making it simple to work with.

As mentioned before, automatic control systems can be classified according to control method, control purpose, etc. Naturally, the details of the specification differ from one type of automatic control system to another. We recall that we divided automatic control systems according to control method into follow-up control systems and automatic regulating systems. In an automatic regulating system, the reference input is fixed at a certain value throughout the operation. Consequently, we need to consider not the response of the controlled variable to a variation in the reference input signal but the variation in the controlled variable due to a disturbance. The major disturbance in an automatic regulating system is usually the load variation, which can be expressed by a step function. On the other hand, the most desirable property of a follow-up control system is that the control variable should follow the variation in the reference input rapidly and accurately. Thus, if the controlled variable follows the variation in the reference input satisfactorily, it will usually also have a satisfactory response to a disturbance in general. Therefore, we do not need to consider the variation in the controlled variable due to a disturbance in a follow-up control system except in special cases.

Automatic control systems can also be classified according to manufacturing method or control purpose into servomechanisms, automatic regulators, and process control systems. These systems differ in structure, manufacturing processes, operational conditions, and response velocities. Accordingly, the premises for the synthesis of their characteristics also differ somewhat.

For the design of a servomechanism, the client specifies only the quality of the performance; details such as the structure or the components to be used are usually left to the manufacturer's discretion. Since a servomechanism is a follow-up control system whose controlled variable is a position or an angle, the response speed is not extremely high.

An automatic regulator is an automatic control system that controls a velocity, a voltage, or a current, and the response speed is higher than that of any other type of automatic control system. In the design of an automatic regulator, the client often specifies the control object. Consequently, the subordinate elements to be used are often determined in a natural way. Usually, the constants of the control objects are also specified.

Process control systems are used mainly for controlling chemical processes. The selection of the control object is, of course, not left to the manufacturer, and, in the worst cases, the designer of the system has to start without knowing explicitly the characteristics of the process to be controlled. Since the response of the process itself is much slower than that of other control objects, some response delay in the control system does not hinder the control purpose. This property greatly reduces the technical difficulties involved in the design of a process control system.

As just mentioned, the specifications differ according to type of automatic control system to be designed and the control purposes. Moreover, the specifications written from the operational view point are not necessarily identical with those written from the point of view of design. However, we can divide the specification into the specification of steady-state characteristics and the specification of transient characteristics, since the performance is divided into the steady-state response and the transient response. Furthermore, the specification of transient characteristics can be classified into two major items, the item that specifies the wave form of the transient response and the item that specifies the speed of the transient response. We shall now discuss the specification of the transient and steady-state characteristics.

(1) STEADY-STATE CHARACTERISTICS

Specification of the steady-state characteristics consists in listing various items and stating the admissible steady-state error. We shall discuss each such item.

(a) Accuracy of detecting unit and of reference input. If an error is caused by a detecting unit or if a reference input that should be constant actually varies, an error will result in the controlled variable. The value of this error depends only on the accuracy of the detecting unit or the reference input; it is almost independent of the characteristics of the other elements. The problem of making a detecting unit or reference input sufficiently accurate belongs to manufacturing design rather than characteristic synthesis.

(b) Steady-state error due to disturbance (offset). Even though the detecting unit and the reference input are sufficiently accurate, a steady-state error will occur if there is a disturbance. This steady-state error is called a residual error or an offset. An offset depends on both the magnitude of the disturbance and the point at which it is applied. Thus, it is necessary to specify both these things when stating the allowable range for an offset.

There is a certain ratio, called the regulation, that is often used for specifying a steady-state error. The regulation is a steady-state error, expressed as a percentage, caused by a rated load variation. Sometimes, the steady-state error, expressed in percentages, caused by a half or third of a rated load variation, is also used to specify the regulation. When the regulation is used in the specification, it is also necessary to specify the corresponding load-variation range. Errors caused by disturbances other than a load variation are not called regulations. However, if there are disturbances that cause relatively large variations in the controlled variable, their values must also be specified. Usually, steady-state errors caused by disturbances should be as small as possible. However, for an automatic regulator in which elements of the same type are operated in parallel, a certain value of the regulation for each element may be specified, and it has to be neither larger nor less than the specified value in order to match the load division in the system. Even in the case in which the allowable range for the steady-state error needs to be as small as possible, it is not advisable to narrow the allowable range to an unnecessarily small range, since this often creates difficulties in the synthesis of the transient characteristics, such difficulties are to be avoided.

(c) Steady-state errors from other causes. Besides the steady-state errors mentioned in the preceding paragraphs, there often occur some irregular steady-state errors caused by trembles or dead zones of amplifying units or of control objects, etc. There is no uniform way of specifying these steady-state errors because of the difference between systems and elements.

(d) Velocity and acceleration errors. These steady-state errors occur when a reference input varies with a constant velocity or constant acceleration. For the design of a servomechanism or a follow-up control system, these errors are often included in the specification. It is then necessary to specify also the corresponding values of the velocity or the acceleration of the reference input, since the steady-state errors depend on them.

(2) WAVE FORM OF TRANSIENT RESPONSE

The waveform of a transient response is generally complicated; therefore, it is rather difficult to specify it exactly. Even if it is specified in an exact form, it is not always possible to design an automatic control system with the exactly specified wave form of transient response. Fortunately, it is not actually necessary to specify a wave form of transient response exactly. It is sufficient to specify the approximate form or to specify the values of certain important constants. In actual synthesis, it is convenient to approximate an automatic control system by a simple second-order system or by the dominant components of the response and to specify the form of the approximate transient response. Often, the characteristics that are convenient for describing the performance in operation, such as allowable ranges for an overshoot or the maximum value of a transient response, are specified in the specification. Then, it is necessary to express them in terms of different characteristics that are convenient for design.

We shall discuss here only the specification of transient characteristics in the case in which the transient responses of the systems can be approximated by those of suitable second-order systems or by their dominant components.

As stated above, the wave form of a transient response should be somewhat but not exceedingly oscillatory. In fact, a desirable wave form of transient response does not differ greatly from one system to another. We may assume that the desirable wave form of transient response has a fixed pattern for any one type of automatic control system. The values of the important constants characterising the desirable wave forms of transient responses are computed for each type of system and are listed in Table 6.2.

Now, we shall discuss several constants that characterise a transient response. These constants are often used to specify a transient characteristic in a specification and to determine the form of a transient response.

(a) The damping ratio ζ and the damping coefficient γ_0 of the dominant characteristic root. When the transient response of an automatic control system is approximated by that of a second-order automatic control system, the damping ratio ζ is used to describe the waveform of the transient response of the second-order automatic control system. If we write the characteristic equation of this second-order system in the standard form

$$s^2+2\zeta\omega_n s+\omega_n^2=0 \tag{6.1}$$

then ζ in this equation is the damping ratio. Denoting by r_0 the characteristic roots (which are assumed to be oscillatory roots), we have

$$\begin{aligned} r_0 &= -\zeta\omega_n \pm j\sqrt{1-\zeta^2}\,\omega_n \\ &= (-\zeta \pm j\sqrt{1-\zeta^2})\omega_n \end{aligned} \tag{6.2}$$

On the other hand, if we denote by

$$r_t=-\alpha_0 \pm j\omega_0 \tag{6.3}$$

the dominant roots of a higher-order automatic control system, then α_0 / ω_0 is the damping coefficient γ_0 of the dominant roots. That is, we have

$$\gamma_0=\frac{\alpha_0}{\omega_0} \tag{6.4}$$

The dominant roots can then be written

$$r_t=(-\gamma_0 \pm j)\omega_0 \tag{6.5}$$

Since the damping ratio ζ is a constant expressing the wave form of the transient response of a second-order system (the approximation of the higher-order system) and the damping coefficient γ_0 is a constant associated with the dominant roots of the higher-order system, r_0 in equation (6.2) and r_t in equation (6.5) are different characteristic roots. However, in practice, we may treat their values as equal to each other. Thus, if we set $r_0 = r_t$, we obtain from equations (6.2) and (6.5) the following relation between γ_0 and ζ :

$$\gamma_0=\frac{\zeta}{\sqrt{1-\zeta^2}} \tag{6.6}$$

The damping ratio ζ is convenient for synthesis by the frequency response method, and the damping coefficient γ_0 is convenient for synthesis by the root configuration method.

(b) The resonant value M_p . A resonant value is a value obtained by dividing the ratio of the output signal to the input signal at the resonant angular frequency by the ratio of the output signal to the input signal at an extremely low frequency, under the assumption that the reference input is a sinusoidal wave. For a second-order system, the relation between the resonant value M_p and the damping ratio ζ is

$$M_p=\frac{1}{2\zeta\sqrt{1-\zeta^2}} \tag{6.7}$$

as was shown in equation (4.113). The resonant value M_p is a convenient specification of a transient response for synthesis by the vector locus method.

(c) The phase margin ϕ_m . The phase margin is the angle obtained by subtracting -180° from the phase angle corresponding to a 0 [dB] gain in the frequency response of an open loop transfer function. Specification of the phase margin is convenient for synthesis by the Bode diagram method. Since the accuracy of the approximation of a transient response in terms of the phase margin is lower than that of the approximation by the resonant constant M_p , it is advisable to specify a transient response in terms of M_p for a synthesis that requires a high accuracy. For a second-order system, we have the relation

$$\phi_m = 90° - \tan^{-1}\sqrt{\frac{1}{4}\sqrt{4+\frac{1}{\zeta^4}}-\frac{1}{2}} \tag{6.8}$$

between the phase margin ϕ_m and the resonant value M_p , as was shown by equation (4.129)

(d) Overshoot Θ_m . The overshoot is the ratio of the maximum deviation of a controlled variable from its steady-state value to the steady-state value when the reference input varies stepwise, and it is usually expressed as a percentage. Since the overshoot is the most descriptive constant for representing the wave form of a transient response, it is often used in specifications that are written from the operational viewpoint. However, for synthesis, it has to be transformed into an equivalent value of ζ , γ_0 , M_p , or ϕ_m . For a second-order system, the relation between the overshoot Θ_m and the damping coefficient γ_0 is

$$\Theta_m = -\epsilon^{-\gamma_0 \pi} \tag{6.9}$$

as was shown by equation (3.88). By use of this equation, Θ_m can be transformed into the equivalent value of γ_0 .

(e) The maximum instantaneous error ϵ_m . The maximum instantaneous error is the maximum value of an error that occurs instantaneously when a certain disturbance is applied. Sometimes, this constant is significant as a description of a transient response from the operational point of view. For a follow-up control system, the maximum instantaneous error is always equal to the variation in the reference input when the reference input varies stepwise, and it is independent of the transient characteristics of the system.

TABLE 6.1 EQUIVALENT VALUES OF IMPORTANT CONSTANTS

damping ratio ζ	damping coefficient γ_0	resonant value M_p	phase margin ϕ_m	overshoot Θ_m
0.25	0.259	2.09	28.0°	43.2[%]
0.30	0.315	1.75	33.4°	37.2[%]
0.35	0.374	1.53	38.5°	30.8[%]
0.40	0.437	1.35	43.4°	25.4[%]
0.45	0.505	1.25	47.7°	20.6[%]
0·50	0.578	1.16	52.0°	16.4[%]

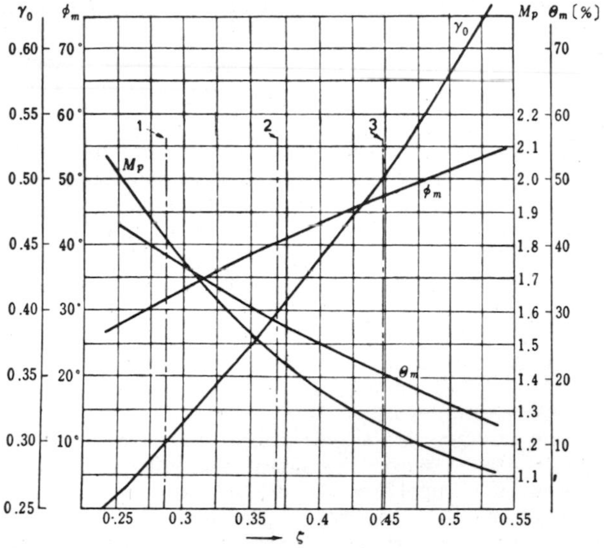

Fig. 6.1 Relations between important constants generally used for specification of transient responses

Therefore, specification of a transient response in terms of the maximum instantaneous error is meaningless for the synthesis of a follow-up control system. For an automatic regulating system, the maximum instantaneous error takes different values according to the wave form of the disturbance and the place where the disturbance is applied. Consequently, when this error is used as a specification of a transient response, it is necessary also to specify the wave form and place of application.

As shown above, there are certain relationships connecting the damping ratio ζ, the damping coefficient γ_0 of the dominant roots, the resonant value M_p, the phase margin ϕ_m, and the overshoot Θ_m, each of which can be used for the specification of a transient response. Table 6.1 gives a numerical representation of these relations, and Fig. 6.1 gives a graphical representation. Table 6.2 shows the standard values of the important constants corresponding

TABLE 6.2 STANDARD VALUES OF IMPORTANT CONSTANTS FOR THE WAVE FORM OF A DESIRED TRANSIENT RESPONSE

	damping ratio ζ	damping coefficient γ_0	resonant value M_p	phase margin ϕ_m	overshoot Θ_m.
servomechanism	0.45	0.5	1.25	48°	21 [%]
automatic regulator	0.37	0.4	1.45	41°	28 [%]
process control system	0.29	0.3	1.80	32°	38 [%]

to the wave form of the desired transient response for each type of automatic control system. Their graphical representations for a second-order system are shown in Fig. 3.10.

3. RAPIDITY OF TRANSIENT RESPONSE

For us to be able to compare rapidities of transient responses numerically, the wave forms of the transient responses have to be similar to each other. Strictly speaking, the transient response takes a different wave form for each system. However, the wave form of the transient response of a well designed automatic control system can be well approximated by that of a suitable second-order system, as mentioned before, and hence the rapidity of the transient response of a well-designed higher-order system can also be well approximated by that of a second-order system or that of the dominant component. The quantities listed below are usually used to express the rapidity of a transient response.

(a) The damped angular frequency ω_0. When the transient response of a higher-order automatic control system can be approximated by its dominant component, the damped angular frequency for the approximate transient response is the absolute value of the imaginary part of the dominant root. This constant is used together with the damping coefficient γ_0 to specify a transient response for synthesis by the root configuration method.

(b) The specific angular frequency ω_n. The specific angular frequency (also called the undamped natural angular frequency) is the oscillation angular frequency of the sustained oscillation of a second-order system (which is an approximation of a higher-order system) obtained by assuming that the attenuation term in the equation of the second-order system is 0. It is a convenient specification of a transient response for synthesis by the frequency response method. It is also convenient for the theoretical treatment of automatic control systems.

(c) The resonant frequency ω_r. The resonant frequency is the angular frequency at which the amplitude of the frequency response of a controlled variable attains its maximum value when the reference input is sinusoidal. That is, the resonant frequency is the angular frequency at which the resonance of the frequency response occurs. The specification of the transient response by this constant is convenient for synthesis by the frequency response method. In particular, it often used together with the resonant value M_p for synthesis using the Nyquist diagram.

(d) Cross-over angular frequency ω_c. The cross-over angular frequency is the angular frequency at which the frequency response of an open loop transfer function has 0 [dB] gain. That is, the cross-over angular frequency is the angular frequency at which the gain characteristic curve crosses the 0 [dB] line. This constant is used together with the phase margin ϕ_m to specify the transient response for synthesis using the Bode diagram.

The relations between these constants vary, depending on the structure of the automatic control system. However, for a second-order system, they are expressed by the following equations:

$$\omega_0=\sqrt{1-\zeta^2}\,\omega_n \tag{6.10}$$

$$\omega_r=\sqrt{1-2\zeta^2}\,\omega_n \tag{6.11}$$

$$\omega_c=\sqrt{\sqrt{4\zeta^4+1}-2\zeta^2}\,\omega_n \tag{6.12}$$

If we express ω_0, ω_r, and ω_c in terms of γ_0, their curves are as shown in Fig. 6.2. Table 6.3 gives numerical values of these constants for the standard wave form of the desirable transient response for each type of automatic control system.

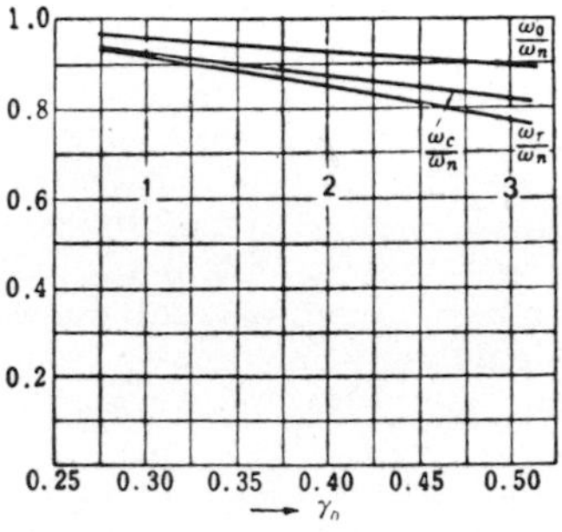

1 - *process control system*; 2 - *automatic regulator*; 3 - *servomechanism*

Fig. 6.2 Relations between the constants usually used for specifying the rapidity of a transient response

TABLE 6.3 NUMERICAL VALUES OF THE CONSTANTS FOR THE STANDARD WAVE FORM OF A DESIRABLE TRANSIENT RESPONSE

	damping coefficient γ_0	damping ratio ζ	ω_0/ω_n	ω_r/ω_n	ω_c/ω_n
servomechanism	0.5	0.45	0.893	0.772	0.821
automatic regulator	0.4	0.37	0.929	0.851	0.874
process control system	0.3	0.29	0.957	0.913	0.920

(c) The settling time T_s. The settling time is the duration of time between the instant at which a unit step disturbance is applied and the instant at which the transient error falls into the acceptable range of steady-state error for an automatic control regulating system. This is a convenient constant for describing the rapidity of a transient response from the operational viewpoint. For a second-order system, the envelope of the error response is $\sqrt{1+\gamma_0^2}\ exp-(\gamma_0\omega_0 t)$. Consequently, if we denote by δ the admissible steady-state error, then the time t that satisfies the equation

$$\sqrt{1+\gamma_0^2}\,e^{-\gamma_0\omega_0 t}=\delta$$

is the settling time. If we denote it by T_s, we get, from the above equation,

$$T_s = -\frac{1}{\gamma_0 \omega_0} \ln \frac{\delta}{\sqrt{1+\gamma_0^2}} \tag{6.13}$$

where γ_0 is the damping coefficient, ω_0 is the damped angular frequency, and δ is the admissible steady-state error. For synthesis, a suitable constant should be chosen from the constants used in equation (6.13), and it has to be specified.

6.3. SYNTHESIS OF STEADY-STATE CHARACTERISTICS

Synthesis of the steady-state characteristics is the first step in designing an automatic control system. It consists in choosing a suitable control method and determining properly the gain constant of the open-loop transfer function and the other constants that characterise the steady-state characteristics so that the specified steady-state characteristics will be realised. Here, we assume that the reference input and the detecting unit are sufficiently accurate (because of proper manufacturing design). We shall discuss a synthesis method by which we can let a designed automatic control have a specified steady-state error due to a variation in the reference input or to a disturbance.

If the steady-state error or the regulation is specified to be 0, we should use an integral control (an astatic control). An integral control system has a velocity error or an acceleration error according to the number of integral elements used in the system. If it is specified that the velocity error should have a certain non-zero value, we choose an integral control that uses only one integral element (that is, a type 1 integral control), and we determine by the method discussed in Section 3.4 the velocity error (that is the gain constant), as specified. If it is specified that the velocity should be 0 and that the acceleration should have a certain non-zero value, we choose an integral control that uses two integral elements, and we determine, by the previous method, the acceleration error (that is, the gain constant) as specified.

If the steady-state error or the regulation need not be exactly 0, it is advisable to use a proportional control (static control). A proportional control has superior transient characteristics to those of an integral control. If we denote the steady-state error or the regulation by η, the regulation of the controlled object by η_0, and the gain constant of the open-loop transfer function of a proportional control system by A, then from what was said in Section 3.4, we have

$$\eta = \frac{\eta_0}{1+A} \tag{6.14}$$

Therefore, the regulation η will have a specified value if the gain constant A of the open-loop transfer function is

$$A = \frac{\eta_0}{\eta} - 1 \tag{6.15}$$

where η_0 is the regulation of the control object.

In most cases, it is desired that the steady-state error be as small as possible, and the maximum allowable value of the steady-state error or the regulation is specified. Then, we can compute the minimum allowable value of the gain constant A by equation (6.15).

As mentioned above, an exact value may sometimes be specified for the steady-state error or the regulation, and the designed proportional control system is then required to have first that value because of the distribution of the load or some other reason. This requirement will be satisfied by letting the gain constant of the open loop transfer function keep the value computed from equation (6.15) for the specified value of the steady-state error or of the regulation. However, the gain constant A of the open loop transfer function of a single closed-loop system does not always take a fixed value; it varies slightly according to variations in the electric power source, the velocity of the driving motor, etc. Moreover, actual elements of an automatic control system have nonlinear

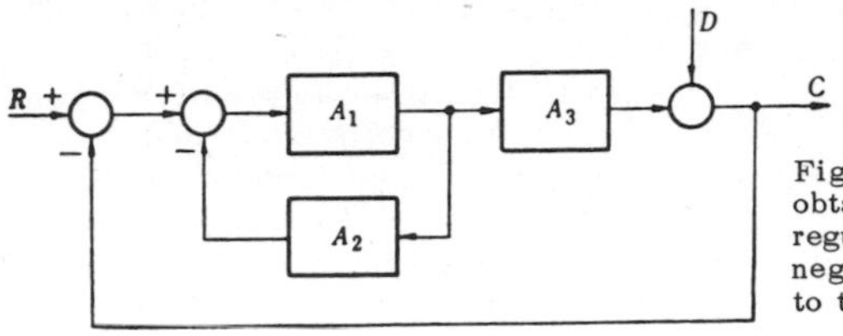

Fig. 6.3 A method of obtaining a constant regulation by adding a negative feedback device to the controlled variable

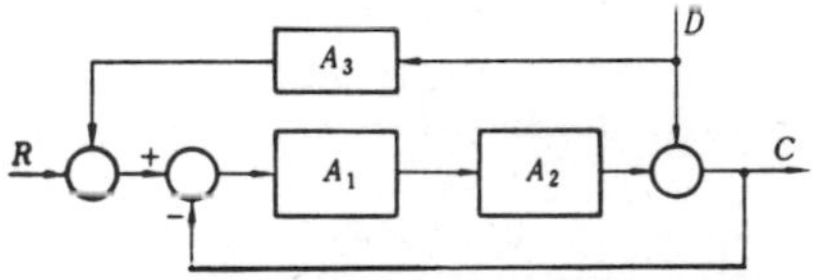

Fig. 6.4 A method of obtaining a constant regulation by varying the reference input according to the load variation

characteristics; hence, the effective gain constants of the elements vary according to the levels of the input signals or the variations in the positions of the working points. Therefore, in order to maintain the regulation at a fixed value for a wide range of load values, it is necessary to adopt certain special devices. Figs. 6.3, and 6.4 show the block diagrams of proportional control systems with such devices. In Fig. 6.3, a feedback amplifier is used as the amplifying unit to improve the linearity of the amplifying unit. If each component amplifier has the amplification factor shown in Fig. 6.3, and if the value of A_1 is sufficiently large, then the gain constant $A = A_3/A_2$ and the steady-state error η is computed from equation (6.14):

$$\eta = \frac{\eta_0}{1 + \frac{A_3}{A_2}} \tag{6.16}$$

This method is effective for obtaining a constant regulation only when the controlled object has an excellent linearity and A_3 is practically constant. This method is now applied to the velocity regulator for steam turbines and hydroturbines in power plants.

In Fig. 6.4, the regulation is almost nullified by giving a sufficiently large value to the gain constant of the open-loop transfer function. Then a certain portion of the disturbance is subtracted from the reference input. This method is quite effective even when the regulation of the control object varies with variation in the load. It is now applied to the automatic voltage regulation of a d.c. generator, to power factor regulation, and to the automatic voltage regulation of a generator of a power plant.

6.4. METHODS OF SYNTHESIS OF TRANSIENT CHARACTERISTICS

Once the gain constants of an automatic control system to be designed are determined by synthesis of the steady-state characteristics, we need to select suitable components and assemble them in the correct manner, so that the designed system will have the specified steady-state and other characteristics. This belongs to manufacturing design, yet it affects significantly the various characteristics of the designed automatic control system, especially the transient characteristics. Therefore, one should consider the expected transient characteristics when selecting the components and assembling them. Though the transient characteristics can be determined exactly only after synthesis of the transient characteristics, the following remarks are helpful for obtaining better transient characteristics in general.

1. It is desirable to reduce as much as possible the number of time delays contained in the system. If there are no more than two time delays, the system is stable. If an integral control is used, we count it as a time delay.
2. When three or more time delays are contained in the system the system can be more easily stabilised if the values of the time constants differ greatly from each other.
3. If we multiply every time constant by $1/a$ then the response velocity of the system is a times the original response velocity, provided the system is not an integral control system. If the system is an integral control system, we must, in addition, multiply the gain constant of the system by a^n to obtain the same effect on the response velocity as before.
4. Since a dead time has a bad effect on the transient response in general, it is advisable to reduce as much as possible the number of dead times contained in the system. However, if the only concern in the synthesis is the waveform of the transient response, we can obtain a better form for the transient response by adding only one first-order time delay with a sufficiently large time constant. The larger the time-constant of the first-order time delay, the better will be the waveform of the transient response obtained.
5. The maximum value of the transient error of an automatic regulating system can be reduced by giving a large value of the time

constant of the disturbance transfer function.

Even if transient characteristics are synthesised by the techniques suggested in the above five remarks, they may not satisfy the given specification. In such a case, we need to improve the transient characteristics so that they may satisfy the given specification. Actual methods for the improvement of the transient characteristics are the following: (i) change in the values of the constants; (ii) insertion of compensating networks; (iii) change in the components or the structure of the system.

In the first method, the constants whose values are changed for an improvement of the transient response are usually the gain-constant and the time constant of each element. Since a change in the value of the gain constant has a considerable effect on the transient characteristics, this property can be used to improve the transient response. However, it also has a considerable effect on the steady-state characteristics. This should be taken into consideration in the change of gain-constant. Naturally, the change of gain constant is allowed only within a limit that will not deteriorate the steady-state characteristics. For a proportional control system, the gain constant is related to the steady-state characteristics by equation (6.14). Thus, an excessive reduction of the value of the gain constant results in poor steady-state characteristics. For a type 1 integral control system with a constant reference input, the steady-state error is always 0, and hence a change in the gain constant does not affect the steady-state error. It is clear, however, that if the reference input varies at a constant rate, then the steady-state error is inversely proportional to the gain constant.

Similarly, for a type 2 integral control system, a change in the gain constant value does not affect the steady-state error when the reference input varies at a constant rate. These properties can be used to improve the transient characteristics of the system to be designed. If we decrease the value of the gain constant, we usually obtain a better wave form for the transient response. However, the speed of the transient response generally decreases at the same time. Consequently, change of gain constant may not be a suitable method for improving the transient characteristics when the wave form and the response speed are both specified.

It is clear that if we reduce the value of each time constant, the response speed of the system will increase. If we make the difference between the time constants great, the damping will increase. These properties can also be used to improve the transient characteristics. However, the application of this method, which makes use of the changes in the gain constant and the time constant, is restricted in practice because of certain undesirable effects that changes in these constants have on other characteristics.

In contrast with the first method, insertion of a compensating network is the method with the widest application in practice. This method is to insert a particular network, used for a compensation of the transient characteristics, into the system in order to improve the transient characteristics. Such a network is called a compensating network. We classify the compensation methods into two

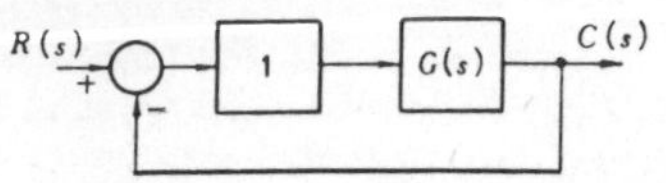

1 - *compensating network*
Fig. 6.5 Series compensation

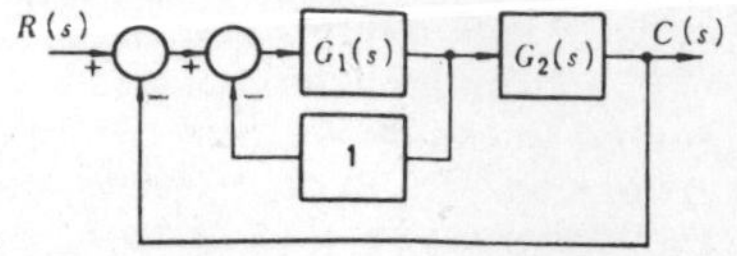

1 - *compensating network*
Fig. 6.6 Parallel compensation

types according to the method of insertion. They are (i) series (or cascade) compensation and (ii) parallel (or feedback) compensation. Sometimes both are used simultaneously.

As shown by the block diagram in Fig. 6.5, in series compensation the compensating network is connected to the primary closed loop in series (or in cascade). In parallel compensation, the compensating network is connected to the primary closed loop in parallel (or in feedback), as shown in Fig. 6.6. In either method of compensation, it is most effective to insert the compensating network at a place where the power level is low. In particular, it is most effective to insert the compensating network immediately before an amplifier. In general, series compensation is suitable for an automatic control system whose amplifier is an electronic tube amplifier, and parallel compensation is suitable for an automatic control system whose amplifier requires some power for the application of the input. For example, parallel compensation is suitable for a system with a magnetic or rotary amplifier. In parallel compensation, the compensating network should be connected in such a way that the input to the compensating network has a higher power level than that of the point to which the output of the compensating network is applied. When the compensating network is connected in the reverse direction, we need to use an amplifier in the compensating network itself, and hence the compensation may then not always be practical.

6.5. VARIOUS COMPENSATING NETWORKS AND THEIR CHARACTERISTICS

Although many types of compensating networks exist, practically usable ones are limited to certain types because of other factors. The compensation networks in each category (series and parallel) can be further classified according to the number of degrees of freedom they have in changing the values of the constants. In general, they are classified according to whether they have two, or more than three degrees of freedom. Tables 6.4 and 6.5 show compensating networks that are suitable for series compensation. Compensating networks with two and three degrees of freedom are shown in Table 6.4 and Table 6.5 respectively. Tables 6.6 and 6.7 show the compensating networks that are suitable for parallel compensation. These have respectively two and three degrees of freedom.

Each table gives examples of compensating networks, their transfer functions, the approximate wave forms of their frequency responses, and their pole-zero configurations. These are all typical compensating networks. However, other types of compensating network give the same compensating results inasmuch as their transfer functions are the same as those above. The letter *s* in the first column of these tables indicates series compensation and the letter *P* indicates parallel compensation. The first number following the *S* or *p* denotes the number of degrees of freedom. The second number is merely for numbering the networks.

We shall now briefly discuss the compensation characteristics and some precautions to be taken in the use of each of the compensating networks shown in Tables 6.4-6.7. The networks shown in Tables 6.4 and 6.5 are all series compensating networks. Their chief characteristic is that the amplifiers contained in them all have non-zero amplification factors. Unless the gain constant of the compensating network is 1, insertion of the network into the primary closed-loop will obviously change the original steady-state characteristics. Specifically, it changes the magnitude of the steady-state error in the case of a proportional control system, and the steady-state error corresponding to a variation of the reference input at a constant rate in the case of an integral control system. The networks S2-1 and S2-2 in Table 6.4 are mainly used as controllers of process control systems. Non-electrical networks whose transfer functions are equal to those of the above two networks are also frequently used as controllers of process control systems. These controllers are usually not considered as compensating networks. However, these are connected to the primary closed-loop, and they perform amplification and series compensation. Thus, we may treat them as series compensating networks. The time constants of these networks are generally much larger than those of the usual type of series compensating networks. The network S2-1 is called a proportional-plus-derivative control compensator or a PD network; it is often used as a controller of an industrial control system. Insertion of this network is quite useful for advancing the phase angle of the open-loop transfer function in the high frequency range so that the system may be stabilised and that the speed of the response may be increased. The network S2-2 is called a porportional-plus-integral control system as a PI network; it is also often used as a controller of an industrial system. If this network is connected to the primary closed-loop in series, the whole system becomes an integral network. The open-loop amplification can be made ∞ by the insertion; hence the steady-state error, that is, the offset, can be made 0. Insertion of this network usually causes a phase lag in the system in the low frequency range. Therefore, it has the disadvantage of decreasing the speed of the transient response.

The network S2-3 is called a lead network. Insertion of this network into the closed-loop of a system causes a phase lead to the system in the high frequency band. This property is quite useful for increasing the response speed of the system, but the lead network acts as a high pass filter simultaneously. Thus, the insertion also increases the ripple or other noise level in the high frequency band, and it causes saturation of the amplifiers in the original system, thus disabling them. This should be taken into consideration when one uses this network as a compensating network. The network S2-4 is usually called a lag-network; insertion of this network causes an increase in the damping in the high-frequency band. This property is used in the compensation. Such a compensating network is effective for improving the wave form of the transient response. However, it causes a decrease in the response speed. This should be taken into consideration when a lag network is used as a compensating network.

The network S2-5 is another type of lead network. Its compensating characteristics are quite similar to those of S2-3. Only the compensating range of this network is different from that of S2-3. However, the gain constant of this network is not 1, and hence insertion of this network may upset the steady-state performance of the system.

Table 6.5 shows typical series compensating networks with three degrees of freedom.

The network S3-1 is called a lead-lag network. This network can achieve not only the compensation effect of the lag network S2-4 but also that of the lead network S2-5. Since the gain constant of this network is always 1, there is no danger in deteriorating the steady-state characteristics of the original system. Moreover, it does not have the disadvantage of increasing ripple or other noise in the high-frequency band, since it, unlike the lead network S2-3, has no high-pass filtering characteristics. Thus, this lead-lag network is one of the most effective compensating networks.

The network S3-2 is called a proportional-plus-integral-plus-derivative network; it is used as a controller of a process control system. It is also called a three-term controller. Compensation by this network yields a zero steady-state error of the system just as the PI compensating network does, and it increases the response speed of the system. This three-term controller has a wide compensating range, and its compensating characteristics are similar to those of S3-1.

The networks S3-3 and S3-4 are respectively a lead and a lag network each with three degrees of freedom. These networks are obtained by adding a gain constant k to the lead network S2-3, with two degrees of freedom, and to the lag network S2-4, with two degrees of freedom. The value of the gain constant k can be chosen freely. The network S3-3 is a convenient compensating network since we can change other component waves of the transient response than the dominant one if necessary. The network S3-4 is effective for improving the steady-state characteristics by giving an appropriately large value to k.

Tables 6.6 and 6.7 show various parallel compensating networks. In general, the gain constants of parallel compensating networks are zero. If not, the parallel compensation by these networks exerts considerable influence on the steady-state characteristics of the system. As mentioned before, when we construct the minor loop for parallel compensation, the parallel compensating network should be connected in such a way that the signal is transmitted through the network from the higher power-level point to the lower power-level point. This condition naturally determines where the compensating should be inserted. Table 6.6 shows the most common parallel compensating network with two degrees of freedom.

The network P2-1.1 is called a differentiating network; it is widely used as a parallel compensating network. It gives various compensating effects, depending on where it is inserted and the method of insertion. If this network is used as a negative feedback compensating network, it is effective for improving the wave form of the response but it decreases the speed of the response. If it is used as a positive feedback compensating element, it may be effective for increasing the response speed.

The networks P2-1.2 and P2-1.3 are often called damping transformers. Their transfer functions have the same form as does the network P2-1.1; also, their compensating characteristics are almost the same as those of P2-1.1. These networks are sometimes preferred to P2-1.1 because of other requirements imposed on the system to be designed. The network P2-1.3 is a suitable compensating network for an automatic control system of the type in which the reference input and the output of the system are electric currents and a magnetic amplifier or a rotary amplifier whose input is also an electric current is used as an element of the system.

The input and the output of the network P2-1.2 are voltages. This network is of almost the same type as P2-1.1. However, P2-1.2 is more convenient for practical use, since the primary and secondary coils are isolated.

Table 6.7 shows parallel compensating networks with three degrees of freedom. The network P3-1 is a lead-lag network that is frequently used as a parallel compensating element. This network has a wide compensating range, and it is effective for reducing the ripple in the minor loop. The network P3-2 has the same transfer function as does P3-1, but the input and the output of this network are electric currents.

EXERCISE PROBLEMS

1. Given the open-loop transfer function

$$\frac{5}{s(1+0.2\,s)\,(1+0.05\,s)}$$

construct the Bode diagram and find the phase margin ϕ_m. Find the resonant value M_p from the vector locus. Then read the phase margin corresponding to M_p and find the ratio of this phase margin to the phase margin ϕ_m found from the Bode diagram.

2. Given the open-loop transfer function

$$\frac{K}{s(1+0.5s)\,(1+0.1\,s)}$$

construct the root locus and determine the value of K so that the damping coefficient γ_0 will be 0.5. Construct the Bode diagram of the above open-loop transfer function with the determined value of K. Then find the phase margin from the Bode diagram and find the ratio of this phase margin to the phase margin shown in Table 6.1.

TABLE 6.4 SERIES COMPENSATING NETWORKS WITH TWO DEGREES OF FREEDOM

network number	compensating network	compensation transfer function and values of free parameters.	frequency response	pole-zero configuration
S2-1 (*P D* network)	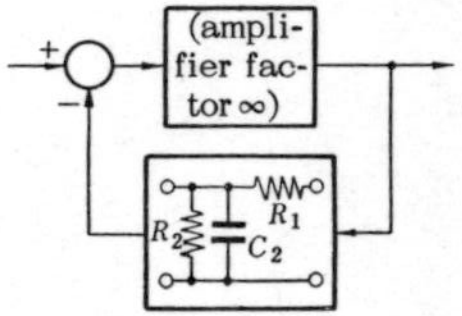	$F_c(s)=k(1+s/\omega_s)$ $\begin{cases} k=\dfrac{R_1}{R_2}+1 \\ \omega_s=\dfrac{1}{C_2}\left(\dfrac{1}{R_1}+\dfrac{1}{R_2}\right) \end{cases}$	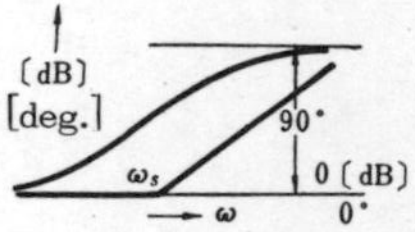	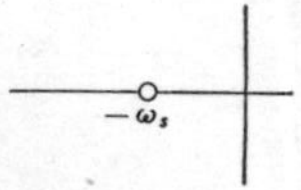
S2-2 (*P I* network)	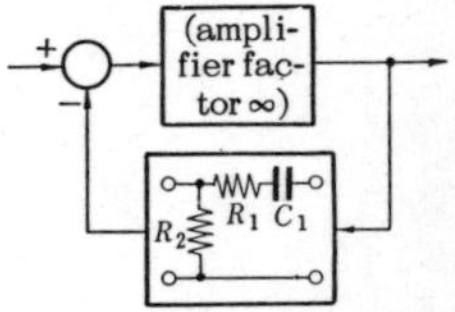	$F_c(s)=k(1+\omega_s/s)$ $\begin{cases} k=\dfrac{R_1}{R_2}+1 \\ \omega_s=\dfrac{1}{C_1(R_1+R_2)} \end{cases}$	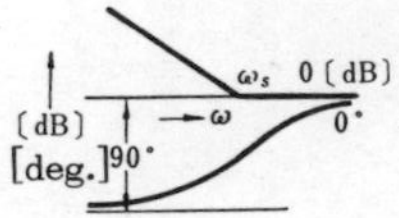	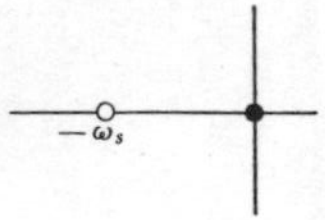
S2-3 (lead network)	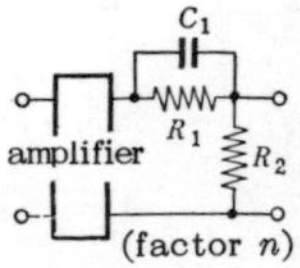	$F_c(s)=\dfrac{1+s/\omega_s}{1+s/n\omega_s}$ $\begin{cases} n=\dfrac{R_1}{R_2}+1 \\ \omega_s=\dfrac{1}{C_1R_1} \end{cases}$	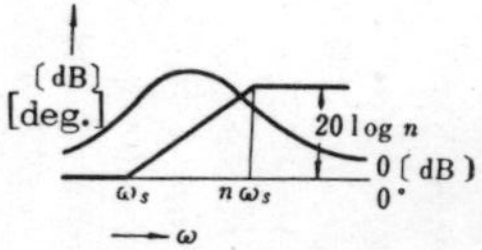	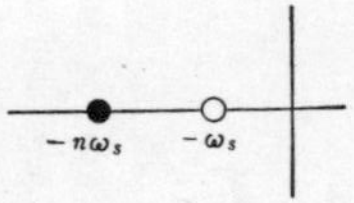

TABLE 6.4 (cont.)

network number	compensating network	compensation transfer function and values of free parameters.	frequency response	pole-zero configuration
S2-4 (lag network)	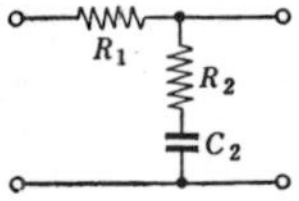	$F_c(s)=\frac{1+s/\omega_s}{1+sn/\omega_s}$ $\begin{cases} n=\frac{R_1}{R_2}+1 \\ \omega_s=\frac{1}{C_2R_2} \end{cases}$	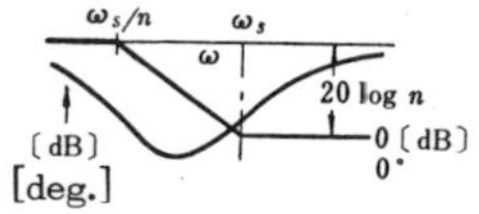	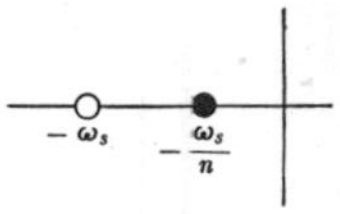
S2-5 (lead network)	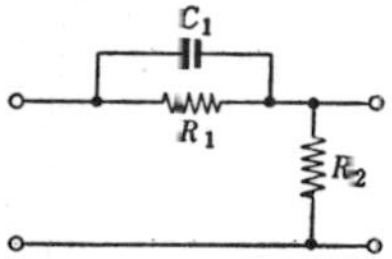	$F_c(s)=\frac{1}{n}\left(\frac{1+s/\omega_s}{1+s/n\omega_s}\right)$ $\begin{cases} n=\frac{R_1}{R_2}+1 \\ \omega_s=\frac{1}{C_1R_1} \end{cases}$	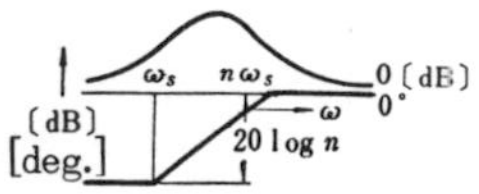	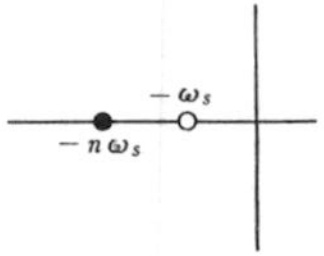
S2-6 (*PID* network)	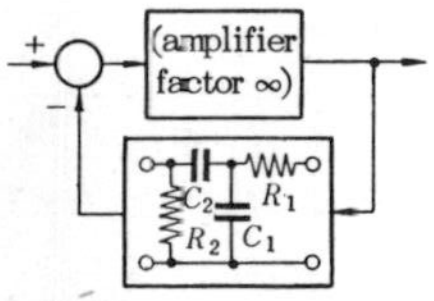	$F_c(s)=1+\frac{s}{\omega_{s1}}+\frac{\omega_{s2}}{s}$ $\begin{cases} \omega_{s1}=\frac{1}{C_1R_1} \\ \omega_{s2}=\frac{1}{C_2R_2} \end{cases}$ where $C_1 \gg C_2$	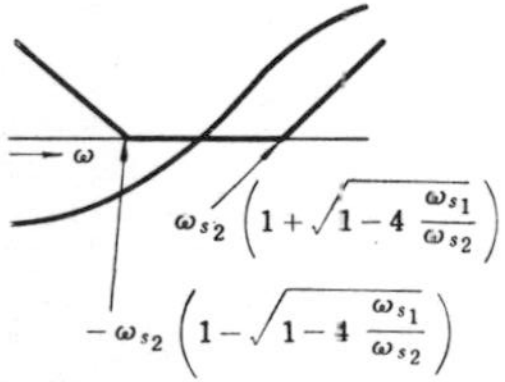	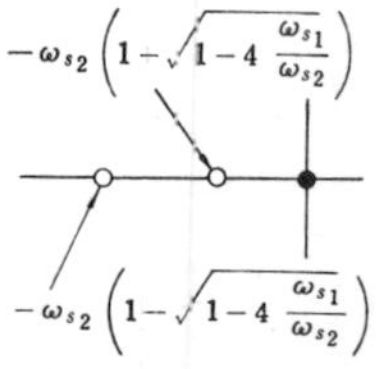

TABLE 6.5 SERIES COMPENSATING NETWORKS WITH THREE DEGREES OF FREEDOM

network number	compensating network	compensation transfer function and values of free parameters.	frequency response	(●: pole) (○: zero)
S3-1 (lead-lag network)	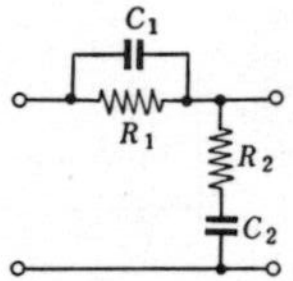	$F(s)=\dfrac{\left(1+\dfrac{s}{\omega_{s1}}\right)\left(1+\dfrac{s}{\omega_{s2}}\right)}{\left(1+\dfrac{s}{n\omega_{s1}}\right)\left(1+\dfrac{sn}{\omega_{s2}}\right)}$ $\omega_{s_1}=\dfrac{1}{C_1R_1}$ $\omega_{s_2}=\dfrac{1}{C_2R_2}$ $(n-1)\left(\dfrac{1}{\omega_{s_2}}-\dfrac{1}{n\omega_{s_2}}\right)=C_2R_1$ $n>1$ where $n\omega_{s_1}>\omega_{s_2}$	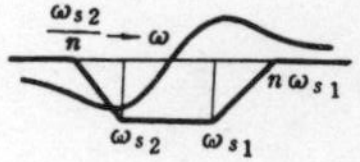	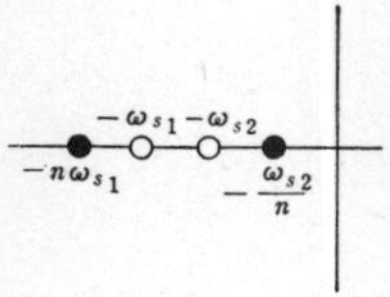
S3-2 (*PID* network)	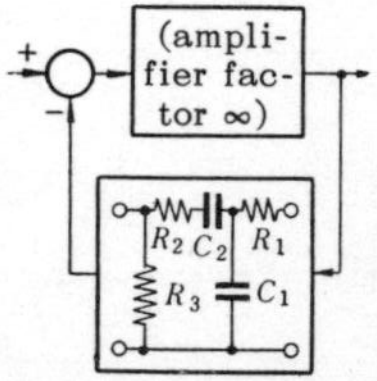	$F_c(s)=k\left(1+\dfrac{s}{\omega_{s_1}}+\dfrac{\omega_{s_2}}{s}\right)$ $\omega_{s_1}=\dfrac{1}{C_1R_1}$ $\omega_{s_2}=\dfrac{1}{C_2(R_2+R_3)}$ $k=\dfrac{R_2}{R_3}+1$ where $C_1\gg C_2$	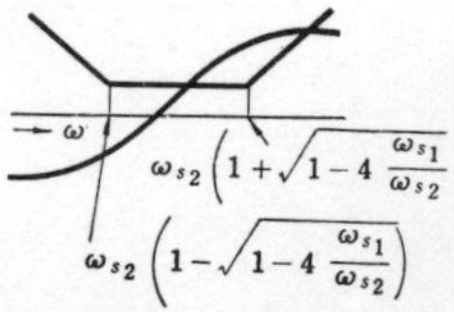	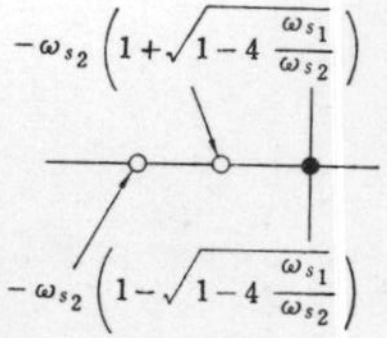

N

TABLE 6.5 (cont.)

network number	compensating network	compensation transfer function and values of free parameters.	frequency response	(●: pole) (○: zero)
S3-3 (lead network)	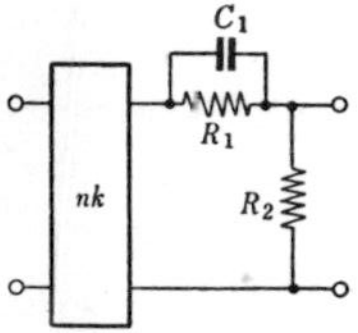 $n=\frac{R_1+R_2}{R_2}$	$F_c(s)=k\left(\frac{1+\frac{s}{\omega_s}}{1+\frac{s}{n\omega_s}}\right)$ $\omega_s=\frac{1}{C_1R_1}$ $n=\frac{R_1}{R_2}+1$ k: amplifaction factor	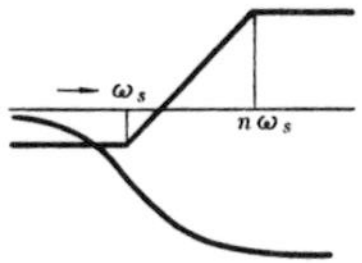	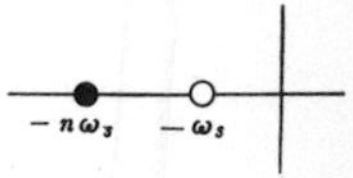
S3-4 (lag network)	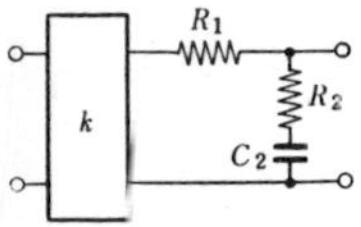	$F_c(s)=k\left(\frac{1+\frac{s}{\omega_s}}{1+\frac{sn}{\omega_s}}\right)$ $\omega_s=\frac{1}{C_2R_2}$ $n=\frac{R_1}{R_2}+1$ k: amplification factor	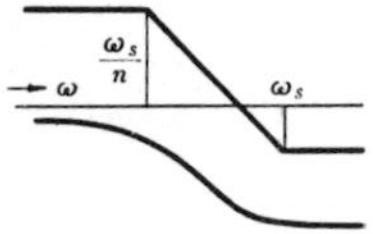	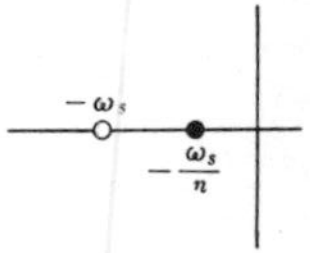

TABLE 6.6 PARALLEL COMPENSATING NETWORKS WITH TWO DEGREES OF FREEDOM

network number		compensating network	compensation transfer function and values of free parameters.	frequency response	pole-zero configuration
P2-1 (differential networks)	P 2-1·1	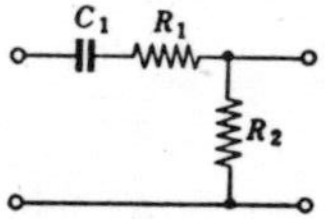 CR network	$\dfrac{n\frac{s}{\omega_s}}{1+\frac{s}{\omega_s}}$ $n=\dfrac{R_2}{R_1+R_2}$ $\omega_s=\dfrac{1}{C_1(R_1+R_2)}$	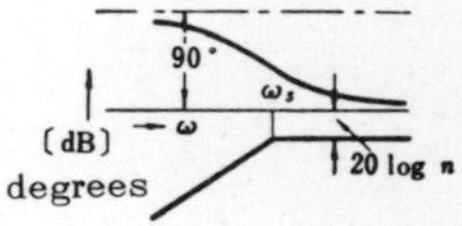	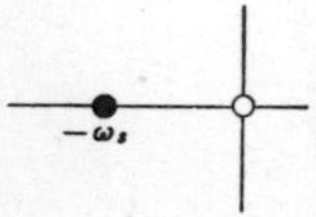
	P 2-1·2	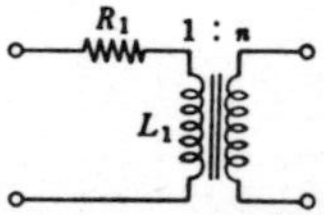 damping transformer	$\dfrac{n\frac{s}{\omega_s}}{1+\frac{s}{\omega_s}}$ n: turns ratio $\omega_s=\dfrac{R_1}{L_1}$	as above	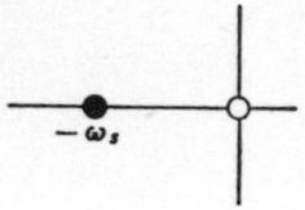
	P 2-1·3	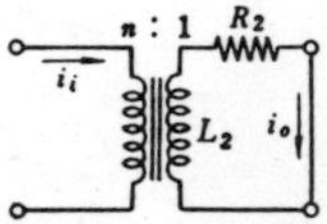 damping transformer	$\dfrac{n\frac{s}{\omega_s}}{1+\frac{s}{\omega_s}}$ n: turns ratio $\omega_s=\dfrac{R_2}{L_2}$	as above	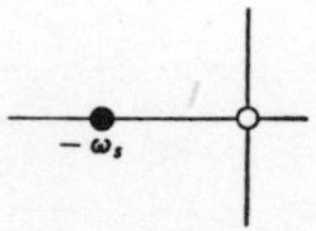

TABLE 6·7 PARALLEL COMPENSATING NETWORKS WITH THREE DEGREES OF FREEDOM

network number	compensating network	Compensation transfer function and values of free parameters	frequency response	pole-zero configuration
P3-1 (lead-lag network)	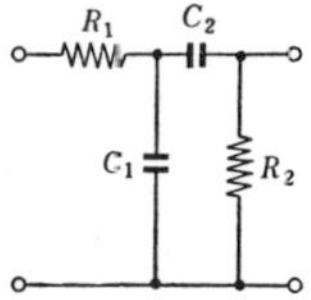	$\dfrac{sn/\omega_{s_2}}{(1+s/\omega_{s_1})(1+s/\omega_{s_2})}$ $\omega_{s1}=\dfrac{1}{nR_1C_1}$ $\omega_{s_2}=\dfrac{n}{R_2C_2}$ $\dfrac{n-1}{n}\left(\dfrac{1}{\omega_{s_1}}-\dfrac{n}{\omega_{s_2}}\right)=C_2R_1$	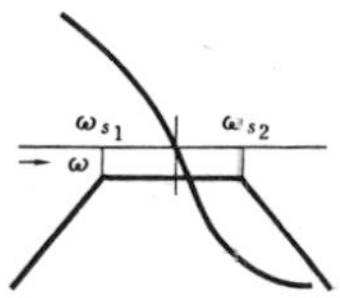	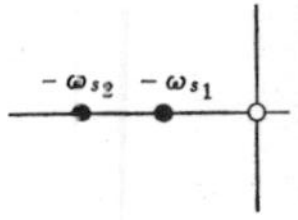
P3-2 (lead-lag network)	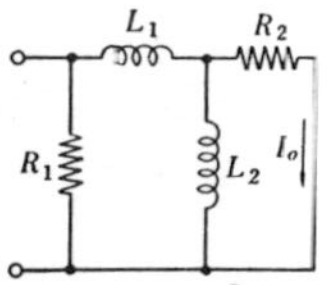	$\dfrac{sn/\omega_{s2}}{(1+s/\omega_{s_1})(1+s/\omega_{s_2})}$ $\omega_{s_1}=\dfrac{R_1}{nL_1}$ $\omega_{s_2}=\dfrac{nR_2}{L_2}$ $\dfrac{n-1}{n}\left(\dfrac{1}{\omega_{s_1}}-\dfrac{n}{\omega_{s_2}}\right)=\dfrac{L_2}{R_1}$	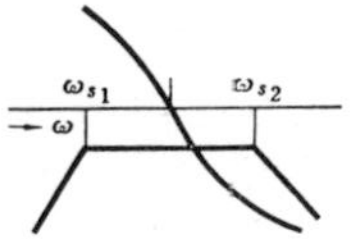	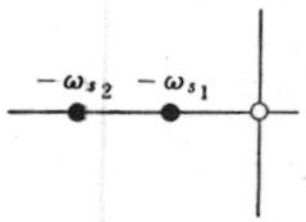

3. Let the allowable error be 2 per cent and let the settling time be 1 sec. Find the approximate value of the damped angular frequency ω_0, assuming that the damping coefficient γ_0 is 0.4.
4. Consider an automatic regulating system whose block diagram is as shown below. The numerical values and the A in the blocks are amplification factors of the elements. The load variation is assumed to be the only disturbance. Find the range of values of A for which the variation in the controlled variable corresponding to 100 per cent load variation is less than 0.5 per cent.

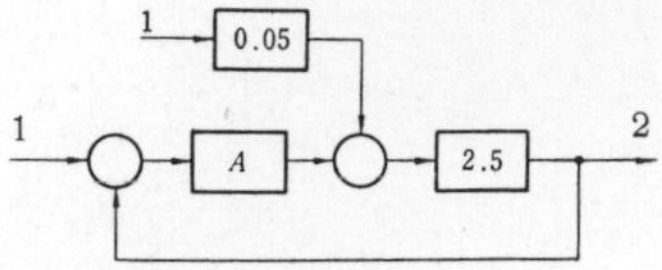

1 - *constant reference input*; 2 - *controlled variable*

5. The diagram below shows an automatic speed regulator for a hydroturbine in a power plant. Suppose that the characteristics of the elements of the revolution regulator are as follows:
(i) If the load of the hydro turbine changes from 0 to the full load when the manipulating piston is in a fixed position, then the rate of rotation of the hydroturbine decreases by 40 per cent.
(ii) If the rate of rotation N of the hydroturbine varies by 1 per cent, then the left end of the floating lever is displaced 1 cm.
(iii) If the manipulating piston is displaced downward by 10 cm when the load is fixed, then the rate of rotation of the hydroturbine varies by 20 per cent and the lever is displaced by 1 cm.
(iv) The floating lever has the structure shown in the diagram.
Find the length l [cm] for which the variation in the rate of rotation is 1 per cent.

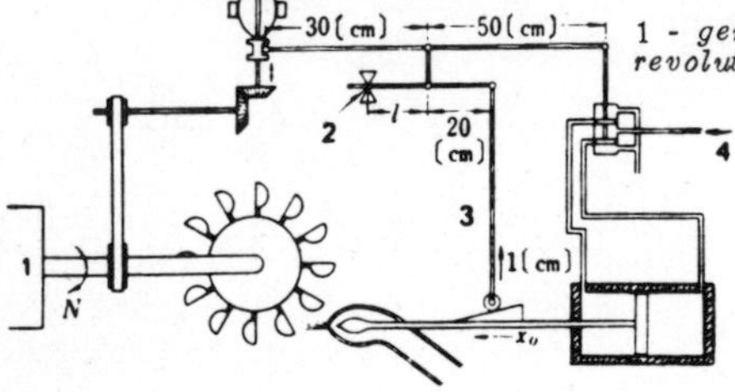

1 - *generator*; 2 - *fulcrum for setting the revolution variation rate*; 3 - *lever* 4 - *compressed oil*

6. The diagram below shows an automatic voltage regulator for a magnetic amplifier. We assume that the open-loop amplification factor is so large that it may be regarded as ∞. Let i_e be the load current and i_d the current fed back to the controlling coil. Determine the ratio of i_e to i_d such that the voltage variation ratio corresponding to 100 per cent load variation will be η per cent. Here, i_r is the reference input current, i_e is the feedback current, and i_0 is the full load current of the generator. We also assume that the impedance of the controlling coil of the magnetic

amplifier is sufficiently small. Suppose that the rated voltage of the generator is equal to the output voltage with no load and that it is 110 [v]. We know that the full load current is 120 [A] when i_e = 20 [mA]. Determine i_e [A] so that the voltage variation ratio is 2 per cent.

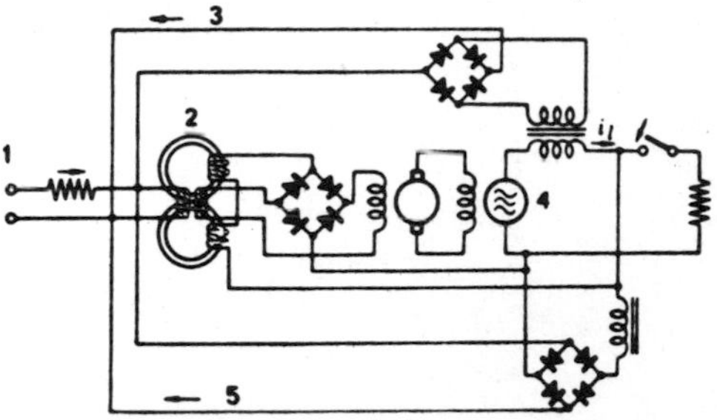

1 - *constant current* i_r
2 - *magnetic amplifier*
3 - *a d.c.* i_d, *proportional to the load current*; 4 - *a.c. generator*; 5 - *a d.c.* i_e, *proportional to the load current*

7. The diagram shows a device by which we can obtain an output air-pressure P_0 proportional to the input displacement x_i of the lever end. We assume that the length of the bellows varies in proportion to the air pressure in the bellows. The lever length is divided as shown in the diagram. Give the ratio K of P_0 to x_i, determine the ratio of the air pressure in the bellows to the variation in length of the bellows. Construct the block diagram of the device also.

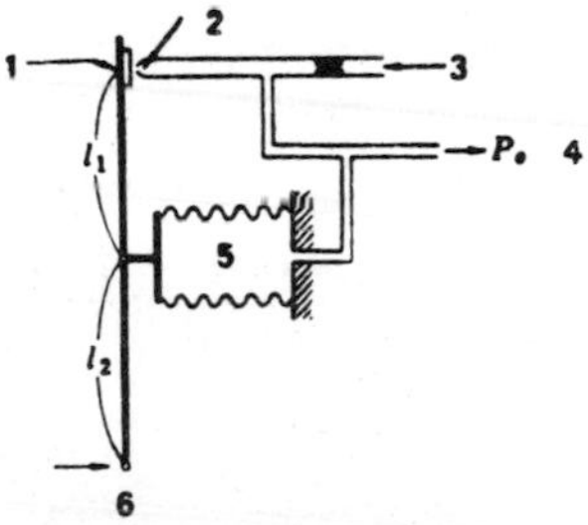

1 - *flapper*; 2 - *nozzle*; 3 - *air supply*
4 - *output air pressure* P_0; 5 - *bellows*
6 - *input displacement* x_i

8. Consider the apparatus shown in the diagram below. The air-flow rate at the throttle 0_z is proportional to the difference between the pressure on one side of the throttle and that on the other side. Find the transfer function when the displacement x_i is the input signal and the pressure P_0 is the output signal.

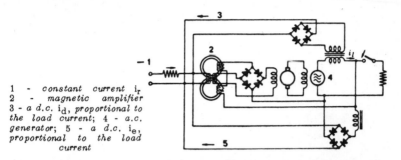

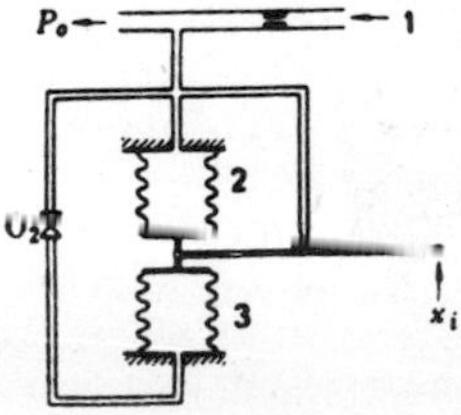

1 - *air supply*; 2 - *bellows*; 3 - *bellows*

9. The diagram below shows a mechanical compensating network. Find the transfer function when the displacement x_i is the input and the displacement x_o is the output. Here, k_1 and k_2 are the compliances of the springs and D_2 is the damping coefficient of the dashpot. The damping coefficient is defined as the ratio of the force exerted on the piston to the velocity of the piston.

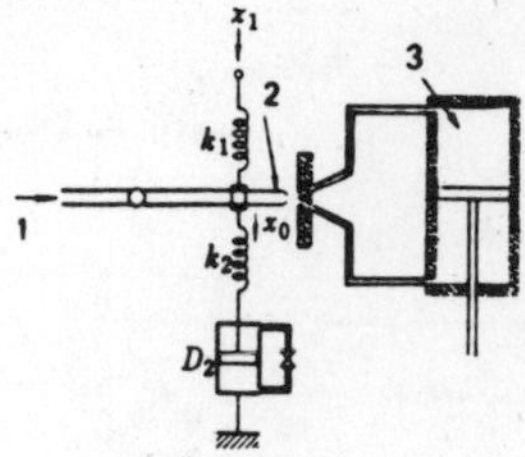

1 - *oil under pressure*; 2 - *nozzle*; 3 - *oil-pressure motor*

10. We wish to construct a mechanical compensating network whose transfer function is equal to that of the lead network S2-5 and whose structure is similar to that of the mechanical compensating network shown in problem (9). Determine the structure of the desired mechanical compensating network.

11. Consider the system shown in the diagram below. Find the transfer function of the system when the input signal is x_i and the output signal x_o. Here, we assume that the amplification factor x_o / x_p of the unit consisting of the pilot valve and the oil-pressure motor is sufficiently large and that the response of the unit is extremely rapid.

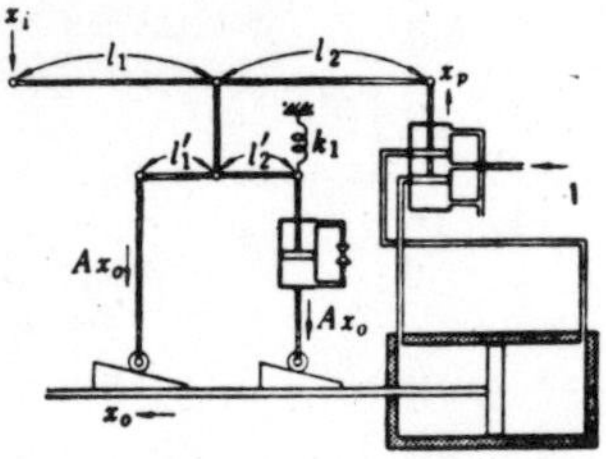

1 - *oil under pressure*

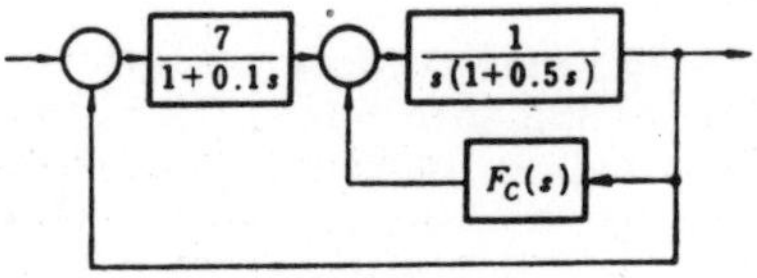

(a)

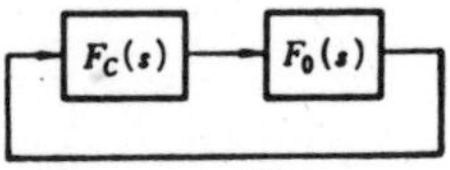

(b)

12. Consider the parallel compensation shown in diagram (a). Compute $F_c(s)$ when we regard the parallel compensation as the series compensating network shown in diagram (b).

7

Frequency Response Method

7.1 DETERMINATION OF COMPENSATING NETWORK CONSTANTS BY THE FREQUENCY RESPONSE METHOD

When we use a compensating network to improve the transient characteristics to be synthesised, we need to determine the constants of the compensating network properly so that the transient characteristics will meet the specifications. As mentioned before, there are two methods of determining these constants: the frequency response method and the root configuration method.

In this chapter, we shall discuss in detail the technique of determining a required gain constant of the system or the constants of a compensating network by using the frequency response method. The necessary properties of the frequency response for this technique have been already treated in Chapter IV. In that chapter, we introduced three kinds of representation for a frequency response: (i) vector locus (Nyquist diagram); (ii) logarithmic vector locus; (iii) Bode diagram. Accordingly, there are three different methods of designing a compensating network. However, we may classify the methods into two main kinds, the vector locus method and the Bode diagram method, since the vector locus and the logarithmic vector locus are essentially the same except that different scales are used. When a compensating network is designed by use of the vector locus or the logarithmic vector locus, the resonant value M_p and the resonant angular frequency ω_r are used to specify the transient response waveform and the transient response velocity respectively. When the Bode diagram method is employed, the phase margin ϕ_m and the cross-over angular frequency ω_c are used to specify the above characteristics of the transient response. In practice, it is difficult to synthesise a transient response that satisfies simultaneously both the specified resonant value and the specified resonant angular frequency. Therefore, we often specify only the waveform of the transient response and not the velocity of the transient response. We sometimes have to use a compensator and a gain change together to synthesise the specified transient response. This method must be used with caution since it may upset the steady-state characteristics.

Computation by the vector locus or logarithmic vector locus method is highly accurate but it involves a more complicated synthesis procedure. On the other hand, the Bode diagram method is convenient for finding approximate values of the constants, but this method lacks a high degree of accuracy. Therefore, from a practical viewpoint, it is advisable to carry out a rough synthesis by the Bode diagram method first and then check by the vector locus method whether the synthesised transient characteristics really have the specified resonant value M_p and the specified resonant angular frequency ω_n. If this check indicates that a correction is necessary in the synthesis, it may be made by the same procedure which consists of the following steps.

(a) Construction of Bode diagram. Plot the Bode diagram of the given open-loop transfer function of the automatic control system to be designed.

(b) Selection of compensating network. Read the cross-over angular frequency ω_c and the phase margin ϕ_m from the plotted Bode diagram, and find the required compensation of the phase angle and the gain by comparing the resonant value M_p and the resonant angular frequency ω_r that are read from the Bode diagram with the specified values. Then, select a suitable compensating method and a suitable compensating network on the basis of the required compensation, taking into consideration the various factors related to the compensation.

(c) Selection of suitable values for the free parameters contained in the compensating transfer function. Compare the frequency response of the selected compensating network with that of the given open-loop transfer function of the automatic control system to be designed, and select suitable values for the free parameters contained in the compensating transfer function, so that the specified transient characteristics will be realised.

(d) Examination of transient characteristics. Plot the Bode diagram of the automatic control system with the selected compensating network added to it, read the values of the phase margin and the cross-over angular frequency from the Bode diagram, and check whether these values coincide with the specified values.

(e) Correction of the selected values of the free parameters. If the values of the phase margin and the cross-over angular frequency read from the Bode diagram differ greatly from the specified values, correct the selected values of the free parameters and repeat step (d) for the corrected values. Repeat the correction until the values of the phase margin and the cross-over angular frequency coincide with the specified values.

(f) Examination of synthesis. If a very high accuracy is required in the synthesis of the transient response, plot the vector locus or the logarithmic vector locus of the automatic control system designed in steps (a)-(e), draw the M_p - circle, and note whether the resonant value M_p and the resonant angular frequency ω_r have the specified values. If these differ greatly, correct the selected values of the free parameters.

(g) Analysis of the synthesised transient response. If it is required to know the transient response of the designed system with a high degree of accuracy, carry out the analysis by manual calculation or use a computer.

(h) Determination of the constants of the compensating network. Compute the constants of the adopted compensating network from the finally determined values of the free parameters.

The above procedure seems quite complicated, but it is really not so cumbersome if the student acquires some experience. Often steps (a)-(d) are sufficient for ordinary synthesis of the transient characteristics unless a high degree of accuracy is required by the given specifications.

7.2. EXAMPLE I (SYNTHESIS USING CHANGE OF GAIN CONSTANT AND SERIES COMPENSATION BY A LAG NETWORK)

Suppose that the open-loop transfer function of an automatic control system is given by

$$F_0(s)=\frac{5}{s(1+0.5\,s)(1+0.1\,s)} \tag{7.1}$$

Suppose (1) that the waveform of the transient response is given by $M_p = 1.3$ (where M_p is the resonant value); (2) that the velocity of the transient response is specified by the requirement that the resonant angular frequency ω_r be larger than 0.5 [rad/sec]; and (3) that the gain constant is no less than the given value. Let us synthesise the transient characteristics with this specification.

(a) Construction of the Bode diagram. We plot the Bode diagram of the given open-loop transfer function (7.1) and obtain the Bode diagram shown in Fig. 7.1*.

(b) Selection of compensating network. The Bode diagram in Fig. 7.1 shows that the cross-over angular frequency is 3.0 [rad/sec] and that the phase margin is 17°. On the other hand, it is specified that $M_p = 1.3$ and that the equivalent phase margin ϕ_m is 45° (see Fig. 6.1). Thus, the phase margin of the given transfer function is less than the specified phase margin and must be improved by some means. According to the Bode diagram, the angular frequency ω at which the phase margin is 45° is $\omega = 1.5$ [rad/sec] and the gain at $\omega = 1.5$ [rad/sec] is 9 [dB]. Therefore, if we reduce the gain constant by 9 [dB], that is, if we reduce the gain constant by a factor of 1/2.82, the cross-over angular frequency becomes 1.5 [rad/sec] and the phase margin becomes 45°, as specified. Consequently, if the other characteristics of the transient response meet the specifications, the synthesis will be complete. The open-loop transfer function with the reduced gain constant is

$$F_1(s)=\frac{5/2.82}{s(1+0.5\,s)(1+0.1\,s)} \tag{7.2}$$

Since decrease in the gain constant upsets the steady-state characteristics, we need to improve the transient characteristics further,

*The most important parts of a Bode diagram are the gain curve and the phase curve in the vicinity of the cross-over angular frequency. Thus, to construct a good Bode diagram, the following procedure is recommended: construct approximations of the gain curve and the phase curve by plotting their asymptotes. Then refine these approximate curves to greater accuracy by using the curves in 4.14 and 1.16.

keeping or improving the steady-state characteristics of the open-loop transfer function $F_1(s)$ given by equation (7.2). To do this, we have to use a compensator. Since the given specification allows a somewhat lower cross-over angular frequency than that of the given transfer function (7.1), which is 3.0 [rad/sec], we select a lag network* (S2-4 in Table 6.4) for the compensating network. (c), (d), (e). Selection of the values for the free parameters contained in the compensating transfer function, examination of the

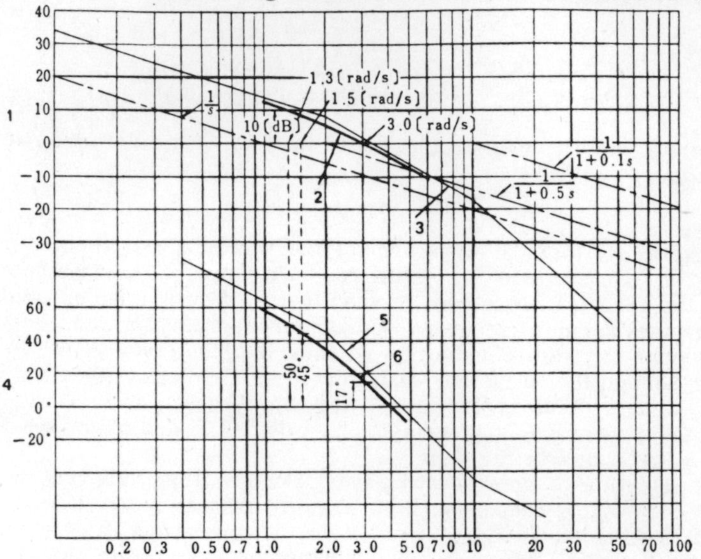

1 - *gain* [dB]; 2 - *gain curve*; 3 - *asymptote of gain curve*; 4 - *phase margin* [*degrees*]; 5 - *asymptote of the phase curve*; 6 - *phase curve*

Fig. 7.1 Bode diagram of the transfer function

$$F(s) = \frac{5}{s(1 + 0.5s)(1 + 0.1s)}$$

synthesised transient characteristics, and correction of the selected values of the free parameters. As stated before, to let the phase margin be 45° (which is equivalent to $M_p = 1.3$), it is sufficient to reduce the gain by 9 [dB] at $\omega = 1.5$ [rad/sec]. The compensating transfer function $F(c)$ (that is, the transfer function of the lag network) is

$$F_c(s) = \frac{1+\dfrac{s}{\omega_s}}{1+\dfrac{sn}{\omega_s}} \tag{7.3}$$

If we choose the value of n so that

$$9\ [\text{dB}] = 20 \log n \tag{7.4}$$

*If we are required to increase the response velocity, we should use a lead network (S2-3 in Table 6.4) or a lead-lag network (S3-1 in Table 6.5) as the compensating network.

$$n=10^{0.45}=2.82 \tag{7.5}$$

we shall obtain an attenuation of 9 [dB] for a sufficiently high frequency range relative to ω_s. Accordingly, it seems proper to choose a value of ω_s so that the above high frequency range will be a neighbourhood of $\omega = 1.5$ [rad/sec.]. However, an extremely small value of ω_s is likely to make construction of the compensating network difficult. Therefore, it is quite common to use 1/10 of 1.5 [rad/sec].

The Bode diagram of the lag network with $n = 2.82$ is shown in

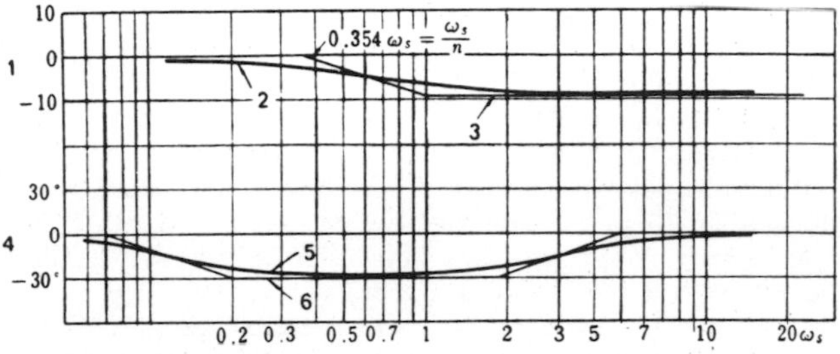

1 - *gain* [dB]; 2 - *gain curve*; 3 - *asymptote*; 4 - *phase angle* [*degrees*]; 5 - *phase curve*; 6 - *asymptote*

Fig. 7.2 Frequency response of a lag network (compensating network)

Fig. 7.2. As is clear from this Bode diagram, the damping is slightly less than 9 [dB] and the phase lag is approximately 5° at 10 ω_s. Accordingly, if we choose the value of ω_s so that 10 ω_s will be 1.5 [rad/sec], then the phase margin of the automatic control system being designed will be approximately 40° and hence will not satisfy the specification. To correct the phase margin, we read from Fig. 7.1 the angular frequency at which the phase margin of the original transfer function is 50° (i.e. 45° + 5°). Then the angular frequency is

$$\omega=1.3 \text{ [rad/s]} \tag{7.6}$$

Therefore, if we take the value of ω_s at

$$\omega_s=\frac{\omega}{10}=\frac{1.3}{10}=0.13 \text{ [rad/s]} \tag{7.7}$$

then the phase margin will be 45°, as desired. However, the required damping at the angular frequency $\omega = 1.3$ [rad/sec] becomes 10 [dB]. Thus, the value of n is determined to be

$$20\log n=10 \text{ [dB]} \tag{7.8}$$

$$n=3.2 \tag{7.9}$$

Then, the compensating transfer function becomes

$$F_c(s) = \frac{1+\dfrac{s}{\omega_s}}{1+\dfrac{sn}{\omega_s}} = \frac{1+\dfrac{s}{0.13}}{1+\dfrac{3.2\,s}{0.13}} = \frac{1+7.7\,s}{1+24.6\,s} \tag{7.10}$$

If we compensate the original open-loop transfer function in series by this compensating transfer function, we obtain

$$F(s) = \frac{5(1+7.7\,s)}{s(1+0.5\,s)(1+0.1\,s)(1+24.6\,s)} \tag{7.11}$$

The Bode diagram of this open-loop transfer function is shown in Fig. 7.3. This Bode diagram indicates that the given specification is approximately satisfied by using the series compensation with the compensating transfer function (7.10).

(f) Examination of synthesis. If we plot the vector locus of the synthesised transfer function in the previous step, we obtain the Nyquist diagram shown in Fig. 7.4. This diagram shows that the resonant value M_p = 1.3 and that the resonance angular frequency is approximately 1 [rad/sec]. Thus, the synthesis satisfies the specification with a very high accuracy.

(g) Analysis of the synthesised transient response. Fig. 7.5 (b) shows the waveform of the synthesised transient response calculated by an analogue computer. Fig. 7.5 (a) shows the transient response before compensation.

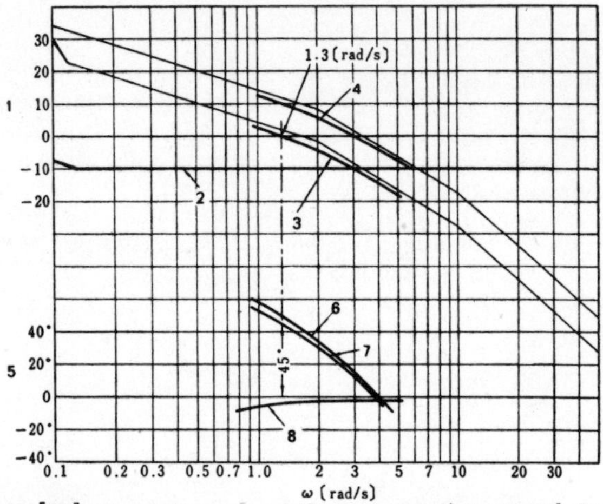

1 - *gain* [dB]; 2 - *gain curve of the compensating network (asymptote)* 3 - *gain curve after compensation*; 4 - *gain curve before compensation* 5 - *phase margin* [*degrees*]; 6 - *phase curve before compensation*; 7 - *phase curve after compensation*; 8 - *phase curve of the compensating network*

Fig. 7.3 Bode diagram of the system obtained by using a lag network with transfer function $\dfrac{1+24{\cdot}6s}{1+7{\cdot}7s}$ to compensate the system whose Bode diagram is Fig. 7.1

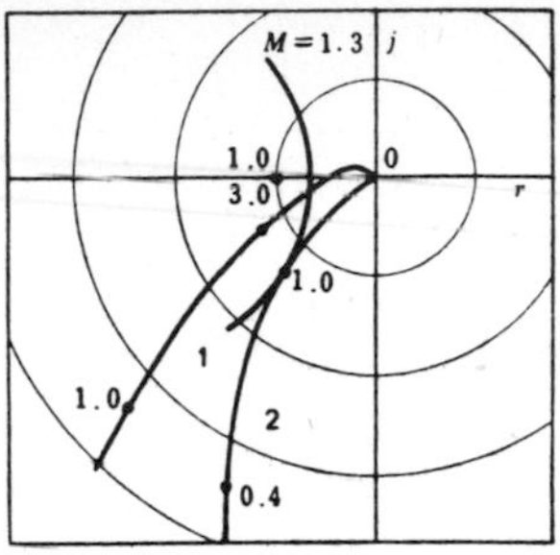

(1) *before compensation*; (2) *after compensation*

Fig. 7.4 Nyquist diagram

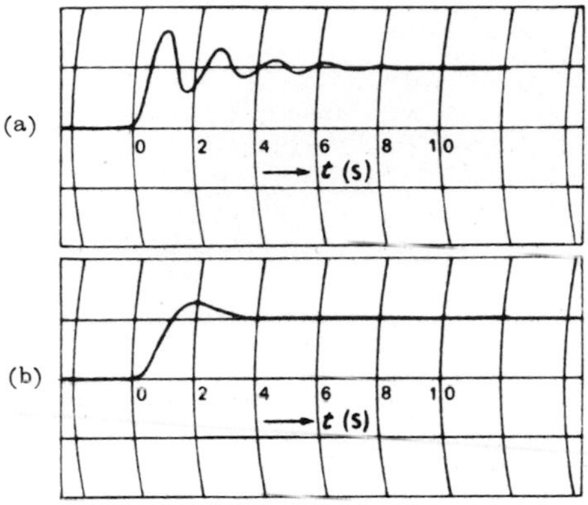

Fig. 7.5 Transient responses calculated by an analogue computor: (a) Transient response before compensation; (b) Transient response after compensation

(h) Determination of the constants of the compensating network. As shown in Table 6.4, the following relations hold between the network constants and the free parameters of the lag network S2-4:

$$n = \frac{R_1}{R_2} + 1 \tag{7.12}$$

$$\omega_s = \frac{1}{C_2 R_2} \tag{7.13}$$

We need to compute R_1, R_2, and C_2 from these equations for $n = 3.2$ and $\omega_s = 0.13$ [rad/sec]. Since there are two degrees of freedom and the number of network constants to be found is 3, we can give an arbitrary value to one of the three network constants. If we assign an arbitrary value to C_2, then

$$R_2 = \frac{1}{C_2 \omega_s} \tag{7.14}$$

$$R_1 = \frac{1}{C_2 \omega_s}(n-1) \tag{7.15}$$

Therefore, if we set $C_2 = 10$ [μF] and if we assign to ω_s and n the values given by equations (7.7) and (7.9), then the values of R_1 and R_2 are

$$R_2 = 0.77 \text{ [M}\Omega\text{]}$$

$$R_1 = 1.6 \text{ [M}\Omega\text{]}$$

Figure 7.6 shows the lag network with these constants.

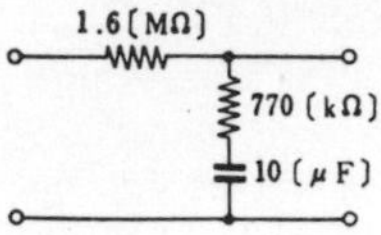

Fig. 7.6 Lag network used as compensating network

7.3 EXAMPLE II (SYNTHESIS USING SERIES COMPENSATION BY LEAD NETWORKS)

Consider the same open-loop transfer function

$$F_0(s) = \frac{5}{s(1+0.5s)(1+0.1s)} \tag{7.16}$$

as in example I and suppose that the waveform of the transient response is specified by setting $M_p = 1.3$ and that it is specified that the response velocity be as large as possible. Moreover, we assume that a slight sacrifice of the steady-state characteristics is allowed. Under these conditions, we shall synthesise the transient characteristics.

(a) Construction of Bode diagram. The given open-loop transfer function is the same as in example I, and Bode diagram is the one shown in Fig. 7.1.

(b) Selection of compensating network. Since the primary purpose is to increase the response velocity, we use series compensation by means of a lead network (S3-3 in Table 6.5) with three degrees of freedom.

(c), (d), (e) Selection of values for the free parameters contained in the compensating transfer function, examination of synthesised transient characteristics, and correction of the selected values of the free parameters. The transfer function of the compensating network is

$$F_c(s) = k\frac{1+\dfrac{s}{\omega_s}}{1+\dfrac{s}{n\omega_s}} \tag{7.17}$$

In order to achieve series compensation, we let the time constant $1/\omega_s$ in the numerator of the compensating transfer function be equal to the largest time constant in the denominator of the given open-loop transfer function (7.16):

$$\frac{1}{\omega_s}=0.5 \quad \text{or} \quad \omega_s=2 \tag{7.18}$$

The larger the value of n, the better will be the compensating effect. However, if the value of n is extremely large, it will be difficult to construct the compensating network. Consequently, it is advisable to take a value within the range 5-50. Thus, we choose

$$n=20 \tag{7.19}$$

The compensating transfer function then becomes

$$F_c(s)=k\frac{1+0.5\,s}{1+0.025\,s} \tag{7.20}$$

Therefore, the open-loop transfer function obtained by compensating the given open-loop transfer function with the compensating network whose transfer function is (7.20) is as follows:

$$=\frac{5\,k}{s(1+0.1\,s)(1+0.025\,s)} \tag{7.22}$$

$$=\frac{5\,k}{s\left(1+\frac{s}{10}\right)\left(1+\frac{s}{40}\right)} \tag{7.23}$$

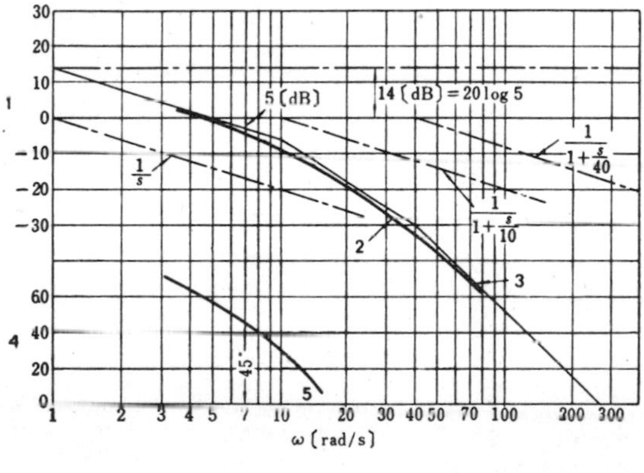

1 - *gain* [*dB*]; 2 - *gain curve*; 3 - *asymptote of gain curve*
4 - *phase margin* (*degrees*); 5 - *phase curve*

Fig. 7.7 Bode diagram of the open-loop transfer function obtained by compensating the original open-loop transfer function with a lead network

If we set $k=1$, then the Bode diagram of the compensated open-loop transfer function is as shown in Fig. 7.7. The Bode diagram indicates that the angular frequency at which the phase margin is 45° is 7 [rad/sec] and that the gain at 7 [rad/sec] is precisely -5.0 [dB]. Accordingly, if we increase the gain by 5.0 [dB], then the gain curve crosses the 0 [dB]-line at $\omega=7$ [rad/sec] and the phase margin is 45° at $\omega = 7$ [rad/sec]. Thus, it is sufficient to assign to k the value corresponding to 5.0 [dB]. This value is

$$k=1.78 \tag{7.24}$$

Then, the compensating transfer function becomes

$$F_c(s)=1 \tag{7.25}$$

and the open loop transfer function obtained by compensation is

$$F(s)=\frac{5\times 1.78(1+0.5\,s)}{s(1+0.5\,s)(1+0.1\,s)(1+0.025\,s)} \tag{7.26}$$

$$=\frac{8.9}{s(1+0.1\,s)\,(1+0.025\,s)} \tag{7.27}$$

(f) Examination of the synthesis. Plotting the vector locus of the open-loop transfer function obtain by compensation, we have the Nyquist diagram shown in Fig. 7.8. The diagram shows that the resonance value M_p is 1.3 as specified, that the resonance angular frequency is $\omega_r = 8$ [rad/sec], and that the gain constant is larger than that of the original transfer function.

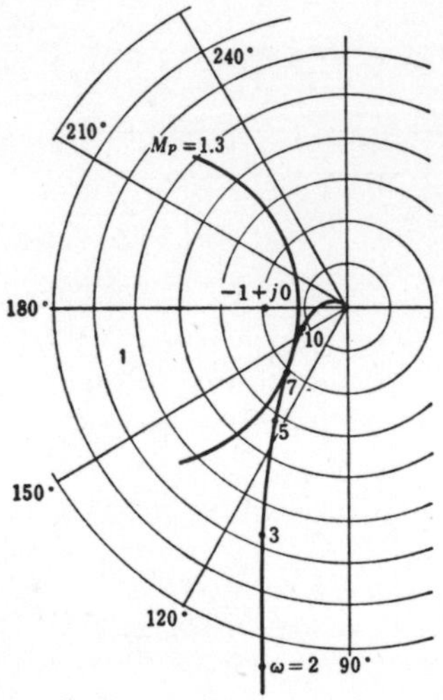

1 - *centre*: (x = 2.45, y = 0), *radius*: 1.88

Fig. 7.8 Nyquist diagram of the open-loop transfer function obtained by compensation

(g) Analysis of the synthesised transient response. The synthesised transient responses as calculated by an analogue computer are shown in Fig. 7.9 (b). Fig. 7.9 (a) shows the transient response before compensation. When we compare Fig. 7.9 (b) with Fig. 7.5 (a), which shows the transient response of the open-loop transfer function obtained by the lag compensation, we see that the transient response obtained by the lead compensation is approximately eight times as fast as that obtained by the lag compensation.

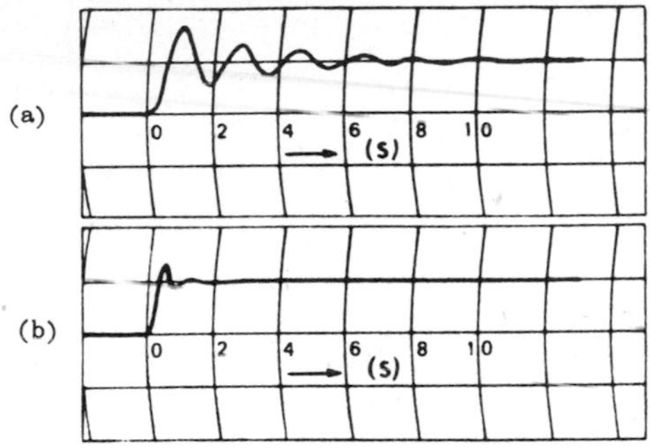

Fig. 7.9 Transient responses calculated by analogue computor: (a) transient response before compensation: (b) transient response after compensation

EXERCISE PROBLEMS

1. Given an automatic control system whose transfer function is

$$F(s)=\frac{40}{s(1+0.25\,s)\,(1+0.0625\,s)}$$

compensate this system with the lag network (S2-4), so that the resonant value will be $M_p = 1.3$.

2. Examine the result when the automatic control system of problem 1 is compensated with a lead network to satisfy the same specification.

3. Compensate an automatic control system whose transfer function is $0.25/s^2(1+0.25s)$ in such a way as to satisfy the specification that $M_p = 1.3$.

4. The diagram below shows a lead-lag network. Find the transfer function of this network and plot the Bode diagram. Discuss the optimum approach for series compensation with this lead-lag network.

8

Root Configuration

8.1. ANALYSIS AND SYNTHESIS FROM ROOT CONFIGURATION

In Chapter V, we discussed a method for finding the root configuration from the open-loop transfer function and the distribution of the zeros of a given automatic control system and also a method for finding the transient characteristics from the root configuration Specifically, we discussed the root locus method for finding the transient characteristics. Although this method can be used for the synthesis of an automatic control system, it is primarily developed for the analysis of a given automatic control system and is not a direct method for synthesis. Therefore, we again need to select suitable values for the constants of the system being designed, and to examine the synthesised transient characteristics with these constants until we obtain a proper synthesis, just as with synthesis by the frequency response method. Analysis of the characteristics of an automatic control system by the frequency response method is relatively simple. However, analysis by the root locus method is not so simple except in certain special cases. Moreover, selection of suitable values for the constants of the automatic control system that is being designed is rather difficult with the root locus method; hence, synthesis by this method naturally involves more repetition of the selection of suitable values for the constants and examination of the synthesised transient characteristics. Therefore, it is not practical to carry out the synthesis of transient characteristics by using only the root configuration or the root locus.

In this chapter, we shall develop a new method for synthesis of transient characteristics, which is based on the root configuration and root locus, and we shall discuss the procedure for synthesis by this method. More specifically, we shall show how to select a compensating network so as to let the dominant roots of the system being designed be equal to the specified values, and how to determine the constants of the compensating network by manual or graphical computations. This synthesis method is called the 'root specifying method'. This method is relatively simple and yields a relatively high accuracy in the synthesis.

8.2. THEORETICAL ASPECTS OF THE ROOT SPECIFYING METHOD

When transient characteristics are synthesised by use of the root configuration, the damping coefficient γ_0 of the dominant root and the damped angular frequency ω_0 of the dominant root are given as the specification of the waveform and velocity of the transient response respectively. That is, it is required that we design an automatic control system with a dominant root

$$(-\gamma_0+j)\omega_0=r_0 \tag{8.1}$$

Sometimes, we are required to design an automatic control with no dominant roots.

Then, different types of specifications are necessary for the different cases.

As indicated by equation (8.1), the dominant root r_0 consists of two mutually independent quantities, namely, ω_0 and γ_0. Accordingly, in order to satisfy the specified values of these two quantities, the open-loop transfer function of the system being designed must contain two mutually independent quantities x and y (real numbers) to which we can freely assign any value, as shown in Fig. 8.1. In other words, the open-loop transfer function must have two degrees of freedom. If we can determine suitable values for the two free parameters, it means that we can synthesise the specified transient characteristics.

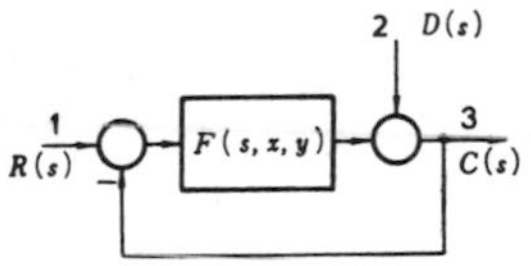

1 - *input*; 2 - *disturbance*; 3 - *output*

Fig. 8.1 Block diagram indicating that the open-loop transfer function must have two degrees of freedom to specify the dominant root

Before taking up the general use, let us consider a simple example. Suppose that the automatic control system whose block diagram is shown in Fig. 8.2* is given and that the amplification factor and resistance R can be assigned any suitable values. That is, the free parameters x and y are identical with K and R:

$$\left.\begin{array}{l} x\equiv K \\ y\equiv R \end{array}\right\} \tag{8.2}$$

The characteristic equation of the given automatic control system is

$$\frac{-K}{s^2LC+sCR+1}=1 \tag{8.3}$$

Then,

$$-K=s^2LC+sCR+1 \tag{8.4}$$

*In Fig. 8.2 the feedback transfer function is $\epsilon^{j\pi}$. This means a 180° phase lag. We recall that $\epsilon^{j\pi}=-1$

Substituting equation (8.2) into this equation, we obtain

$$-x=s^2LC+sCy+1 \tag{8.5}$$

Let the specified dominant root be

$$r_0=(-\gamma_0+j)\omega_0 \tag{8.6}$$

If we substitute the dominant root r_0 for s in equation (8.5), we obtain

$$-x=\{(-\gamma_0+j)\omega_0\}^2LC+(-\gamma_0+j)\omega_0Cy+1 \tag{8.7}$$

Therefore, in order to synthesise transient characteristics with the specified dominant root r_0, it is sufficient to find the values of x and y for which equation (8.7) holds. Since equation (8.7) has complex coefficients, it can be expanded into the two equations,

$$-x=(\gamma_0^2-1)\omega_0^2LC+1-\gamma_0\omega_0Cy \tag{8.8}$$

$$\omega_0Cy-2\gamma_0\omega_0^2LC=0 \tag{8.9}$$

by separating the real and the imaginary parts. Therefore, it is sufficient to solve these two equations for x and y. From equation (8.9), y, which is the resistance R, is calculated to be

$$y=R=2\gamma_0\omega_0L \tag{8.10}$$

Substituting this value of y into equation (8.8), we obtain the value of x, which is the amplification factor K:

$$x=K=(\gamma_0^2+1)\omega_0^2LC-1 \tag{8.11}$$

In this manner, we can easily calculate the values that $y \equiv R$ and $X \equiv K$ must have for the system given in Fig. 8.2 to have the specified characteristic root $r_0 = (-\gamma_0 + j)\omega_0$. It should be noted here that we only need to solve linear equations for the synthesis of a transient response, whereas we need to solve a quadratic equation for the analysis of a transient response. This remarkable fact often holds even for higher-order systems.

In this example, the characteristic equation of the given system is a quadratic equation, and hence the roots of the specified characteristic equation are the dominant roots. In many cases, however, the automatic control system being designed is of order 3 or higher, and hence the specified characteristic root is not necessarily the dominant root. Specifically, the residue of the specified charac-

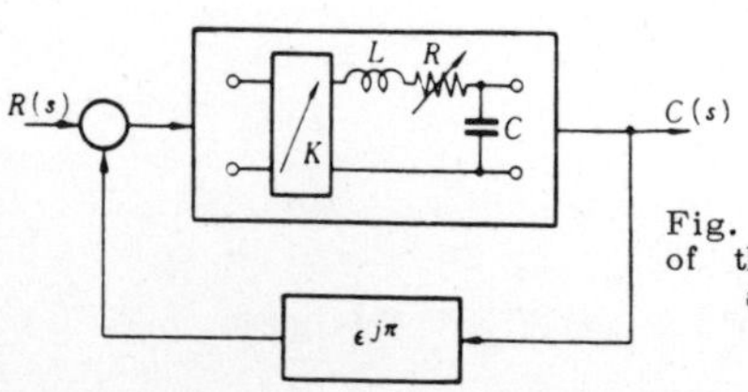

Fig. 8.2 Determination of the values of the parameters K and R for a specified characteristic root

teristic root may not satisfy the condition for the dominant root.

As mentioned before, a compensating network is customarily used to synthesise specified transient characteristics. That is, the transient characteristics are compensated only by inserting a compensating network with two or more degrees of freedom, as shown in Fig. 8.3. We shall discuss below how to apply the root specifying method to the case in which a transient response is compensated by use of a compensation network. We have already mentioned that there are two kinds of compensation, namely, parallel and series. However, parallel compensation can always be converted into an equivalent series compensation, and hence the compensation can always be described by the block diagram shown in Fig. 8.3.

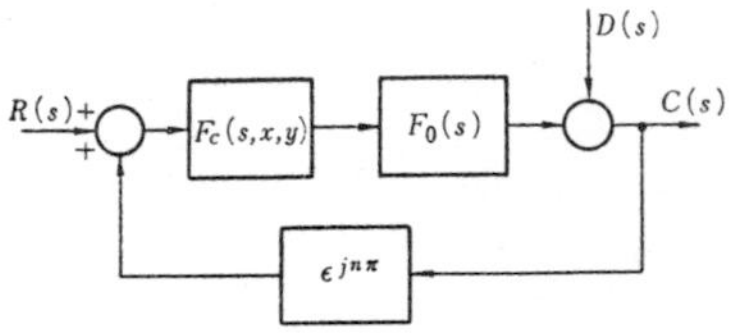

Fig. 8.3 Block diagram of degree of freedom necessary in compensation networks generally

The characteristic equation of the system given by Fig. 8.3 is

$$\epsilon^{jn\pi}F_c(s,\ x,\ y)F_0(s)=1 \tag{8.12}$$

where $F_0(s)$ is the open-loop transfer function of the system without compensation, and $F_c(s, x, y)$ is the compensating transfer function, that is, the transfer function of the compensating network. Here, n is an odd integer. Thus, $\epsilon^{jn\pi}$ represents increase in the phase angle by $n\pi$. Hence,

$$\epsilon^{jn\pi}=-1 \tag{8.13}$$

As already mentioned in Chapter V, the root locus is the locus of those characteristic roots on the complex plane that satisfy the conditions that the phase angle is an odd number n times π and that the branches of the locus can be classified by the value of n. That is, there are m characteristic roots if the degree of the characteristic roots is m, and these m roots can be classified into classes each of which has phase angle π, 3π, 5π, etc. We used $\epsilon^{jn\pi}$ instead of -1 equation (8.12) since it is necessary to classify the characteristic roots in such a manner. It is clear that a characteristic root with phase angle larger than π (such as 3π, 5π, ..., etc.) lies on the root plane to the left of a characteristic root with phase angle π and that the effect of the former on the transient is much less than that of the latter in general. Thus, if a system has a dominant root, this root belongs to the class of characteristics with phase angle π (that is, the class with $n = 1$). Since the class with phase angle π may contain more than a pair of characteristic roots, a characteristic with phase angle π is not always a dominant root. We shall be concerned only with dominant roots in what follows, and hence we assume that $n = 1$ in equation (8.12).

Suppose that the dominant root of equation (8.12) is equal to the specified root r_0. Then, equation (8.12) must hold for $s = r_0$:

$$\epsilon^{j\pi} F_c(r_0, x, y) F_0(r_0) = 1 \tag{8.14}$$

This equation can be written

$$F_c(r_0, x, y) = \frac{\epsilon^{-j\pi}}{F_0(r_0)} \tag{8.15}$$

Here, $F_0(r_0)$ is the value of the open-loop transfer function $F_0(s)$ of the given (uncompensated) system evaluated at r_0; hence it is a known quantity. Accordingly, the right-hand side of equation (8.15) can be expressed by a vector representation as follows:

$$\frac{\epsilon^{-j\pi}}{F_0(r_0)} = g_c \underline{/\phi_c} = g_c \epsilon^{j\phi_c} \tag{8.16}$$

The vector quantity $g_c \epsilon^{j\phi_c}$ is called the compensating vector for the specified root r_0.

Substitution of equation (8.16) into equation (8.15) yields

$$F_c(r_0, x, y) = g_c \epsilon^{j\phi_c} \tag{8.17}$$

This equation with complex coefficients can be split into the following two equations with real coefficients:

$$R_e\{F_c(r_0, x, y)\} = g_c \cos \phi_c \tag{8.18}$$

$$I_m\{F_c(r_0, x, y)\} = g_c \sin \phi_c \tag{8.19}$$

where R_e denotes the real part and I_m the imaginary part. These two equations form a system of simultaneous equations in the two unknowns x and y. The desired values for the free parameters x and y of the compensating transfer function can be determined by solving them. Hence, with this compensation, we can let the system have the specified root. The compensated system has also the conjugate root $r_0{}^* = (-\gamma_0 - j)\omega_0$.

The characteristic roots r_0 and $r_0{}^*$, however, are not necessarily the dominant roots of the compensated system. It is true that these are the characteristic roots for which the angle condition is satisfied with the value π since we assumed that $n = 1$ in equation (8.12). Therefore, it is quite possible that they will be the dominant roots but this will not necessarily be the case. Therefore, we need to examine whether they actually are the dominant roots.

In practice, the phase angle of $F_c(r_0, x, y)$ in equation (8.17) is usually within the range of $\pm 90°$, and the unnatural phenomenon often arises† when it is not within the range of $\pm 180°$. Thus, the phase angle difference of an integer times 2π cannot be neglected.

One can easily determine whether a characteristic root is a dominant root by using the method discussed in Section 5.3. That is, it is sufficient to find the residue of the characteristic and examine whether or not the residue is within a certain region. We

†For example, a situation in which the constants of the compensating network have to have negative values may arise.

shall discuss the detailed procedure of the examination in Section 8.5. We may find that the dominant root of the compensated system is not equal to the specified root. This situation usually happens when the compensating network is not the correct one or the specification of the transient characteristics is itself incorrect. From a theoretical point of view, if we have two degrees of freedom, we can let the system have the specified dominant root but it is impossible to let the system have both the specified dominant root and the specified residue of the dominant root. To meet both requirements, we must use a compensating network with four or more degrees of freedom. In practice, however, the allowable region of values of the residue for a characteristic root to be a dominant root is fairly large, and hence we can let a system have a specified dominant root by compensation with two or three degrees of freedom.

A network with more than three degrees of freedom is useful for compensation that will be used to obtain several specified characteristics simultaneously. Synthesis of such a network can be carried out by a method based on the synthesis of a network with two degrees of freedom, as we have already pointed out. Procedure of the synthesis will be discussed in detail in Chapter IX.

8.3. COMPENSATING FORMULAE, COMPENSATING CHARTS, AND COMPENSATING LIMITS

The main problems in the synthesis of transient characteristics by use of a compensating network are (1) selection of a suitable compensating network and (2) determination of the network constants of the selected compensating network.

Moreover, the synthesis of the compensating network should be such that it can be easily constructed in practice.

We shall show how to solve these problems by the root-specifying method. Suppose that the compensating transfer function of Fig. 8.3 is given in the following form:

$$F_c(s, x, y) = k(1 + s/\omega_s) \tag{8.20}$$

where k and ω_s are the free parameters (unknowns). Let $r_0 = (-\gamma_0 + j)\omega_0$ be the specified root. We shall determine the values of k and ω_s.

From the defining equation (8.16), the compensating vector is

$$g_c\epsilon^{j\phi_c} = \frac{\epsilon^{j\pi}}{F_0(r_0)} \tag{8.21}$$

which can be written in polar form as follows:

$$g_c\epsilon^{j\phi_c} = g_c(\cos\phi_c + j\sin\phi_c) \tag{8.22}$$

If we substitute $s = r_0$ in equations (8.20) and (8.22) and then substitute the resulting equations into equation (8.17), we obtain

the relation
$$F_c(r_0, x, y) = k\left(1+\frac{r_0}{\omega_s}\right) \tag{8.23}$$
$$= g_c(\cos\phi_c + j\sin\phi_c) \tag{8.24}$$

The substitution $r_0 = (-\gamma_0 + j)\,\omega_0$ in the last relation yields
$$k\left\{1+(-\gamma_0+j)\frac{\omega_0}{\omega_s}\right\} = g_c(\cos\phi_c + j\sin\phi_c) \tag{8.25}$$

Separating the real and imaginary parts in this equation, we obtain the following two equations:
$$k\left(1-\gamma_0\frac{\omega_0}{\omega_s}\right) = g_c\cos\phi_c \tag{8.26}$$
$$k\frac{\omega_0}{\omega_s} = g_c\sin\phi_c \tag{8.27}$$

These two equations can be solved for k and ω_s, which are the free parameters of the compensating transfer function, and we obtain
$$\omega_s = \omega_0(\gamma_0 + \cot\phi_c) \tag{8.28}$$
$$k = g_c(\cos\phi_c + \gamma_0\sin\phi_c) \tag{8.29}$$

These two equations, by means of which we can find the values of the two free parameters of the compensating transfer function for a given compensating vector, are collectively called the 'compensating formulae'.

We can derive the corresponding compensating formulae for other compensating transfer functions by the same approach. We omit the details of the calculations. However, the compensating formulae for various compensating transfer functions are shown in Tables 8.1-8.7.

Using the compensating formulae, we can easily compute the values of the two free parameters for a compensating transfer function. It is more convenient for the synthesis to have a chart from which we can read directly the values of the two free parameters. Such a chart can be constructed as follows.

For example, consider the compensating formula consisting of equations (8.28) and (8.29) for the compensating transfer function (8.20). In order to represent the compensating vector in rectangular coordinate form, we apply the transformation
$$\left.\begin{aligned} g_c\cos\phi_c &= X \\ g_c\sin\phi_c &= Y \end{aligned}\right\} \tag{8.30}$$

to equations (8.28) and (8.29). We then obtain
$$\frac{\omega_s}{\omega_0} = \gamma_0 + \frac{X}{Y} \tag{8.31}$$
$$k = X + \gamma_0 Y \tag{8.32}$$

To simplify these equations, we use the quantity defined by

$$\frac{\omega_s}{\omega_0}=\Omega_s \tag{8.33}$$

which is called the relative break frequency. Equations (8.31) and (8.32) can then be written as follows:

$$\Omega_s=\gamma_0+\frac{X}{Y} \tag{8.34}$$

$$k=X+\gamma_0 Y \tag{8.35}$$

If γ_0, Ω_s, and k are all constant, these two equations represent two lines on the complex XY plane on which the compensating vector is to be plotted. The value of γ_0 is given as an item of the

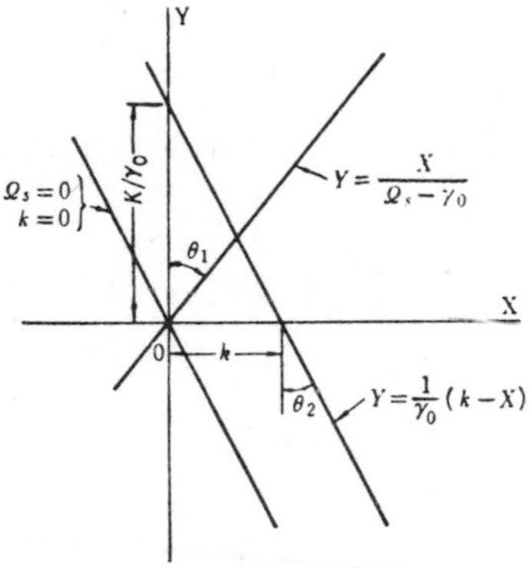

Fig. 8.4 Rectangular coordinate representation of the compensating formula defined by equations (8.28) and (8.29)

specification, but it is practically a fixed value for a particular type of automatic control system*. Therefore, for a single type of automatic control system, the line representing equation (8.34) depends only on the value of Ω_s and the line representing equation (8.35) depends only on the value of k. That is, these lines determine Ω_s and k respectively. We shall call them the Ω_s-line and the k-line respectively. Fig. 8.4 shows an Ω_s-line and a k-line for a particular value of Ω_s and k.

Equation (8.34) can be written as

$$Y=\frac{X}{\Omega_s-\gamma_0} \tag{8.36}$$

This is the equation of a line passing through the origin of the XY-plane with slope $1/(\Omega_s-\gamma_0)$. Equation (8.35) is the equation of a line passing through $(k, 0)$ with slope $1/\gamma_0$.

If we plot the Ω_s-lines and k-lines for various values of Ω_s and k on the compensating-vector plane, we can immediately read the values of $\Omega_s=\omega_s/\omega_0$ and the free parameter k of a compensating transfer function by simply plotting the compensating vector on this plane. Since ω_0 is also given as an item of the specification, we can easily calculate the value of the free parameter ω_s from the value of Ω_s. A compensating-vector plane

* See Table 6.1

TABLE 8.1 COMPENSATING NETWORK SYNTHESIS (I)

compensating network number	compensating transfer function	application
S 2-1 (proportional + derivative network)	$k\left(1+\dfrac{s}{\omega_s}\right)$	industrial regulator

compensating formula	$\omega_s=\omega_0(\gamma_0+\cot\phi_c)$ $k=g_c(\cos\phi_c+\gamma_0\sin\phi_c)$

EXAMPLE OF COMPENSATING NETWORK

construction	free parameters	network constants
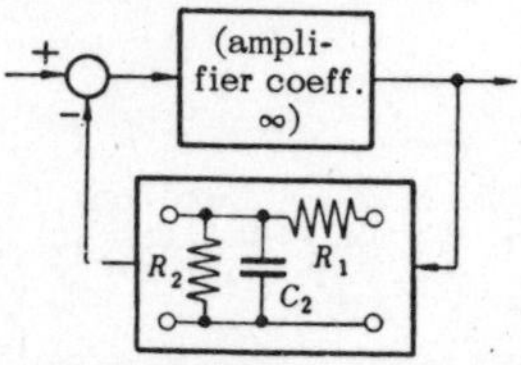	$\omega_s=\dfrac{1}{C_2}\left(\dfrac{1}{R_1}+\dfrac{1}{R_2}\right)$ $k=\dfrac{R_1}{R_2}+1$	$R_1=\dfrac{1}{C_2}\cdot\dfrac{k}{\omega_s}$ $R_2=\dfrac{1}{C_2}\cdot\dfrac{k}{(k-1)\omega_s}$

COMPENSATING CHART

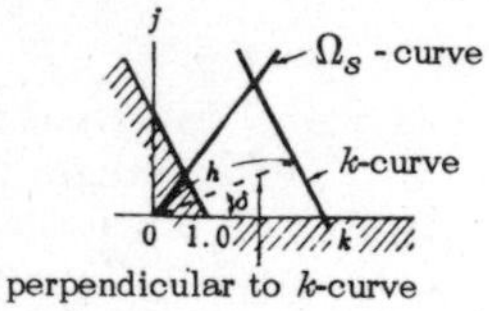

(1) $\Omega_s=\omega_s/\omega_0$

(2) compensation region
$\infty>\Omega_s>0$
$\infty>k>1$
(unshaded region)

SCALING CURVES

	Ω_s - curve	k-curve
type	straight line	straight line
location	(1) pass through origin (2) slope is $\beta=\cot^{-1}(\Omega_s-\gamma_0)$	(1) distance from the origin is $h=k\cos\delta$ (2) slope of perpendicular (broken line) to k-curve is $\delta=\tan^{-1}\gamma_0$ (3) line passes through k on x-axis

TABLE 8.2 COMPENSATING NETWORK SYNTHESIS (II)

compensating network number	compensating transfer function	application
S 2-2 (proportional + integrating network)	$k\left(1+\frac{\omega_s}{s}\right)$	industrial regulator (for series compensation)

compensating formula

$$\omega_s=\frac{\omega_0(1+\gamma_0^2)}{\gamma_0-\cot\phi_c}$$

$$k=g_c(\cos\phi_c-\gamma_0\sin\phi_c)$$

EXAMPLE OF COMPENSATING NETWORK

construction	free parameters	network constants
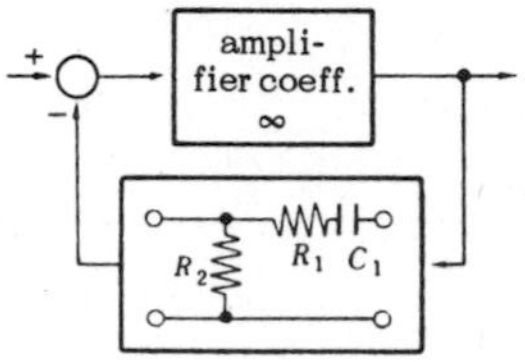	$\omega_s=\frac{1}{C_1(R_1+R_2)}$ $k=\frac{R_1}{R_2}+1$	$R_1=\frac{1}{C_1}\cdot\frac{k-1}{k\omega_s}$ $R_2=\frac{1}{C_1}\cdot\frac{k}{\omega_s}$

COMPENSATING CHART

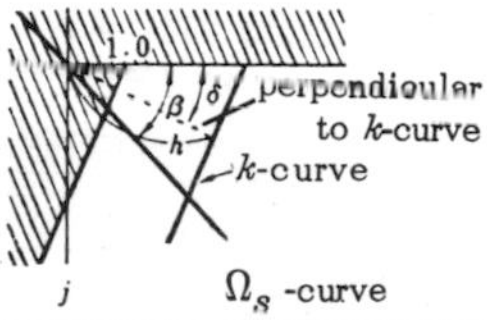

(1) $\Omega_s=\omega_s/\omega_0$

(2) compensation region
$\infty>\Omega_s>0$
$\infty>k>1$
(unshaded region)

SCALING CURVES

	Ω_s - curve	k-curve
type	straight line	straight line
location	(1) passes through origin (2) slope is $\beta=\cot^{-1}\left(\gamma_0-\frac{1+\gamma_0^2}{\Omega_s}\right)$	(1) distance from the origin is $h=k\cos\delta$ (2) slope of perpendicular (broken line) to k-curve is $\delta=\tan^{-1}(-\gamma_0)$

TABLE 8.3 COMPENSATING NETWORK SYNTHESIS(III)

compensating network number	compensating transfer function	application
S 2-3 (lead network)	$\dfrac{1+\dfrac{s}{\omega_s}}{1+\dfrac{s}{n\omega_s}}$	general automatic control system

compensating formula

$$\omega_s=\frac{\omega_0(1+\gamma_0^2)\sin\phi_c}{g_c-\cos\phi_c+\gamma_0\sin\phi_c}$$

$$n=\frac{g_c-\cos\phi_c+\gamma_0\sin\phi_c}{\cos\phi_c+\gamma_0\sin\phi_c-1/g_c}$$

EXAMPLE OF COMPENSATING NETWORK

construction	free parameters	network constants
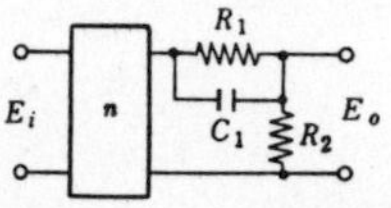	$\omega_s=\dfrac{1}{C_1R_1}$ $n=\dfrac{R_1}{R_2}+1$	$R_1=\dfrac{1}{C_1\omega_s}$ $R_2=\dfrac{1}{C_1}\cdot\dfrac{1}{(n-1)\omega_s}$

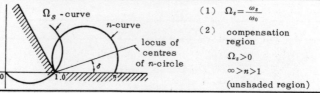

COMPENSATING CHART

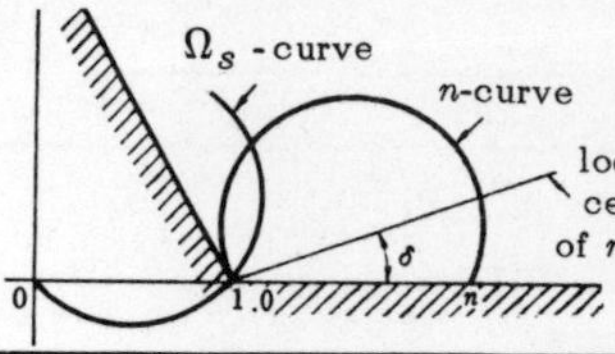

(1) $\Omega_s=\dfrac{\omega_s}{\omega_0}$

(2) compensation region

$\Omega_s>0$

$\infty>n>1$

(unshaded region)

SCALING CURVES

	Ω_s - curve	k-curve
type	circle	circle
location	(1) circle passes through origin and (1,0) (2) coordinates of centre are: $X=\dfrac{1}{2}$, $Y=\dfrac{1+\gamma_0^2-\gamma_0\Omega_s}{2\gamma_0}$	(1) circle passes through (1,0) and (n, 0) (2) locus (fine line) of circle centres passes through (1,0); slope $\delta=\tan^{-1}\gamma_0$

TABLE 8.4 COMPENSATING NETWORK SYNTHESIS (VI)

compensating network number	compensating transfer function	application
S 2-4 (lag network)	$\dfrac{1+\dfrac{s}{\omega_s}}{1+\dfrac{ns}{\omega_s}}$	general automatic control system (for series compensation)

compensating formula

$$\omega_s=\frac{\omega_0(1+\gamma_0^2)\sin\phi_c}{g_c-\cos\phi_c+\gamma_0\sin\phi_c}$$

$$n=\frac{\cos\phi_c+\gamma_0\sin\phi_c-1/g_c}{g_c-\cos\phi_c+\gamma_0\sin\phi_c}$$

EXAMPLE OF COMPENSATING NETWORK

construction	free parameters	network constants
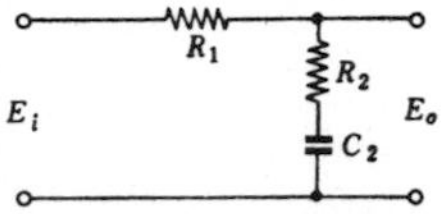	$\omega_s=\dfrac{1}{C_2R_2}$ $n=\dfrac{R_1}{R_2}+1$	$R_1=\dfrac{1}{C_2}\ \dfrac{n-1}{\omega_s}$ $R_2=\dfrac{1}{C_2}\ \dfrac{1}{\omega_s}$

COMPENSATING CHART

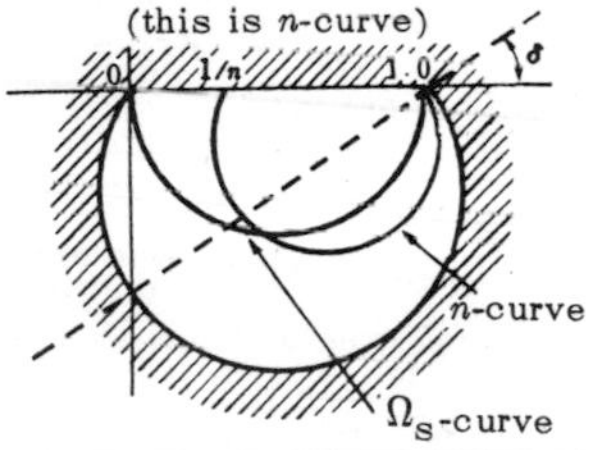

(1) $\Omega_s=\dfrac{\omega_s}{\omega_0}$

(2) compensation region
$\Omega_s>0$
$\infty>n>1$
(unshaded region)

SCALING CURVES

	Ω_S - curve	n-curve
type	circle	circle
location	(1) circle passes through origin and (1,0) (2) coordinates of centre are: $X=\dfrac{1}{2},\quad Y=\dfrac{1+\gamma_0^2-\gamma_0\Omega_s}{2\gamma_0}$	(1) circle passes through (1,0) and (1/n, 0) (2) locus (broken line) of centres of circle passes through (1,0); slope $\delta=\tan^{-1}\gamma_0$

TABLE 8.5 COMPENSATING NETWORK SYNTHESIS (V)

compensating network number	compensating transfer function	application
S 2-5 (lead network)	$\frac{1}{n}\left(\frac{1+\frac{s}{\omega_s}}{1+\frac{s}{n\omega_s}}\right)$	general automatic control system

compensating formula

$$\omega_s=\frac{\omega_0(\cos\phi_c+\gamma_0\sin\phi_c-g_c)}{\sin\phi_c}$$

$$n=\frac{1/g_c-\cos\phi_c+\gamma_0\sin\phi_c}{\cos\phi_c+\gamma_0\sin\phi_c-g_c}$$

EXAMPLE OF COMPENSATING NETWORK

construction	free parameters	network constants
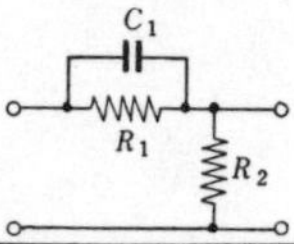	$\omega_s=\frac{1}{C_1R_1}$ $n=\frac{R_1}{R_2}+1$	$R_1=\frac{1}{C_1\omega_s}$ $R_2=\frac{1}{C_1}\ \frac{1}{(n-1)\omega_s}$

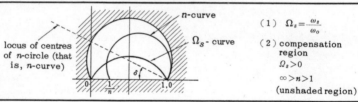

COMPENSATING CHART

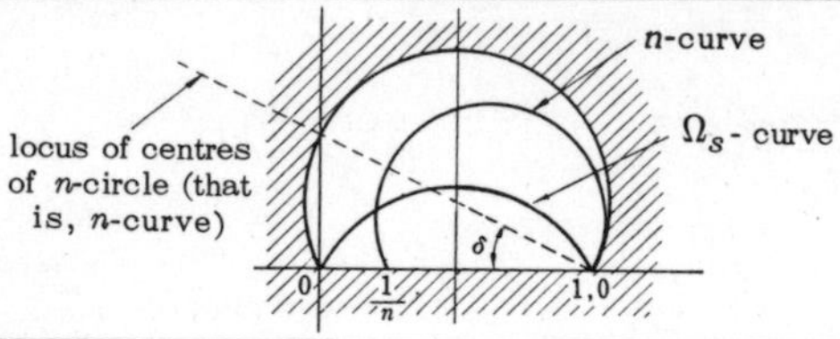

(1) $\Omega_s=\frac{\omega_s}{\omega_0}$

(2) compensation region
$\Omega_s>0$
$\infty>n>1$
(unshaded region)

SCALING CURVES

	Ω_s - curve	n-curve
type	circle	circle
location	(1) circle passes through origin and (1,0) (2) co-ordinates of the centre are: $X=\frac{1}{2}$ $Y=-\frac{\gamma_0+\Omega_s}{2}$ (3) the radius is $\sqrt{\left(\frac{1}{2}\right)^2+\left(\frac{\gamma_0+\Omega_s}{2}\right)^2}$	(1) circle passes through (1,0) and (1/n, 0) (2) locus (broken line) of centres of circle through (1,0); slope $\delta=-\tan^{-1}\gamma_0$

TABLE 8.6 COMPENSATING NETWORK SYNTHESIS (VI)

compensating network number	compensating transfer function	application
S 2-6 (proportional + differentiating + integrating network)	$1+\frac{s}{\omega_{sD}}+\frac{\omega_{sI}}{s}$	industrial regulator for series compensation

compensating formula

$$\omega_{sD}=\frac{2\gamma_0\omega_0}{1-g_c\cos\phi_c+\gamma_0 g_c\sin\phi_c}$$

$$\omega_{sI}=\frac{(\gamma_0^2+1)\omega_0}{2\gamma_0}(1-g_c\cos\phi_c-\gamma_0 g_c\sin\phi_c)$$

EXAMPLE OF COMPENSATING NETWORK

construction	free parameters	network constants
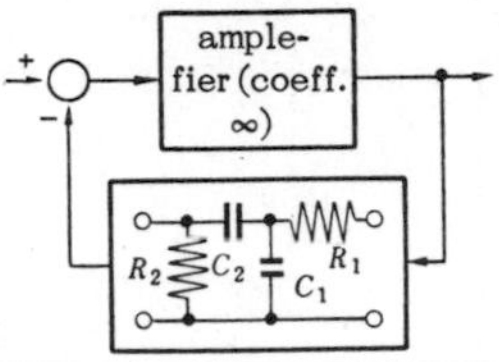	$\omega_{sD}=\frac{1}{C_1R_1}$ $\omega_{sI}=\frac{1}{C_2R_2}$ where $R_1 \ll R_2$	$R_1=\frac{1}{C_1}\;\frac{1}{\omega_{sD}}$ $R_2=\frac{1}{C_2}\;\frac{1}{\omega_{sI}}$ where $R_1 \ll R_2$ and $C_1 \ll C_2$

COMPENSATING CHART

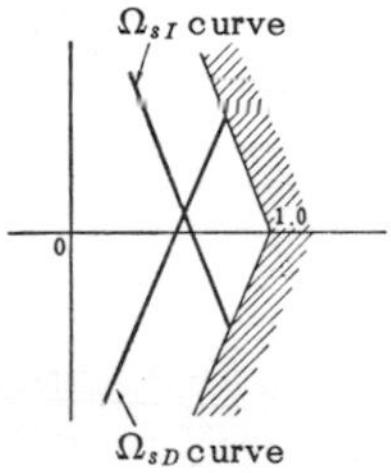

(1) $\Omega_{sD}=\frac{\omega_{sD}}{\omega_0}$

$\Omega_{sI}=\frac{\omega_{sI}}{\omega_0}$

(2) compensation region

$\infty>\Omega_{sD}>0$

$\infty>\Omega_{sI}>0$

(unshaded region)

SCALING CURVES

	Ω_{sD} - curve	Ω_{sI}-curve
type	line	line
location	(1) the slope is $+\cot^{-1}\gamma_0$ (2) line passes through $1-\frac{2\gamma_0}{\Omega_{sD}}$	(1) the slope is $-\cot^{-1}\gamma_0$ (2) line passes through $1-\frac{2\gamma_0}{\gamma_0^2+1}\Omega_{sI}$

TABLE 8.7 COMPENSATING NETWORK SYNTHESIS (VII)

compensating network number	compensating transfer function	application
P 2-1 (differentiating network)	$\dfrac{s\dfrac{k}{\omega_s}}{1+\dfrac{s}{\omega_s}}$	general automatic control system

compensating formula: $\omega_s = \dfrac{\omega_0(1+\gamma_0^2)}{\gamma_0+\cot\phi_c}$ $\quad k = \dfrac{g_c}{\cos\phi_c+\gamma_0\sin\phi_c}$

EXAMPLES OF COMPENSATING NETWORK

construction		free parameters	network constants
P 2-1·1	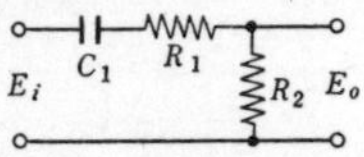	$\omega_s = \dfrac{1}{C_1(R_1+R_2)}$ $k = \dfrac{R_2}{R_1+R_2}$	$R_1 = \dfrac{1}{C_1}\cdot\dfrac{1-k}{\omega_s}$ $R_2 = \dfrac{k}{C_1\omega_s}$
P 2-1·2	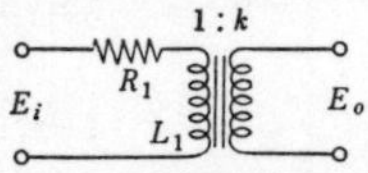	$\omega_s = R_1/L_1$ k: turns ratio	$R_2 = L_1\omega_s$
P 2-1·3	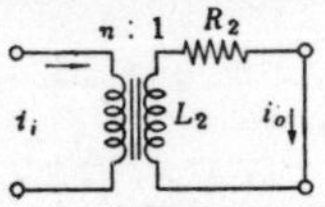	$\omega_s = R_2/L_2$ n: turns ratio	$R_1 = L_2\omega_s$

COMPENSATING CHART

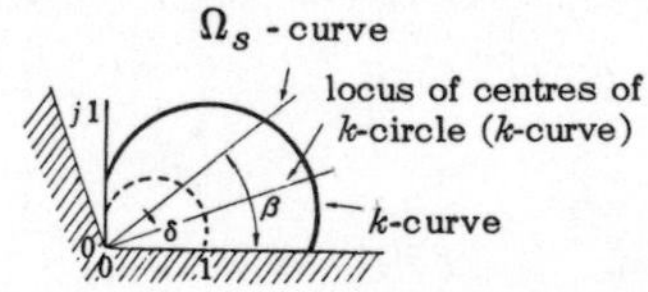

(1) $\Omega_s = \omega_s/\omega_0$

(2) compensation domain $\Omega_s > 0$

for P2 - 1·1, $1 > k > 0$ (interior of broken circle); for P2 - 1·2 and P2 - 1·3, $k > 0$ (unshaded region)

SCALING CURVES

	Ω_s-curve	k-curve
type	$k > 0$ (unshaded region)	circle
location	(1) the line passes through origin (2) the slope is $\beta = \cot^{-1}\left(\dfrac{1+\gamma_0^2}{\Omega_s} - \gamma_0\right)$	(1) locus of centres of circle has slope $\delta = \tan^{-1}\gamma_0$ (2) the radius is $k\sqrt{1+\gamma_0^2}$ (3) circle passes through origin and $(k, 0)$

with Ω_s-lines and k-lines is called a compensating chart. Fig. 8.5 shows the compensating chart for the transfer function (8.20).

Once suitable values are found for the free parameters of the transfer function by use of the compensating chart, the next task is to synthesise a compensating network with the determined transfer function.

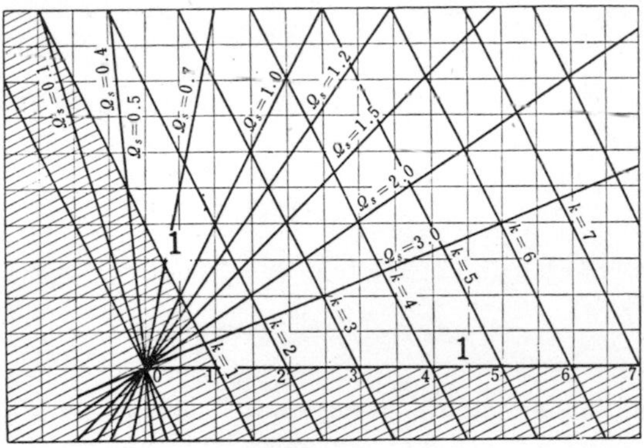

1 - *compensating limit*

Fig. 8.5 Compensating chart for the transfer function $K(1 + s/\omega_s)$ ($\gamma o = 0.5$)

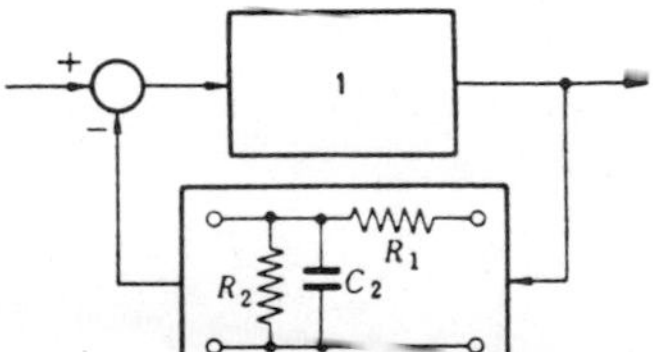

Fig. 8.6 Compensation network employing the transfer function $k(1 + s/\omega_s)$

For example, consider again the compensating transfer function

$$F_c(s) = k\left(1 + \frac{s}{\omega_s}\right) \tag{8.37}$$

Here, we assume that k and ω_s are known values found from the compensating chart. Fig. 8.6 shows a compensating network whose transfer function is the one given by equation (8.37). The feedback transfer function $H(s)$ of the network is expressed by

P

$$H(s) = \frac{R_2}{R_1+R_2} \quad \frac{1}{1+sC_2\dfrac{R_1R_2}{R_1+R_2}} \tag{8.38}$$

If we denote by A the amplification coefficient of the amplifier and by $F_c(s)$ the transfer function with input E_i and output E_o, then

$$F_c(s) = -\frac{A}{1+AH(s)} \tag{8.39}$$

If A is sufficiently large in this expression, $F_c(s)$ can be approximated as follows:

$$F_c(s) \doteqdot \frac{1}{H(s)} \tag{8.40}$$

Substitution of equation (8.38) into this equation yields

$$F_c(s) \doteqdot \frac{R_1+R_2}{R_2}\left(1+sC_2\frac{R_1R_2}{R_1+R_2}\right) \tag{8.41}$$

Comparing this equation with equation (8.37), we get

$$k = \frac{R_1+R_2}{R_2} = \frac{R_1}{R_2}+1 \tag{8.42}$$

$$\omega_s = \frac{1}{C_2}\left(\frac{1}{R_1}+\frac{1}{R_2}\right) \tag{8.43}$$

Now, we only need to determine the values of R_1, R_2, and C_2 from these two equations. Since we have three network constants and two equations, one of the network constants, let us say C_2, may take an arbitrary value. Then,

$$R_1 = \frac{1}{C_2} \quad \frac{k}{\omega_s} \tag{8.44}$$

$$R_2 = \frac{1}{C_2} \quad \frac{k}{(k-1)\omega_s} \tag{8.45}$$

Clearly C_2 has to be positive. It is also desirable that R_1 and R_2 be positive since, otherwise, construction of the compensating network may be difficult. Therefore, the following conditions should be satisfied:

$$\frac{k}{\omega_s}>0, \quad \frac{k}{(k-1)\omega_s}>0$$

that is,

$$\omega_s>0, \quad k>1$$

Consequently, the Ω_s-line and the k-line (on the compensating chart) corresponding to $\omega_s = 0$ (that is, $\Omega_s = \omega_s / \omega_0 = 0$) and $k = 1$ represent the boundary of a region for which the compensating network can be constructed in practice. In the compensating charts shown above, the region for which construction of the compensating network is impossible is indicated by shading. The boundary of the region for which the compensating network is realisable is called the compensating limit. If for each network we specify the compensating limit on the compensating chart, we can immediately determine whether this compensation is possible or not merely by plotting the compensating vector on the chart. Sometimes there are several different networks for one compensating transfer function. When this is the case, we can use the same chart for all syntheses of such networks. However, different networks generally have different compensating limits.

8.4. PRACTICAL COMPENSATING CHART AND ITS APPLICATION TO NETWORK SYNTHESIS*

As stated in the preceding section, if we construct a compensating chart for a given compensating vector, we can determine from this chart whether compensation by use of the network is possible. If compensation by use of the network is possible, we can immediately read from the chart suitable values of the free parameters for achieving compensation. However, there may still be some inconveniences. For example, if the magnitude of the compensating vector is much less than 1, there may well be a large error in plotting the compensating vector and in reading the values of the free parameters. Or, if the magnitude of the compensating vector is extremely great, it cannot in practice be plotted on the compensating chart. To remove these inconveniences, we use a logarithmic plane instead of the usual complex plane. That is, we use a logarithmic scale for the horizontal axis (which represents the magnitude g_c of the compensating vector) and the usual scale for the vertical axis (which represents the value of the phase angle ϕ_c as shown in Fig. 8.7. The Ω_s -curves and the k -curves can also be plotted on this logarithmic plane. The logarithmic plane with the Ω_s -curves and the k -curves is called a logarithmic compensating chart or simply a compensating chart. By means of it, we can maintain a high accuracy in reading the values of the free parameters throughout a wide range of magnitudes of the compensating vector. There is another advantage in using the logarithmic compensating chart. Ordinary compensating charts differ, depending on the compensating network and the value of the specified damping coefficient γ_0. However, the Ω_s -curves and k -curves on the logarithmic compensating charts retain their shapes when the compensating network or the value of γ_0 is changed. Thus, one logarithmic compensating chart can be used for more networks and values of γ_0 than can one ordinary compensating chart. Moreover, a logarithmic compensating chart can be more easily constructed.

We shall discuss the properties, construction, and use of this highly practical logarithmic compensating chart.

*This section treats the method of constructing Tables I-VI of the appendix and the principles involved in applying these tables to the synthesis of a compensating network. If the reader wishes to acquire the technique of using tables the for synthesis, he can omit this section and examine the tables in which their applications are illustrated.

(1) THE COMPENSATING CHART OF NETWORK S2-1

As shown in Table 8.1, the compensating formula for the compensating network S2-1 is

$$\Omega_s = \gamma_0 + \cot \phi_c \tag{8.46}$$

$$k = g_c(\cos \phi_c + \gamma_0 \sin \phi_c) \tag{8.47}$$

where (relative break angular frequency),

$$\Omega_s = \omega_s / \omega_0 \tag{8.48}$$

and γ_0 is the specified damping coefficient. Since γ_0 is a constant determined by the type of automatic control system, Ω_s depends only on ϕ_c. Therefore, on the logarithmic plane (where the vertical axis represents ϕ_c and the horizontal axis with a logarithmic scale represents g_c), we may use the vertical axis for representing Ω_s, as shown in Fig. 8.8, that is, we may attach the scaling for Ω_s to the vertical axis in addition to the scaling for ϕ_c. However, this double scaling will complicate the chart. In practice it is more convenient to use a curve for conversion of the Ω_s scale to the ϕ_c scale such as the curve (a) in Fig. 8.8. This scale conversion curve changes its shape with the value of γ_0.

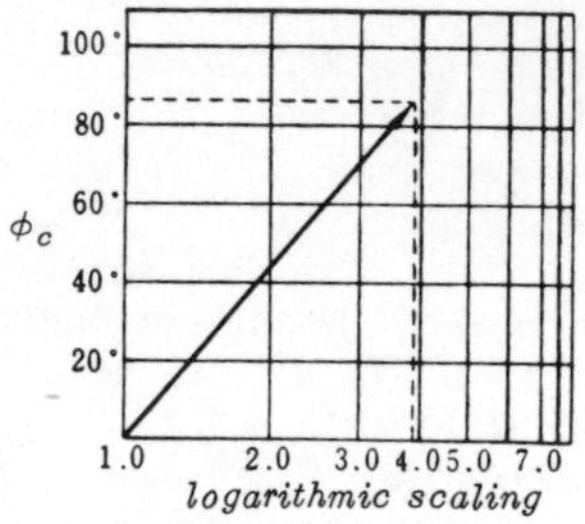

Fig. 8.7 Representation of a compensating vector on the logarithmic plane

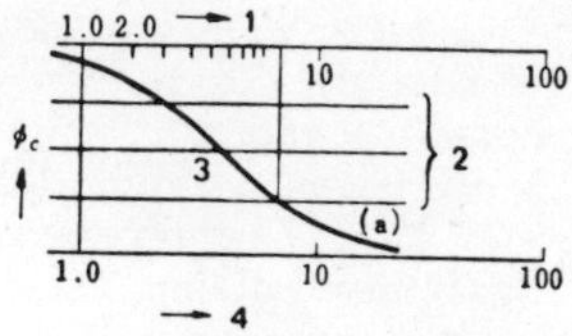

1 - Ω_s *scale*; 2 - *lines of scaling* Ω_s; 3 - *curve for conversion of* Ω_s *scale to* ϕ_c *scale* 4 - (*logarithmic scaling*)

Fig. 8.8 Curve for conversion of Ω_s scale to ϕ_c scale (for the compensating network S2-1)

We shall now discuss k-curves. A k-curve is a (g_c-ϕ_c)-curve corresponding to a certain value of k. Equation (8.47) can be written

$$\frac{k}{g_c} = \sqrt{1+\gamma_0^2} \cos(\phi_c - \tan^{-1}\gamma_0) \tag{8.49}$$

which in turn can be written

$$\frac{\sqrt{1+\gamma_0^2}}{k} g_c \cos(\phi_c - \tan^{-1}\gamma_0) = 1 \tag{8.50}$$

Taking the natural logarithm of the last equation, we obtain

$$\ln g_c + \ln\sqrt{1+\gamma_0^2} - \ln k + \ln\cos(\phi_c - \tan^{-1}\gamma_0) = 0 \tag{8.51}$$

Since γ_0 is a constant, this equation defines a curve corresponding to the value of k on the logarithmic plane, as shown in Fig. 8.9. Such curves, corresponding to various values of k are the scaling curves for k; they are called k-curves. Clearly, the curve of equation (8.51) is the translation of the curve of the equation

$$\ln g_c + \ln\sqrt{1+\gamma_0^2} + \ln\cos(\phi_c - \tan^{-1}\gamma_0) = 0 \tag{8.52}$$

along the real axis by an amount $\ln k$ to the right. The curve of equation (8.52) can be obtained as shown in Fig. 8.10, by translating the curve of the equation

$$\ln g_c + \ln\cos\phi_c = 0 \tag{8.53}$$

or the equation

$$g_c \cos\phi_c = 1 \tag{8.54}$$

along the real axis by an amount $-\ln\sqrt{1+\gamma_0^2}$ and along the imaginary axis by an amount $\tan^{-1}\gamma_0$. That is, the curve of equation (8.52) can be obtained from the curve of equation (8.54) simply by moving the coordinate origin to the point $\ln\sqrt{1+\gamma_0^2} - j\tan^{-1}\gamma_0$. This point lies on the curve of equation (8.54). For if we let

$$\sqrt{1+\gamma_0^2} = g_c, \quad -\tan^{-1}\gamma_0 = \phi_c$$

then

$$g_c \cos\phi_c = \sqrt{1+\gamma_0^2}\,\cos(-\tan^{-1}\gamma_0) \tag{8.55}$$

$$= \sqrt{1+\gamma_0^2} \cdot \frac{1}{\sqrt{1+\gamma_0^2}} = 1$$

That is, the point $\ln\sqrt{1+\gamma_0^2} - j\tan^{-1}\gamma_0$ satisfies equation (8.54).

Summarising the above discussion, we may state that the curve

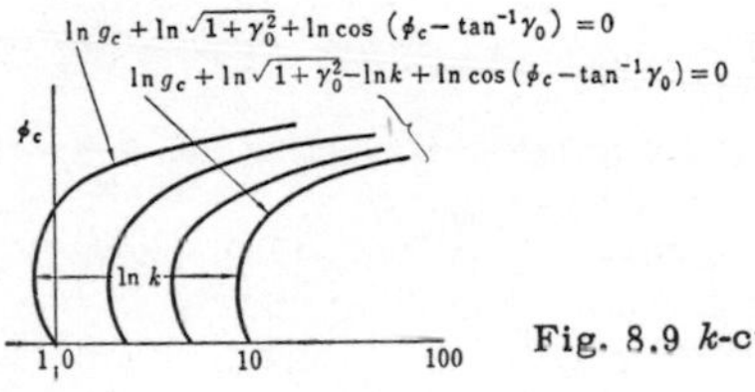

Fig. 8.9 k-curves of the compensating network S2-1

of equation (8.50) can easily be constructed in the manner shown in Fig. 8.10. Specifically, plot the curve (a) of equation (8.54) on the logarithmic plane with origin O′, and move the origin to the point $\ln\sqrt{1+\gamma_0^2} - j\tan^{-1}\gamma_0$. Let us call the new origin O′. Then, we obtain the curve of equation (8.50) corresponding to $k = 1$. The curve of equation (8.50) for another value of k can be obtained simply by translating the curve for $k = 1$ along the real axis by an amount $\ln k$ (see curves (b) and (c) in Fig. 8.10).

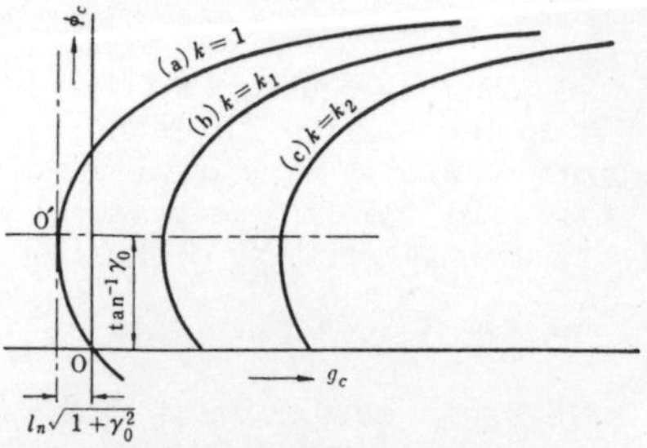

Fig. 8.10 Method of constructing k-curves of compensating network S2-1

So far we have discussed k-curves for a fixed value of γ_0. As is clear from equation (8.54), the shape of the k-curve remains the same for a different value of γ_0. Specifically, the origin is the point on the curve of equation (8.54) such that the phase angle of the vector originating at point O and ending at the point is $-\tan^{-1}\gamma_0$.

Accordingly, if we construct a curved ruler that fits the curve of equation (8.54), it is quite easy to construct the compensating chart. For each value of k, we place the curved ruler in the corresponding position on the logarithmic plane and draw the k-curve along the edge of the ruler. This ruler is useful not only for plotting the k-curves for the compensating transfer functions of the network S2-1 but also for construction of certain other compensating charts. Such a curved ruler is called a compensation-scaling ruler or a scaling ruler.

Table I in the Appendix shows the thus constructed compensating charts of the compensating network S2-1 (a proportional + differentiating + integrating network) given in Table 8.1. In Table I, four compensating charts, corresponding to $\gamma_0 = 0.3$, $\gamma_0 = 0.4$, $\gamma_0 = 0.5$, and $\gamma_0 = 0.6$ (these are the values of γ_0 most frequently used in practice), are constructed together on the same graph. Clearly, the positions of the origins and the shapes of the curves for conversion of Ω_s- scale to ϕ_c- scale differ depending on the value of γ_0 in the table.

The procedure of applying the compensating chart to a synthesis of a compensating network is as follows.

(1) Plot the compensating vector on a semi-transparent graph sheet* with the same scale as the compensating chart.

(2) Place the semi-transparent graph sheet on the compensating chart in such a way that the origin of the former coincides with that of the latter (corresponding to the specified value of γ_0) and both axes of the former are parallel to those of the latter. Read the values of Ω_s and k corresponding to the end point of the compensating vector. Finally, compute the corresponding value of ω_s $(= \Omega_s\omega_0)$ from the value read for Ω_s.

In each table of the Appendix, instructions are given for applying

*It is not strictly necessary to use a semi-transparent graph sheet in this procedure but it is advisable for a reason that will be clarified in section 8·5

the compensating chart. Clearly, the compensating limit can also be read from the compensating chart. Since the compensating limit changes, even for the same compensating transfer function, depending on the compensating network, it is not specified on the compensating charts in the Appendix. However, certain scaling curves for the free parameters will form the compensating limit. In Tables 1-7, the compensating limits are specified.

(2) THE COMPENSATING CHART OF NETWORK S2-2

The compensating formula for the compensating transfer function $k(1+\omega_s/s)$ of the network S2-2 is as follows.

$$\Omega_s = \frac{1+\gamma_0^2}{\gamma_0 - \cot\phi_c} \tag{8.56}$$

$$k = g_c(\cos\phi_c - \gamma_0 \sin\phi_c) \tag{8.57}$$

where $\Omega_s = \omega_s/\omega_0$. The compensating formula for the compensating transfer function $k(1+s/\omega_s)$ of the network S2-1 is

$$\Omega_s = (\gamma_0 + \cot\phi_c) \tag{8.58}$$

$$k = g_c(\cos\phi_c + \gamma_0 \sin\phi_c) \tag{8.59}$$

Comparison of equation (8.57) with equation (8.59) shows that equation (8.57) can be obtained by replacing ϕ_c with $-\phi_c$ in equation (8.59). That is, the k-curves for the compensating transfer function of S2-2 are the reflections of the k-curves for the compensating transfer function of S2-1 in the real axis.

Therefore, the values of the free parameters for the transfer function of S2-2 can be read from the compensating chart of S2-1 by turning upside-down the semi-transparent graph sheet on which the compensating vector is plotted and placing it on the chart. However, we need to make a slight modification in the compensating chart. That is, the scaling lines for Ω_s for the transfer function of S2-2 are the same as those for the transfer function of S2-1, but the curve for conversion from the Ω_s-scale to the ϕ_c-scale is different from that of S2-1. Therefore, we need to plot the conversion curve of S2-2 on to the compensating chart of S2-1.

Figure II in the Appendix shows the compensating chart of the proportional + integrating network S2-2. Instructions for the use of the compensating chart are given in Table 2 in the Appendix.

(3) THE COMPENSATING CHART OF NETWORK S2-3

The transfer function of the lead network S2-3 is

$$F_c(s) = \frac{1+\dfrac{s}{\omega_s}}{1+\dfrac{s}{n\omega_s}} \tag{8.60}$$

where $n > 1$. The values of the free parameters were shown in Table 8.3. However, if we use the relative break angular frequency $\Omega_s = \omega_s / \omega_0$ instead of ω_s, then the values of the two free parameters are

$$\Omega_s = \frac{(1+\gamma_0^2)\sin\phi_c}{g_c - \cos\phi_c + \gamma_0 \sin\phi_c} \tag{8.61}$$

$$n = \frac{g_c - \cos\phi_c + \gamma_0 \sin\phi_c}{\cos\phi_c + \gamma_0 \sin\phi_c - 1/g_c} \tag{8.62}$$

In order to plot the Ω_s -curves, we write equation (8.61) as follows:

$$g_c - \cos\phi_c + \gamma_0 \sin\phi_c = \frac{1+\gamma_0^2}{\Omega_s} \sin\phi_c \tag{8.63}$$

$$g_c = \cos\phi_c + \left(\frac{1+\gamma_0^2}{\Omega_s} - \gamma_0\right) \sin\phi_c \tag{8.64}$$

Therefore,

$$g_c = \sqrt{\left(\frac{1+\gamma_0^2}{\Omega_s} - \gamma_0\right)^2 + 1}\, \cos\left\{\phi_c - \tan^{-1}\left(\frac{1+\gamma_0^2}{\Omega_s} - \gamma_0\right)\right\} \tag{8.65}$$

If we take the logarithm of both sides of this equation, we obtain

$$\ln g_c = \ln\sqrt{\left(\frac{1+\gamma_0^2}{\Omega_s} - \gamma_0\right)^2 + 1} + \ln\left[\cos\left\{\phi_c - \tan^{-1}\left(\frac{1+\gamma_0^2}{\Omega_s} - \gamma_0\right)\right\}\right] \tag{8.66}$$

$$\ln g_c - \ln\sqrt{\left(\frac{1+\gamma_0^2}{\Omega_s} - \gamma_0\right)^2 + 1} = \ln\left[\cos\left\{\phi_c - \tan^{-1}\left(\frac{1+\gamma_0^2}{\Omega_s} - \gamma_0\right)\right\}\right] \tag{8.67}$$

which can be written

$$\ln g_c = \ln\cos\phi_c \tag{8.68}$$

$$\frac{1}{g_c} \cos\phi_c = 1 \tag{8.69}$$

The curve of this equation can be obtained, as shown in Fig. 8.11, by translating the curve of equation (8.68) or (8.69) by the vector quantity P, where P is defined by

$$P = \ln\sqrt{\left(\frac{1+\gamma_0^2}{\Omega_s} - \gamma_0\right)^2 + 1} + j\tan^{-1}\left(\frac{1+\gamma_0^2}{\Omega_s} - \gamma_0\right) \tag{8.70}$$

The curve of equation (8.68) is the curve of the equation obtained by replacing $\ln g_c$ by $-\ln g_c$ in equation (8.53) or equation (8.54). Accordingly, the curve of equation (8.68) is the reflection of the curve equation (8.53) or (8.54) in the imaginary axis; hence, it can also be easily plotted by using the scaling rule used for plotting the curve of equation (8.54).

The point P defined by equation (8.70) varies with the value of Ω_s. The locus of the point P can also be plotted by using the same scaling ruler. For if we set

$$\sqrt{\left(\frac{1+\gamma_0^2}{\Omega_s}-\gamma_0\right)^2+1}=g', \quad \tan^{-1}\left(\frac{1+\gamma_0^2}{\Omega_s}-\gamma_0\right)=\phi' \tag{8.71}$$

equation (8.70) can be written as follows:

$$g'=\sqrt{\tan^2\phi'+1}=\frac{1}{\cos\phi'} \tag{8.72}$$

$$g'\cos\phi'=1 \tag{8.73}$$

and the last equation has the same form as equation (8.54). The locus of the point P is the broken curve in Fig. 8.11.

From what was said above, the Ω_s - curves can easily be constructed by sliding the scaling ruler with its origin on the locus of the point P and by drawing a curve at each position of the scaling ruler. The value of Ω_s corresponding to each Ω_s-curve can be calculated from equation (8.71). Though the shape of the Ω_s-curve does not change for a change in the value of γ_0, the value of Ω_s corresponding to each Ω_s-curve does change with the value of γ_0. Therefore, we need to construct a separate compensating chart for each value of γ_0.

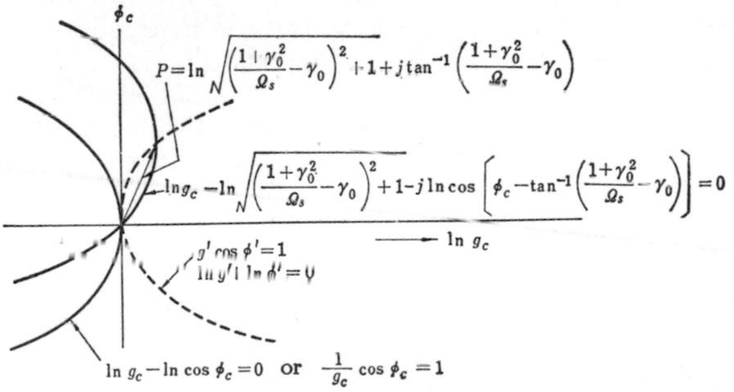

Fig. 8.11 Construction of Ω_s-curves for the network S2-3

We shall now discuss the n-curves. Equation (8.62) can be written

$$n\cos\phi_c+n\gamma_0\sin\phi_c-\frac{n}{g_c}=g_c-\cos\phi_c+\gamma_0\sin\phi_c \tag{8.74}$$

Thus, we obtain the relation

$$g_c+\frac{n}{g_c}=(n+1)\cos\phi_c+(n-1)\gamma_0\sin\phi_c \tag{8.75}$$

$$=\sqrt{(n+1)^2+(n-1)^2\gamma_0^2}\cos\left\{\phi_c-\tan^{-1}\left(\frac{n-1}{n+1}\gamma_0\right)\right\} \tag{8.76}$$

Solving for ϕ_c, we have

$$\phi_c=\tan^{-1}\left(\frac{n-1}{n+1}\gamma_0\right)\pm\cos^{-1}\left(\frac{g_c+\dfrac{n}{g_c}}{\sqrt{(n-1)^2+(n-1)^2\gamma_0^2}}\right) \tag{8.77}$$

Since γ_0 has a fixed value, which is the specified value, the n-curve for a certain value of n is the curve of equation (8.77), where g_c is taken as the independent variable, ϕ_c as the dependent variable, and n as a constant.

As is clear from equation (8.77), two values of g_c correspond to each value of ϕ_c. That is, the n-curve is symmetrical with respect to the horizontal line $\phi_c = \tan^{-1}[(n-1)\gamma_0/(n+1)]$. Equation (8.77) can also be written

$$\phi_c = \tan^{-1}\left(\frac{n-1}{n+1}\gamma_0\right) \pm \cos^{-1}\left\{\sqrt{\frac{n}{(n+1)^2+(n-1)^2\gamma_0^2}}\left(\frac{g_c}{\sqrt{n}}+\frac{\sqrt{n}}{g_c}\right)\right\} \quad (8.78)$$

Even if $g_c/\sqrt{n}$ and $\sqrt{n}/g_c$ are interchanged in this equation, the value of ϕ_c remains the same. That is, the n-curve is also symmetrical with respect to the vertical line $g_c\sqrt{n} = 1$ or $g_c = \sqrt{n}$.

Figures III, IV, V, and VI in the Appendix show compensating charts constructed in this way for the compensating network S2-3 for $\gamma_0 = 0.3$, 0.4, 0.5, and 0.6 respectively.

(4) APPLICATION OF THE COMPENSATING CHARTS TO NETWORK S2-4

The compensating charts constructed by the previous methods are applicable to the synthesis of the lag network S2-4, the lead network S2-5, and the lead-lag network S3-1. We shall discuss only the application of the compensating charts to the synthesis of the lag network S2-4, and leave the discussion of the synthesis of the lead-lag network S3-1 to Chapter IX.

The compensating transfer function of S2-4 is

$$F_c(s) = \frac{1+\dfrac{s}{\omega_s}}{1+\dfrac{ns}{\omega_s}} \quad (8.79)$$

where $n > 1$. The reciprocal $F_c'(s)$ of the compensating transfer function is then

$$F_c'(s) = \frac{1}{F_c(s)} = \frac{1+\dfrac{ns}{\omega_s}}{1+\dfrac{s}{\omega_s}} \quad (8.80)$$

If we set

$$\omega_s' = \frac{\omega_s}{n} \quad \text{i.e.} \quad \omega_s = n\omega_s' \quad (8.81)$$

then $F_c'(s)$ can be written

$$F_c'(s) = \frac{1+\dfrac{s}{\omega_s'}}{1+\dfrac{s}{n\omega_s'}} \quad (8.82)$$

This last equation is of the same form as equation (8.60). Therefore, we can use the compensating chart of the lead network for $F_c'(s)$ that is, the reciprocal of $F_c(s)$. Accordingly, if we rotate 180° the semi-transparent graph sheet on which the compensating vector of S2-4 is plotted around the origin and place it on the compensating chart of the lead network, the value of n in equation (8.82) and the relative break frequency $\Omega_s' = \omega_s'/\omega_0$ can be immediately read from the chart. Then, the value of ω_s in equation (8.81) can be calculated from the equation

$$\omega_s = \omega_0 n \Omega_s' \tag{8.83}$$

where ω_0 is the specified damped angular frequency.

The compensating network S2-5 can also be synthesised by using the compensating charts in Figs. III, IV, V, and VI in the Appendix. However, a detailed discussion of the procedure is omitted and only the result is shown in the Appendix.

8.5. PROCEDURE FOR SYNTHESIS IN PRACTICE

So far, we have discussed the principles behind the root-specifying method and the synthesis of compensating networks on the assumption that explicit numerical values are given for all specification items. In practice, however, a specification for the synthesis of an automatic control system is not always given in the form of numerical values. Even if it is so given, synthesis of an automatic control system that meets all items of the specification exactly may for economic or other reasons be quite difficult. Therefore, we need to consider these facts in the synthesis of an automatic control system. We shall discuss the practical procedure for the synthesis of an automatic control system with such points taken into consideration.

In the previous discussion of the principles of the root-specifying method, we assumed that the dominant root $r_0 = (-\gamma_0 + j)\omega_0$ was given as an item of the specification. That is, we assumed that both the damped angular frequency ω_0 and the damping coefficient γ_0 were specified. In practice, however, they are often not explicitly specified. In general, the damping coefficient γ_0 of a dominant root is a constant which represents the waveform of the transient response, and its optimum value is fixed for a single type of automatic control system. Therefore, we may assume that γ_0 is always explicitly given in the specifications. On the other hand, the damped angular frequency is a constant representing the velocity of the response, and in practice it is not always included in the specifications. Sometimes, only γ_0 is specified and ω_0 can be arbitrary. If so, we need only a compensating transfer function with one degree of freedom, and hence all specified properties can be satisfied simply by gain adjustment.

Since the damped angular frequency ω_0 is a constant representing the velocity of the response, it is usually desirable to have it as great as possible rather than specify a certain value for it. For a synthesis with such a requirement, we first need to find the maximum value of ω_0 that can actually be attained by compensating the automatic control system given at the beginning of our synthesis.

The attainable maximum value of ω_0 depends on two factors.

1. The type of compensation (series or parallel) and the type of

compensating network that can be applied are considerably limited in most cases because of certain other requirements imposed on the system. If we keep on increasing the value of the specified damped angular frequency ω_0, the value of the compensating vector will finally exceed the compensating limit of any practically usable compensating network. The same result happens when the specified value of ω_0 keeps on decreasing. Thus, the range of ω_0 that can be used as a specification is restricted and depends on the compensating network to be used.

2. Frequently, the residue of the specified root for the values of ω_0 larger than a certain value no longer satisfies the condition for the specified root to be a dominant root. This also puts bounds on the value of ω_0 that can be used as a specification.

Therefore, we need to find the maximum value of ω_0 which is within these two limits for an actual synthesis of an automatic control system.

This maximum value of ω_0 can be found in the following manner. First compute the compensating vector for various values of ω_0, plot the computed values to obtain the locus of the compensating vector, and compare the locus with the compensating limit. Since it is convenient to use a logarithmic plane for a compensating chart, the locus of the compensating vector should also be plotted on the same logarithmic plane. The locus of a compensating vector plotted on a logarithmic plane is called a logarithmic compensating vector locus or simply a compensating vector locus.

The region of ω_0 that satisfies the condition for r_0 to be a dominant root can be found by using the methods discussed in Sections 5.2 and 5.3. That is, to construct the locus, we find the values of the free parameters of the compensating network for each value of ω_0, compute the residue of the reciprocal of each specified root γ_0 for the open-loop transfer function, compensated by the compensating transfer function, with the computed values of the free parameters, and plot the computed value of the residue on the residue limit chart of the dominant root. The calculation involved in this procedure seems quite complicated, but once the compensating chart is prepared, the values of the free parameters of the compensating network can be immediately found by plotting the compensating vector on the chart. As was shown in Section 5.3, computation of the residue of the reciprocal of a dominant root is not complicated.

The above procedure is an important part of the actual synthesis. Therefore, we shall present an example showing the details.

Suppose that the automatic control system shown in the block diagram of Fig. 8.12 is given and the open-loop transfer function is

$$F_0(s)=\frac{K}{\left(1+\frac{s}{\omega_{s1}}\right)\left(1+\frac{s}{\omega_{s2}}\right)\left(1+\frac{s}{\omega_{s3}}\right)} \tag{8.84}$$

where

$$\begin{aligned} &\omega_{s1}=1\times10^{-3}\ [\text{rad/s}] \qquad && \omega_{s3}=10\times10^{-3}\ [\text{rad/s}] \\ &\omega_{s2}=3\times10^{-3}\ [\text{rad/s}] && K=5\ [1/\text{s}] \end{aligned} \tag{8.85}$$

Assume that the following specifications are given.

1. The damping coefficient γ_0 should be $\gamma_0 = 0.3$.
2. A series compensation and the compensating network S2-1 shown in Table 6.4 should be used.
3. The damped angular frequency ω_0 should be the maximum value which does not conflict with conditions (1) and (2).

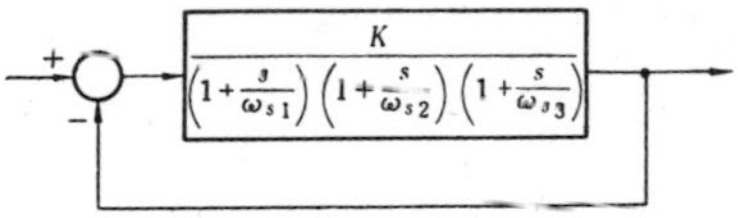

Fig. 8.12 Block diagram illustrating the plotting of the compensating vector

We shall show the actual synthesis procedure. First we perform the calculations necessary for constructing the compensating vector locus.

Let $g_c \epsilon^{j\phi_c} = g_c \angle \phi_c$ be the compensating vector. Then, from equation (8.16),

$$g_c\underline{/\phi_c} = \frac{\epsilon^{-j\pi}}{F_0(r_0)} = \frac{\epsilon^{-j\pi}}{K}\left(1+\frac{r_0}{\omega_{s1}}\right)\left(1+\frac{r_0}{\omega_{s2}}\right)\left(1+\frac{r_0}{\omega_{s3}}\right) \qquad (8.86)$$

If we substitute the specified root $r_0 = (-\gamma_0 + j)\,\omega_0$ into this equation, we get

$$\begin{aligned} g_c\underline{/\phi_c} &= \frac{\epsilon^{-j\pi}}{K}\left\{1+(-\gamma_0+j)\frac{\omega_0}{\omega_{s1}}\right\}\left\{1+(-\gamma_0+j)\frac{\omega_0}{\omega_{s2}}\right\}\left\{1+(-\gamma_0+j)\frac{\omega_0}{\omega_{s3}}\right\} \\ &= \frac{\epsilon^{-j\pi}}{K}\left(1-\gamma_0\frac{\omega_0}{\omega_{s1}}+j\frac{\omega_0}{\omega_{s1}}\right)\left(1-\gamma_0\frac{\omega_0}{\omega_{s2}}+j\frac{\omega_0}{\omega_{s2}}\right)\left(1-\gamma_0\frac{\omega_0}{\omega_{s3}}+j\frac{\omega_0}{\omega_{s3}}\right) \end{aligned} \qquad (8.87)$$

$$\begin{aligned} &= \frac{1}{K}\underline{/-180^\circ} \times \sqrt{\left(1-\gamma_0\frac{\omega_0}{\omega_{s1}}\right)^2+\left(\frac{\omega_0}{\omega_{s1}}\right)^2}\ \underline{\Big/\tan^{-1}\left(\frac{\frac{\omega_0}{\omega_{s1}}}{1-\gamma_0\frac{\omega_0}{\omega_{s1}}}\right)} \\ &\quad \times \sqrt{\left(1-\gamma_0\frac{\omega_0}{\omega_{s2}}\right)^2+\left(\frac{\omega_0}{\omega_{s2}}\right)^2}\ \underline{\Big/\tan^{-1}\left(\frac{\frac{\omega_0}{\omega_{s2}}}{1-\gamma_0\frac{\omega_0}{\omega_{s2}}}\right)} \\ &\quad \times \sqrt{\left(1-\gamma_0\frac{\omega_0}{\omega_{s3}}\right)^2+\left(\frac{\omega_0}{\omega_{s3}}\right)^2}\ \underline{\Big/\tan^{-1}\left(\frac{\frac{\omega_0}{\omega_{s3}}}{1-\gamma_0\frac{\omega_0}{\omega_{s3}}}\right)} \end{aligned} \qquad (8.88)$$

$$\begin{aligned} &= g_0\underline{/\phi_0} \times g_1\underline{/\phi_1} \times g_2\underline{/\phi_2} \times g_3\underline{/\phi_3} \\ &= g_0 g_1 g_2 g_3\underline{/\phi_0+\phi_1+\phi_2+\phi_3} \end{aligned} \qquad (8.89)$$

where

$$g_1 = \sqrt{\left(1-\gamma_0\frac{\omega_0}{\omega_{s1}}\right)^2+\left(\frac{\omega_0}{\omega_{s1}}\right)^2}, \qquad \phi_1 = \tan^{-1}\left(\frac{\frac{\omega_0}{\omega_{s1}}}{1-\gamma_0\frac{\omega_0}{\omega_{s1}}}\right)$$

Contd.,

$$g_2=\sqrt{\left(1-\gamma_0\frac{\omega_0}{\omega_{s2}}\right)^2+\left(\frac{\omega_0}{\omega_{s2}}\right)^2}, \qquad \phi_2=\tan^{-1}\left(\frac{\dfrac{\omega_0}{\omega_{s2}}}{1-\gamma_0\dfrac{\omega_0}{\omega_{s2}}}\right)$$

$$g_3=\sqrt{\left(1-\gamma_0\frac{\omega_0}{\omega_{s3}}\right)^2+\left(\frac{\omega_0}{\omega_{s3}}\right)^2}, \qquad \phi_3=\tan^{-1}\left(\frac{\dfrac{\omega_0}{\omega_{s3}}}{1-\gamma_0\dfrac{\omega_0}{\omega_{s3}}}\right) \tag{8.90}$$

If we substitute the numerical values given in equation (8.85) and $\gamma_0 = 0.3$ into these expressions, we get

$$\left.\begin{aligned}
&g_0=1/5=0.2, \qquad \phi_0=-180^\circ \\
&g_1=\sqrt{\left(1-\frac{0.3\,\omega_0}{1\times10^{-3}}\right)^2+\left(\frac{\omega_0}{1\times10^{-3}}\right)^2}, \quad \phi_1=\tan^{-1}\left(\frac{\dfrac{\omega_0}{1\times10^{-3}}}{1-\dfrac{0.3\,\omega_0}{1\times10^{-3}}}\right) \\
&g_2=\sqrt{\left(1-\frac{0.3\,\omega_0}{3\times10^{-3}}\right)^2+\left(\frac{\omega_0}{3\times10^{-3}}\right)^2}, \quad \phi_2=\tan^{-1}\left(\frac{\dfrac{\omega_0}{3\times10^{-3}}}{1-\dfrac{0.3\,\omega_0}{3\times10^{-3}}}\right) \\
&g_3=\sqrt{\left(1-\frac{0.3\,\omega_0}{10\times10^{-3}}\right)^2+\left(\frac{\omega_0}{10\times10^{-3}}\right)^2}, \quad \phi_3=\tan^{-1}\left(\frac{\dfrac{\omega_0}{10\times10^{-3}}}{1-\dfrac{0.3\,\omega_0}{10\times10^{-3}}}\right)
\end{aligned}\right\} \tag{8.91}$$

From these expressions, we can calculate the values of g_c, g_1, g_2, g_3, ϕ_0, ϕ_1, ϕ_2, and ϕ_3 for various values of ω_0. Substituting them into equation (8.89), we obtain the value of the compensating vector $g_c \angle \phi_c$ for various values of ω_0. Table 8.8 shows the calculated values of $g_c \angle \phi_c$ for various values of ω_0. Though the theoretical allowable range for ω_0 is the entire interval from 0 to ∞, we only need compute the values of $g_c \angle \phi_c$ for a sufficient number of values of ω_0 around that value which is likely to be the damped angular frequency of the synthesised automatic control system.

The range of such values of ω_0 can be roughly estimated by observing the values of the break angular frequencies ω_s of the given open-loop transfer function, the type of automatic control system that is given, and the type of compensating network to be used. More specifically, this range of values of ω_0 is in general the interval from the second-smallest break angular frequency of the given open-loop transfer function to ten times the second largest break angular frequency. However, if the compensating network leads the phase angle of the open-loop transfer, as in the case of a lead network or a proportional + differentiating network, then the above range of values of ω_0 should be shifted slightly toward the high-frequency side. If the compensating network gives a phase-lag effect such as a lag network or a proportional + integrating network, then the above range of values of ω_0 should be shifted slightly toward the low-frequency side. It should be remarked that the angular frequency of a pole located at the origin should be also regarded as a break angular frequency with frequency 0.

If we plot the calculated values shown in Table 8.8 on a logarithmic plane, we obtain the compensating vector locus. The thus constructed compensating vector locus is shown in Fig. 8.13*. From Fig. 8.13, we see that the ω_0 range which corresponds to the inside of the compensating limit ($\Omega > 0$, $k > 1$) is

$$4\times10^{-3}\ [\text{rad/s}] < \omega_0 < 23\times10^{-3}\ [\text{rad/s}] \tag{8.92}$$

in Fig. 8.13. The values of k can be directly read from the compensating chart. The values of ω_S can easily be calculated from the values of Ω_S read from the compensating chart. The values thus found for the free parameters k and ω_S are shown in Table 8.9.

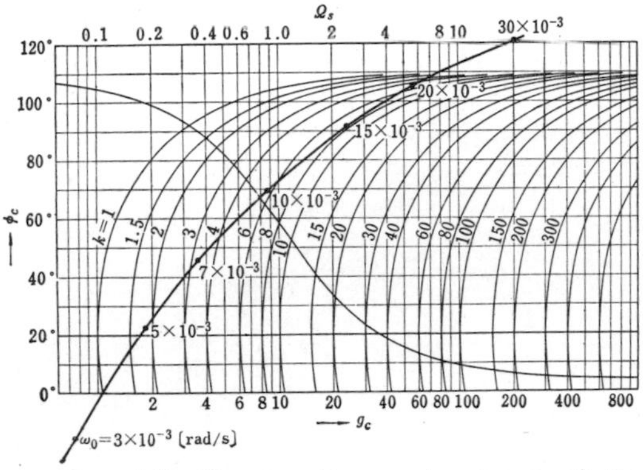

Fig. 8.13 Compensating vector locus of the automatic control system whose transfer function is given by equation (8.84)

Now we shall investigate whether the specified root is really the dominant root of the automatic control system when it is compensated by a compensation network with each set of free parameters shown in Fig. 8.9. For this purpose, we compute the residue of the dominant root of the compensated automatic control system by the method discussed in Section 5.2.

The compensated open-loop transfer function is

$$F(s) = F_0(s)F_c(s) = \frac{Kk\left(1+\dfrac{s}{\omega_s}\right)}{\left(1+\dfrac{s}{\omega_{s1}}\right)\left(1+\dfrac{s}{\omega_{s2}}\right)\left(1+\dfrac{s}{\omega_{s3}}\right)} \tag{8.93}$$

Since this transfer function is of the same form as the transfer function (5.87), the residue of the dominant root can be calculated by using equation (5.95). That is, if we set

$$T_{z1} = \frac{1}{\omega_s},\quad T_{p1} = \frac{1}{\omega_{s1}},\quad T_{p2} = \frac{1}{\omega_{s2}},\quad T_{p3} = \frac{1}{\omega_{s3}},\quad n=0,\ l=3,\ m=1 \tag{8.94}$$

*According to what we said above, we should plot the compensating vector locus on a semi-transparent logarithmic sheet and place it on the compensating chart to read the values of the free parameters. However, it is difficult to practise such a method in a textbook. Therefore, the compensating vector locus is directly plotted on the compensating chart (the chart for γ_0 = 0.3 in Table I of the appendix) in Fig. 8.13.

TABLE 8.8
CALCULATION OF THE VALUES OF THE COMPENSATING VECTOR

ω_0 $(\times 10^{-3})$ [rad/s]	$g_1/\underline{\phi_1}$			$g_2/\underline{\phi_2}$	
	$\frac{\omega_0}{1\times 10^{-3}}$	$1-\frac{0.3\omega_0}{1\times 10^{-3}}$	$g_1/\underline{\phi_1}$	$\frac{\omega_0}{3\times 10^{-3}}$	$1-\frac{0.3\,\omega_0}{3\times 10^{-3}}$
3	3	0.10	3.00/88.1°	1.00	0.70
5	5	−0.50	5.03/95.7°	1.67	0.50
7	7	−1.10	7.08/98.9°	2.33	0.30
10	10	−2.00	10.2/101.3°	3.33	0.00
15	15	−3.50	15.4/103.1°	5.00	−0.50
20	20	−5.00	20.6/104.0°	6.67	−1.00
30	30	−8.00	31.0/104.9°	10.00	−2.00

the reciprocal $1/B_0$ of the residue is

$$\frac{1}{B_0}=2+\frac{1}{1+\frac{r_0}{\omega_s}}-\frac{1}{1+\frac{r_0}{\omega_{s1}}}-\frac{1}{1+\frac{r_0}{\omega_{s2}}}-\frac{1}{1+\frac{r_0}{\omega_{s3}}} \tag{8.95}$$

$$=2+\frac{1}{1+\frac{\omega_0}{\omega_s}(-\gamma_0+j)}-\frac{1}{g_1/\underline{\phi_1}}-\frac{1}{g_2/\underline{\phi_2}}-\frac{1}{g_3/\underline{\phi_3}} \tag{8.96}$$

$$=2+\frac{1}{1-\gamma_0\frac{\omega_0}{\omega_s}+j\frac{\omega_0}{\omega_s}}-\frac{1}{g_1}\underline{/-\phi_1}-\frac{1}{g_2}\underline{/-\phi_2}-\frac{1}{g_3}\underline{/-\phi_3} \tag{8.97}$$

where g_1, g_2, g_3, ϕ_1, ϕ_2, and ϕ_3 are the quantities given in equation (8.91). Since their values have already been calculated for various values of ω_0 (see Fig. 8.8), $1/B_0$ can easily be calculated by use of the table. The values of $1/B_0$ for various values of ω_0 are presented in Tables 8.10 and 8.11.

Figure 8.14 shows the locus of the residue vector plotted on the residue limit chart of the dominant root by using the numerical data shown in Tables 8.10 and 8.11. Observing the chart in Fig. 8.14, we see that the specified root $-r_0 + j\omega_0$, with ω_0 belonging to the range 5×10^{-3} [rad/sec] $< \omega_0 <$ 20×10^{-3} [rad/sec], is the dominant root.

TABLE 8.9 VALUES OF k, Ω_s AND ω_s

$\omega_0\,(\times 10^{-3})$	read values		$\omega_s=\Omega_s\omega_0\times 10^{-3}$
	k	$\Omega_s\times 10^{-3}$	
5	1.75	3.1	15.5
7	3.3	1.4	9.8
10	5.5	0.74	7.4
15	7.5	0.32	4.8
20	5.6	0.10	2.0

TABLE 8.8
(*continued*)

	g_3/ϕ_3			g_c/ϕ_c
g_2/ϕ_2	$\frac{\omega_0}{10\times10^{-3}}$	$1-\frac{0.3\,\omega_0}{10\times10^{-3}}$	g_3/ϕ_3	
1.22/55.0°	0.3	0.91	0.958/18.3°	0.706/−18.6°
1.74/73.4°	0.5	0.85	0.986/30.5°	1.73/19.6°
2.35/82.7°	0.7	0.79	1.06/41.5°	3.52/42.1°
3.33/90.0°	1.0	0.70	1.22/55.0°	8.29/66.3°
5.03/95.7°	1.5	0.55	1.60/69.9°	2.48/88.7°
6.75/98.5°	2.0	0.40	2.04/78.7°	56.1/101.2°
10.2/101.3°	3.0	0.10	3.00/88.1°	199/114.3°

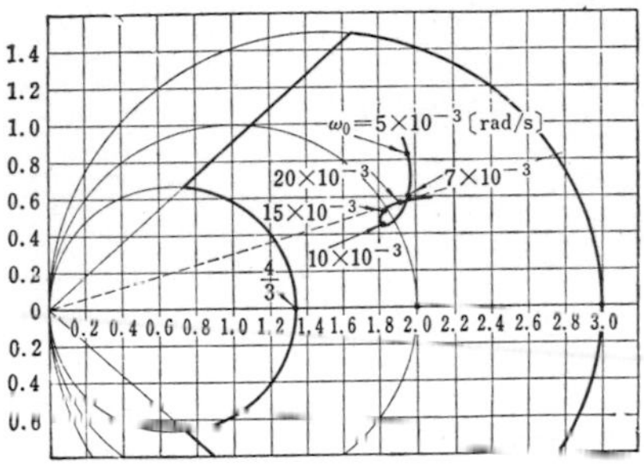

Fig. 8.14 Locus of residue vector of the dominant root plotted on the residue limit chart

The above example shows an outline of the synthesis of an automatic control system. The general procedure of the synthesis is as follows.

(a) Determination of the damping coefficient γ_0. When the damping is not given in the specification, choose a suitable γ_0 according to the type of automatic control system to be synthesised.

(b) Determination of the type of compensation (series or parallel).

(c) Construction of the compensating vector locus. Plot the compensating vector locus for the specified or determined value of the coefficient γ_0 on the logarithmic plane by varying ω_0.

(d) Determination of the range of ω_0. Select a suitable network by comparing the compensating vector and the compensating limits of various networks for the given value of γ_0. Then determine the range of ω_0 for which the given automatic control system can be compensated with the network.

(e) Reading of the values of the free parameters. For each value

TABLE 8.10 NUMERICAL CALCULATION OF THE SECOND TERM ON THE RIGHT SIDE OF EDUATION (8.97)

				$\frac{1}{1-\gamma_0\frac{\omega_0}{\omega_s}+j\frac{\omega_0}{\omega_s}}$		
ω_0 $(\times 10^{-3})$	ω_s $(\times 10^{-3})$	$\frac{\omega_0}{\omega_s}$	$1-0.3\frac{\omega_0}{\omega_s}$	$g/\underline{\phi}$	$\frac{1}{g}/\underline{-\phi}$	$A+jB$
5	15.5	0.32	0.904	$0.965/\underline{19.5^\circ}$	$1.04\ /\underline{-19.5^\circ}$	$0.980-j0.398$
7	9.8	0.72	0.784	$1.06\ /\underline{42.1^\circ}$	$0.944/\underline{-42.1^\circ}$	$0.700-j0.632$
10	7.4	1.35	0.595	$1.48\ /\underline{66.2^\circ}$	$0.672/\underline{-66.2^\circ}$	$0.271-j0.615$
15	4.8	3.13	0.070	$3.10\ /\underline{88.7^\circ}$	$0.323/\underline{-88.7^\circ}$	$0.007-j0.323$
20	2.0	10.0	-2.00	$10.0/\underline{101.2^\circ}$	$0.100/\underline{-101.2^\circ}$	$-0.019-j0.098$

TABLE 8.11 CALCULATION OF THE EXPRESSION (8·97)

ω_0	$\frac{1}{g}/\underline{-\phi}$	$-\frac{1}{g_1}/\underline{-\phi_1}$		$-\frac{1}{g_2}/\underline{-\phi_2}$		$-\frac{1}{g_3}/\underline{-\phi_3}$		$\frac{1}{B_0}$
$(\times 10^{-3})$	A jB	g_1 ϕ_1	A_1 jB_1	g_2 ϕ_2	A^2 jB_2	g_3 ϕ_3	A_3 jB_3	A_0 jB_0
5	0.983 $-j0.348$	5.03 95.7°	0.020 $j0.198$	1.74 73.4°	−0.164 $j0.550$	0.986 30.5°	−0.874 $j0.514$	1.965 $j0.863$
7	0.692 $-j0.635$	708 98.9°	0.022 $j0.139$	2.35 82.7°	−0.055 $j0.423$	1.06 41·5°	−0.709 $j0.628$	1.950 $j0.553$
10	0.273 $-j0.620$	10.2 101.3	0.019 $j0.096$	3.33 90.0°	0 $j0.300$	1.22 55.0°	−0.470 $j0.671$	1.822 $j0.449$
15	0.006 $-j0.317$	15.4 103.1°	0.015 $j0.063$	5.03 95.7°	0.020 $j0.198$	1.60 69.9°	−0.215 $j0.588$	1.826 $j0.532$
20	− 0.019 $-j0.096$	20.6 104°	0.012 $j.047$	6.75 98.5°	0.022 $j0.146$	2.04 78.7°	−0.096 $j0.481$	1.919 $j0.577$

The values of $1/B_0$ were obtained from the equation $1/B_0 = A_0 + jB_0$ where

$$A_0 = 2 + A + A_1 + A_2 + A_3$$

and

$$B_0 = B + B_1 + B_2 + B_3$$

of ω_0 in the above range, read the values of the free parameters of the transfer function.
(f) Construction of the locus of the reciprocal of the residue vector. For various values of ω_0 in the same range, compute the reciprocal $1/b$ of the residue and plot the locus of the reciprocal of the residue vector.
(g) Determination of the optimum value of ω_0. Find the maximum value of ω_0 that satisfies the condition for the characteristic root $(-\gamma_0 + j)\omega_0$ to be the dominant root, by comparing the locus of the reciprocal of the residue vector with the residue limit of the dominant root.
(h) Analysis of synthesised transient response. If it is necessary to know the synthesised transient response exactly, calculate the transient response by manual computation or by the use of an analogue computer, and examine the result.
(i) Determination of the network constants of the compensating network. Compute the network constants of the compensating network from the free parameters corresponding to the optimum value of ω_0.

This is the general synthesis procedure for an automatic control system. In practice, some of the steps can be simplified or omitted, depending on the situation. We shall discuss cases that often occur in the actual synthesis.

The type of compensation to be used in the synthesis is often laid down in the specification. Then, step (b) can be automatically omitted. Even if it is not laid down in the specification, it is often determined naturally by the types of components to be used for construction of the automatic control system. For example, when electron tube amplifiers are used as elements of the automatic control system, it is better to use a series compensation. On the other hand, if magnetic amplifiers or rotary amplifiers are used as elements, parallel compensation is preferred and series compensation is not used in most cases. When it is hard to tell which type of compensation is superior at the beginning of the synthesis, we should decide which kind of compensating network to select according to the final result of the synthesis.

As stated previously, the compensating vector locus is primarily used to determine the region of the damped angular frequency for which compensation is possible with the compensating network by comparing the compensating vector locus with the compensating limit and to find the values of the free parameters of the compensating network. In addition, the compensating vector locus can also be used to find the characteristics of a given automatic control system with no compensation. That is, by use of the compensating vector locus, we can see whether the given automatic control really requires compensation or not, or whether the characteristics of the given automatic control system can be improved by a simple technique without going through all the steps from (d) to (i).

In Section 4.12 we introduced a method of finding whether the damped ratio of every characteristic root is larger than a certain value γ_0 or not, by use of the locus of the complex frequency response $F(-\gamma_0\omega_0 + j\omega_0)$ of an open-loop transfer function $F(s)$.

The compensating vector locus of the vector g_c/ϕ_c is a curve obtained by varying ω_0 in the equation that results from substituting $r_0 = (-\gamma_0 + j)\omega_0$ into equation (8.16). That is, the compensating vector locus is the curve of the equation

$$g_c/\phi_c = \frac{\epsilon^{-j\pi}}{F(-\gamma_0\omega_0 + j\omega_0)} \tag{8.98}$$

when ω_0 varies. Accordingly, if we rotate the locus of the reciprocal of the complex frequency response $F(-\gamma_0\omega_0 + j\omega_0)$ by -180° around the origin, we obtain the compensating locus. Therefore, we can also compare the damping coefficient of every characteristic root with γ_0 by using the compensating vector locus in the same way* as the locus of the complex frequency response.

For example, if the compensating vector locus passes to the right of the point $1 + j0$ (see curve (a) in Fig. 8.15), then the damping coefficient of every characteristic root of the given system is already larger than the specified γ_0 before compensation. Consequently, no compensation is necessary for the given control system. If the compensating vector passes through the point $1 + j0$ (see curve (b) in Fig. 8.15), the given system has a characteristic root whose damping coefficient is exactly equal to the specified damping coefficient γ_0, and this root is $(-\gamma_0 + j)\omega_1$, where ω_1 is the angular frequency corresponding to the point $1 + j0$. If the compensating vector locus passes to the left of the point $1 + j0$, then it is necessary to improve the transient response of the given system by compensation. In this case, if the compensating vector intersects the real axis at a point whose real coordinate is a (where $a < 1$) and if the damped angular frequency corresponding to the point of intersection is ω_2, then we can let the vector locus pass through the point $1 + j0$ by multiplying the compensating vector by a. This means that we can let the system have a characteristic root with a specified damping coefficient by multiplying the open-loop transfer function of the given system by a (where $a < 1$). The damped angular frequency corresponding to the point $1 + j0$ is clearly ω_2. Therefore, if the damped angular frequency is allowed to be arbitrary, we can easily find accurately the value of the gain constant that is necessary for the system to have a characteristic root with the specified damping coefficient γ_0. Fig. 8.16 shows the logarithmic compensating vector loci corresponding to the compensating vector loci shown in Fig. 8.15. The logarithmic vector locus can also be used to compare the damping coefficient of each characteristic root with the specified damping γ_0. The reference point for comparison on the logarithmic plane is the point with coordinates $g_c = 1$ and $\phi_c = 0$ instead of $1 + j0$ on the usual complex plane. It is clear that we will obtain the same comparison results by the same method as before when the logarithmic compensating vector locus is used.

*The point $-1 + j0$ was taken as the reference point for the comparison when the complex frequency locus was used. The reference point should be $1 + j0$ when the compensating vector locus is used.

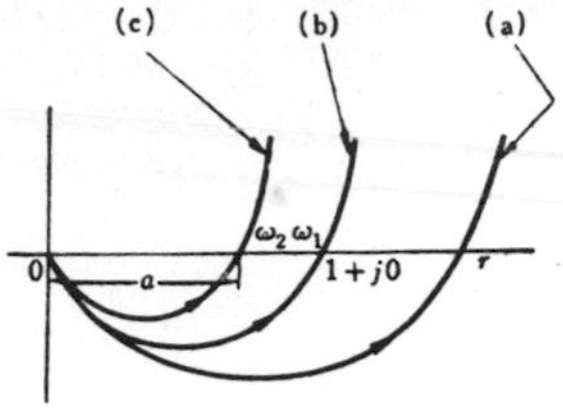

Fig. 8.15 Evaluation of the transient response using compensating vector locus: (a) no compensation needed; (b) system has characteristic root with specified damping ceofficient; (c) compensation needed

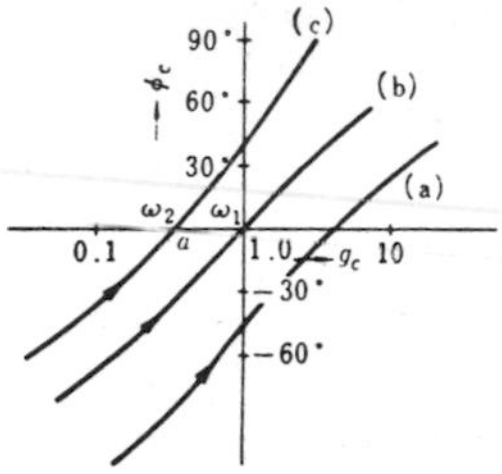

Fig. 8.16 Evaluation of the transient response using logarithmic compensating vector locus: (a) no compensation nedded; (b) system has characteristic root with specified damping coefficient; (c) compensation needed

8.6. AN EXAMPLE ILLUSTRATING THE SYNTHESIS OF A TRANSIENT RESPONSE

We shall give an example that illustrates the root-specifying method of synthesis. Consider the servomechanism shown in Fig. 8.17. Let us improve the transient characteristics by use of a compensating network. The necessary compensating network can be synthesised by the procedure described in Section 8.5.

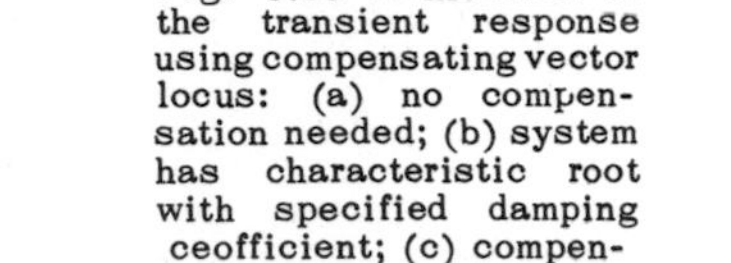

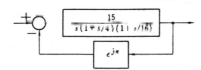

Fig. 8.17 Block diagram of a servomechanism whose transient characteristics require improvement

(a) Determination of the damping coefficient. Since the given system is a servomechanism, it is best to use $\gamma_0 = 0.5$. Then, the dominant root r_0 will be

$$r_0 = (-0.5 + j)\omega_0 \tag{8.99}$$

(b) Determination of the type of compensation. To determine the type of compensation, more detailed information on the given system is necessary. Here we assume that we should take a series compensator.

(c) Construction of the compensating vector locus. The transfer function $F(s)$ given in Fig. 8.17 is

$$F(s) = \frac{15}{s\left(1+\frac{s}{4}\right)\left(1+\frac{s}{16}\right)} \tag{8.100}$$

Thus, the compensating vector $g_c \angle \phi_c$ is

$$g_c\underline{/\phi_c} = \frac{\epsilon^{-j\pi}}{15} r_0\left(1+\frac{r_0}{4}\right)\left(1+\frac{r_0}{16}\right) \tag{8.101}$$

$$= \frac{\epsilon^{-j\pi}}{15}(-0.5+j)\omega_0\left\{1+(-0.5+j)\frac{\omega_0}{4}\right\}\left\{1+(-0.5+j)\frac{\omega_0}{16}\right\} \tag{8.102}$$

Here each term is calculated as follows:

$$g_0\underline{/\phi_0} = \frac{\epsilon^{-j\pi}}{15} = 6.67\times10^{-2}\underline{/-180^\circ} \tag{8.103}$$

$$g_1\underline{/\phi_1} = (-0.5+j)\omega_0 = \sqrt{(0.5)^2+1^2}\,\omega_0\underline{/\tan^{-1}\left(\frac{1}{-0.5}\right)} = 1.12\,\omega_0\underline{/116.8^\circ} \tag{8.104}$$

$$g_2\underline{/\phi_2} = 1+(-0.5+j)\frac{\omega_0}{4} = \sqrt{\left(1-0.5\frac{\omega_0}{4}\right)^2+\left(\frac{\omega_0}{4}\right)^2}\ \underline{/\tan^{-1}\left(\frac{\frac{\omega_0}{4}}{1-0.5\frac{\omega_0}{4}}\right)} \tag{8.105}$$

$$g_3\underline{/\phi_3} = 1+(-0.5+j)\frac{\omega_0}{16} = \sqrt{\left(1-0.5\frac{\omega_0}{16}\right)^2+\left(\frac{\omega_0}{16}\right)^2}\ \underline{/\tan^{-1}\left(\frac{\frac{\omega_0}{16}}{1-0.5\frac{\omega_0}{16}}\right)} \tag{8.106}$$

Numerical calculations of the compensating vector for various values of the damped angular frequency ω_0 are shown in Table 8.12.

(d) Determination of the compensating network. If we plot the compensating vector locus from the numerical values in Table 8.12, we obtain curve (a) of Fig. 8.18.

As indicated in Fig. 8.18, the compensating vector locus intersects the horizontal axis at ω_0 = 3.0 [rad/sec] and the corresponding value of g_c is approximately 0.21. Therefore, if we let

TABLE 8.12
NUMERICAL CALCULATION OF THE COMPENSATING VECTOR FOR THE SERVOMECHANISM SHOWN IN FIG. 8.17

ω_0[rad/s]	$g_1\underline{/\phi_1}$	$g_2\underline{/\phi_2}$	
	$1.12\,\omega_0\underline{/116.8^\circ}$	$\frac{\omega_0}{4}$	$g_2\underline{/\phi_2}$
1	1.12/ "	0.25	$0.910\underline{/16.0^\circ}$
2	2.24/ "	0.50	$0.901\underline{/33.7^\circ}$
3	2.34/ "	0.75	$0.976\underline{/50.2^\circ}$
5	5.60/ "	1.25	$1.305\underline{/73.3^\circ}$
7	7.84/ "	1.75	$1.75\ \underline{/85.9^\circ}$
10	11.2/ "	2.50	$2.51\ \underline{/95.7^\circ}$
15	16.8/ "	3.75	$3.84\ \underline{/103.1^\circ}$
20	22.4/ "	5.00	$5.22\ \underline{/106.7^\circ}$

the gain constant K be 3.15 (by multiplying the given gain constant $K = 15$ by 0.21), then the servomechanism has the damping coefficient $\gamma_0 = 0.5$ as specified, and the corresponding damped angular frequency ω_0 is approximately 0.3 [rad/sec]. If this is the required characteristic of the servomechanism then the principal part of the synthesis has been finished.

As stated previously, the velocity error increases when the gain constant K decreases. Therefore, we often need to improve the transient characteristics without decreasing the value of K. In such a case, we have to use a compensating network. Let us discuss this case.

First, we need to choose a suitable compensating network. Fig. 8.18 shows, besides the compensating vector locus, the compensating limits of a few networks which are likely to be suitable compensating networks. In actual synthesis, we should plot the compensating vector locus on a semi-transparent graph sheet with the same scaling as those of the compensating charts and place the semi-transparent sheet on each compensating chart to determine the suitable range of ω_0, instead of plotting all of them together on one graph sheet.

Reading the range of ω_0 corresponding to the compensating region (that is, the region within the compensating limit) for each compensating network, we obtain the following results.

1. For the region $\omega_0 < 3.0$ [rad/sec], the network S2-4 can be used as the compensating network.
2. For the region 3.0 [rad/sec] $< \omega_0 <$ 7.5 [rad/sec], the network S2-5 can be used.
3. For the region 8.0 [rad/sec] $< \omega_0 <$ 17 [rad/sec], the network S2-5 can be used.
4. For the region $\omega_0 < 7.5$ [rad/sec], the network S3-1 can be used.

Thus, we see that the network S2-3 is the best compensating network for obtaining a fast response.

In addition to this, we can obtain more information from Fig. 8.18 if we consider the following fact. When the gain constant K of the given open-loop transfer function increases or decreases, the

TABLE 8.12
(continued)

$g_3/\underline{\phi_3}$			$g_c/\underline{\phi_c}$
$\frac{\omega_0}{16}$	$1-0.5\frac{\omega_0}{16}$	$g_3/\underline{\phi_3}$	
0.0625	0.969	$0.971/\underline{3.6°}$	$0.0667/\underline{-44.7°}$
0.125	0.937	$0.946/\underline{7.6°}$	$0.128\ /\underline{-21.9°}$
0.187	0.907	$0.926/\underline{11.6°}$	$0.203\ /\underline{-1.4°}$
0.312	0.844	$0.900/\underline{20.4°}$	$0.437\ /\underline{30.6°}$
0.437	0.782	$0.896/\underline{29.5°}$	$0.821\ /\underline{51.3°}$
0.625	0.687	$0.929/\underline{42.3°}$	$1.75\ /\underline{74.8°}$
0.936	0.532	$1.08\ /\underline{60.4°}$	$4.66\ /\underline{100.3°}$
1.25	0.376	$1.31\ /\underline{73.4°}$	$10.2\ /\underline{116.8°}$

compensating vector locus shifts to the left or right, as is clearly shown by equation (8.101). Thus, the compensating region of each compensating network also changes accordingly. Thus we have the following information.

1. If K becomes 1.5 times the given value, the lead network S2-3 is no longer usable as a compensating network.
2. The lag network S2-4, the lead network S2-5, and the lead-lag network S3-1 can all be used as the compensating network even when the gain constant K is increased considerably.
3. When the lead network S2-3 is used as the compensating network, the smaller the gain constant is, the faster will be the response. On the other hand, when the lead network S2-5 or the lead-lag network S3-1 is used as the compensating network, the larger the gain constant is, the faster will be the response; the response velocity for a large gain constant is approximately the same as that for a small gain constant when the lead network S2-3 is used.
4. When the lag network S2-4 is used as the compensating network the response velocity remains almost the same for a change in the value of the gain constant.

The above information can be obtained more accurately in terms of numerical values by simply sliding the semi-transparent sheet on which the compensating vector locus is plotted on the compensating chart to the left or right according to the change in the value of K.

Considering the capability of each compensating network and the other requirements imposed on the servomechanism, we choose a compensating network that best suits our purpose. Here, we assume that we do not change the given value of the gain constant K ($K = 15$) and we choose, as the compensating network, the lead network S2-3, which gives the fastest response velocity to the servomechanism.

(e) Calculation of the free parameters of the compensating transfer function. If we place the compensating vector locus (the semi-transparent sheet) on Fig. V of the Appendix, we can read the values of the free parameters of the lead network S2-3 for $\gamma_0 = 0.5$. Detailed instruction for using Table V is given in Table 3 in the Appendix. By the above method, we can read the values of the relative break angular frequency $\Omega_s = \omega_s / \omega_0$ and n for each value of ω_0. Table 8.13 shows values thus found for the free parameters and the compensating transfer functions with these values of the parameters.

(f) Calculation of the reciprocal of the residue of the dominant root. If we connect the compensating network having the compensation transfer function determined in step (e) with the given system in series, the open-loop transfer function of the compensated servomechanism is

$$F(s) = \frac{15\left(1+\frac{s}{\omega_s}\right)}{s\left(1+\frac{s}{4}\right)\left(1+\frac{s}{16}\right)\left(1+\frac{s}{n\omega_s}\right)} \tag{8.107}$$

Since this transfer function is of the same form as the transfer

TABLE 8.13 VALUES OF Ω_s AND n AND THE COMPENSATING TRANSFER FUNCTIONS WITH THESE VALUES OF THE FREE PARAMETERS

ω_0[rad/s]	Ω_s	ω_s[rad/s]	n	compensating transfer function
10	609·0	6.09	11.4	$\frac{1+s/6.09}{1+s/69.4}$
15	0.34	5.1	45.0	$\frac{1+s/5.1}{1+s/230}$

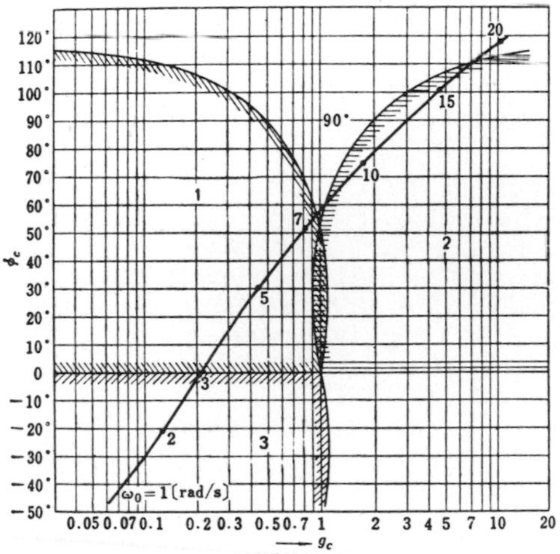

1 - *compensating region of S3-1 and S2-5*
2 - *compensating region of S2-3; 3 - compensating region of S2-1*

Fig. 8.18 Compensating vector locus* for the servomechanism shown in Fig. 8.17

function given in equation (5.87), we use equation (5.95) to compute the reciprocal $1/B_0$ of the residue of the characteristic with which we can examine whether the characteristic root is really the dominant root or not. Then

$$\frac{1}{B_0}=1+3-1+\frac{1}{1+\frac{r_0}{\omega_s}}-\frac{1}{1+\frac{r_0}{4}}-\frac{1}{1+\frac{r_0}{16}}-\frac{1}{1+\frac{r_0}{n\omega_s}} \qquad (8.108)$$

$$=3+\frac{1}{1+\frac{r_0}{\omega_s}}-\frac{1}{1+\frac{r_0}{n\omega_s}}-\frac{1}{g_2/\underline{\phi_2}}-\frac{1}{g_3/\underline{\phi_3}} \qquad (8.109)$$

where $g_2/\underline{\phi_c}$ and $g_3/\underline{\phi_3}$ are given by equations (8.105) and (8.106) respectively. Since their values for various values of ω_0 are already presented in Table 8.12, we can use this table for

*In practice, we do not plot a compensating vector locus directly on a compensating chart but on a semi-transparent graph sheet with the same logarithmic scale as the compensating chart. In order to find a suitable range of the damped angular frequency ω_0, we place the semi-transparent sheet on the compensating chart and read values of ω_0.

evaluating $1/B_0$. The value of $1/D_0$ for ω_0 = 15 [rad/sec] can be calculated as follows:

$$\frac{1}{B_0}=3+\frac{1}{-0.47+j2.94}-\frac{1}{0.967+j0.065}-\frac{1}{3.85\underline{/103.1^\circ}} \tag{8.110}$$

$$-\frac{1}{1.077\underline{/60.4^\circ}}$$

$$=3+0.337\underline{/-99.0^\circ}-1.03\underline{/-0.5^\circ}-0.260\underline{/-103.1^\circ} \tag{8.111}$$

$$-0.928\underline{/-60.4^\circ}$$

$$=3-0.052-j0.333-1.03+j0.01+0.057+j0.253 \tag{8.112}$$

$$-0.459+j0.808$$

$$=1.52+j0.74 \tag{8.113}$$

(g) Determination of the maximum value of ω_0. If we plot the reciprocal of the residue for ω_0 = 15 [rad/sec] on the residue-limit chart of the dominant roots shown in Fig. 5.8, it lies within the residue limit. That is, the characteristic root with damped angular frequency ω_0 = 15 [rad/sec] is indeed the dominant root. Since we prefer the largest value of ω_0, we need not examine the characteristic root with ω_0 = 10 [rad/sec]. Thus, we select the value ω_0 = 15 [rad/sec].

(h) Determination of the network constants of the compensating network. Table 3 in the Appendix shows that the network constants of the compensating network are as follows:

$$R_1=\frac{1}{C_1\omega_s} \tag{8.114}$$

$$R_2=\frac{1}{C_1}\frac{1}{(n-1)\omega_s} \tag{8.115}$$

If we take C_1 = 1 [μF], then

$$R_1=\frac{1}{1\times10^{-6}\times5.1}=196 \quad [\text{k}\Omega] \tag{8.116}$$

$$R_2=\frac{1}{1\times10^{-6}\times(45-1)\times5.1} \tag{8.117}$$

$$=4.45\ [\text{k}\Omega]$$

Therefore, the compensating network is the network shown in Fig. 8.19 and the servomechanism with the compensation has the block diagram shown in Fig. 8.20.

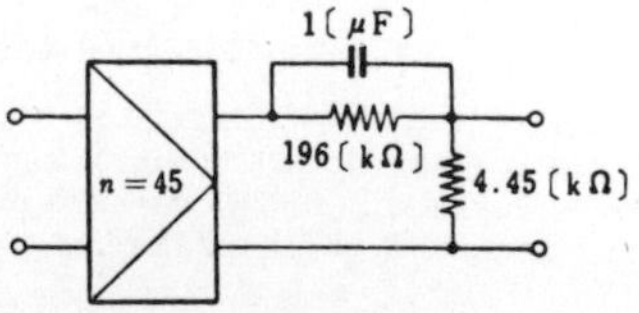

Fig. 8.19 Synthesised compensating network

(i) Accurate calculation of the response waveform. If we calculate the transient response of the servomechanism with the block diagram shown in Fig. 8.20 by using an analogue computer, we obtain the waveform shown in Fig. 8.21.

EXERCISE PROBLEMS

(1) Derive a compensating formula for each of the following series of compensating transfer functions:

(i) $\dfrac{1+\dfrac{s}{\omega_s}}{1+\dfrac{s}{n\omega_s}}$ (ii) $\dfrac{1+\dfrac{s}{\omega_s}}{1+\dfrac{ns}{\omega_s}}$

(iii) $\left(1+\dfrac{s}{\omega_{s_1}}+\dfrac{\omega_{s2}}{s}\right)$ (iv) $k\left(1+\dfrac{\omega_s}{s}\right)$

(2) Find the compensating limit of each of the compensating networks shown below. The compensating formulas are shown in Figs. 8.4 and 8.5. We assume that R_1, R_2, C_1, and C_2 are all positive quantities.

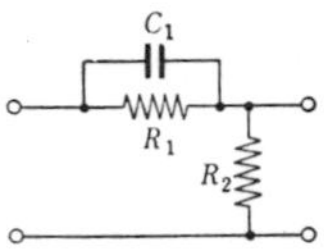

(1)

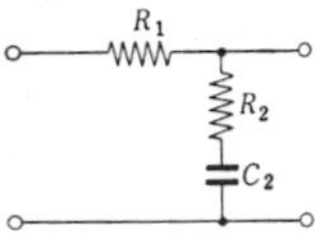

(2)

(3) Plot the compensating vector locus for each of the following transfer functions:

(i) ϵ^{-s}

(ii) ϵ^{-10s}

(iii) $\dfrac{\epsilon^{-s}}{1+0.5s}$

(iv) $\dfrac{1}{(1+3s)^3}$

(v) $\dfrac{50}{(1+2s)(1+0.3s)(1+0.05s)}$

(4) Consider a second-order system given by the block diagram. We wish to let the system have two real characteristic roots a and b. What should the values of K and T_1 be?

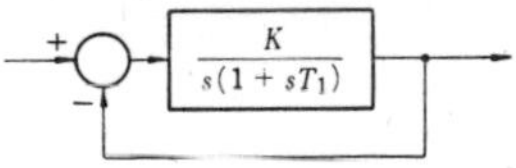

(5) Consider a lead network and a lag network and suppose that both have the same compensating transfer function

$$\frac{1+\dfrac{s}{\omega_{s2}}}{1+\dfrac{s}{\omega_{s_1}}}$$

If the compensating vector is $g_c \angle \phi_c$, find ω_{s1}, ω_{s2}, and the scaling curves.

(6) Find the scaling curves for the free parameters of the compensating transfer function of the compensating network S2-6. Find a method of constructing the compensating chart (the logarithmic compensating chart).

(7) Consider an automatic control system whose open-loop transfer function is

$$F_0(s)=\frac{20\,\epsilon^{-15s}}{1+20\,s}$$

We compensate this system with a compensating network whose compensating transfer function is $k\,(1 + 1/sT_1)$, and we wish to make the response velocity as large as possible. What should the values of k and T_1 be? We assume that the damping coefficient $\gamma_0 = 0.3$.

(8) Consider an automatic control system whose open-loop transfer function is

$$F_0(s)=\frac{2\epsilon^{-s}}{s}.$$

Do the same as in problem (7) for this system. We assume that the same compensating network is used and the same specification is given as in problem (7).

(9) Consider an automatic control system whose open-loop transfer function is

$$F_0(s)=\frac{70}{(1+s)\left(1+\frac{s}{5}\right)\left(1+\frac{s}{20}\right)\left(1+\frac{s}{100}\right)}$$

Apply a series compensation to this sytem, using a compensating network with two degrees of freedom. Here we assume that $\gamma_0 = 0.4$ and that it is required not to change the given gain constant.

9

Applied Synthesis

9.1. SYNTHESIS OF COMPENSATING NETWORKS WITH THREE DEGREES OF FREEDOM

As briefly mentioned in Section 6.5, a network with three degrees of freedom is more flexible than one with two degrees of freedom and it is often convenient for practical synthesis to use a compensating network with three degrees of freedom. Specifically, by giving suitable values to two of the three free parameters, we can let the automatic control system have a specified dominant root, and, by giving a suitable value to the remaining free parameter we can adjust the compensating limit of the compensating network or we can control the effect of another characteristic on the performance of the system.

Let us discuss the synthesis of compensating networks with three degrees of freedom shown in Table 6.5.

(1) SYNTHESIS OF S3-4

The compensating networks S3-3 and S3-4 shown in Table 6.4 are essentially modifications of the lead network (S2-3) and the lag network (S2-4), which are compensating networks with two degrees of freedom such that the gain constants are adjustable. Consequently, the synthesis of these compensating networks is also a modification of the synthesis of the compensating networks with two degrees of freedom.

The compensating transfer function of S3-4 (a lag network with three degrees of freedom) is

$$F_c(s) = \frac{k\left(1+\dfrac{s}{\omega_s}\right)}{1+\dfrac{ns}{\omega_s}} \tag{9.1}$$

as shown in Table 6.5. This compensating network is useful for improving the steady-state characteristics of a given automatic control system by taking a fairly large value for k.

The block diagram for the series compensation with this network is shown in Fig. 9.1. This block diagram can be equivalently written

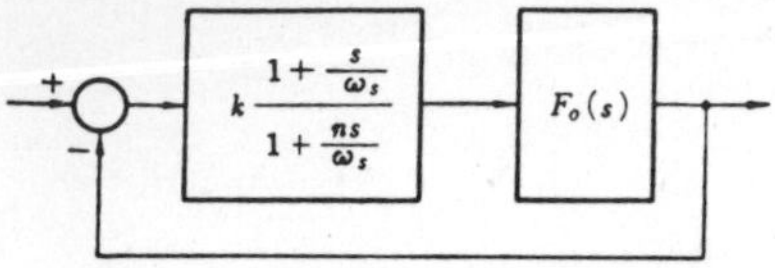

Fig. 9.1 (left) Series compensation by S3-4

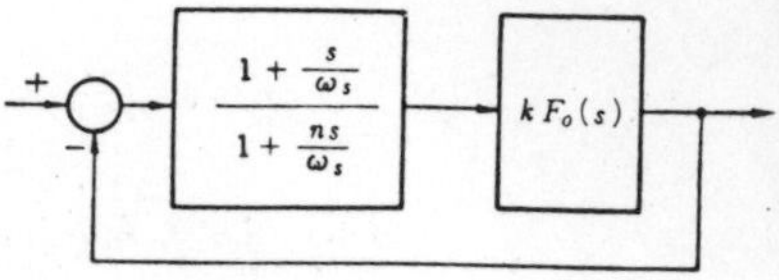

Fig. 9.2 (right) Block diagram equivalent to that shown in Fig. 9.1

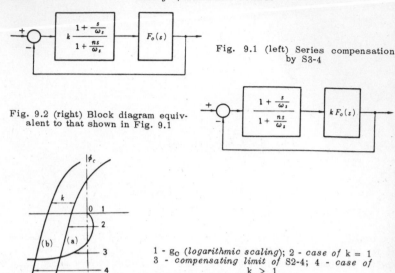

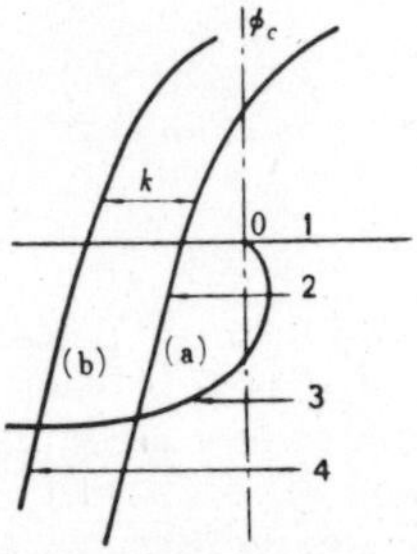

1 - g_c (*logarithmic scaling*); 2 - *case of* k = 1
3 - *compensating limit of* S2-4; 4 - *case of* k > 1

Fig. 9.3 (left) Compensating vector locus

as the block diagram shown in Fig. 9.2. Thus, the method for synthesis of the lag network with two degrees of freedom is directly applicable to the synthesis of this compensating network.

Specifically, we can first plot the compensating vector locus for the block diagram in Fig. 9.2 with $k = 1$ and obtain the curve (a) shown in Fig. 9.3. For another value of k, we can obtain the corresponding compensating vector locus (b) in Fig. 9.3 by appropriately translating the compensating vector locus with $k = 1$ in the horizontal direction according to the value of k, as shown in Fig. 9.3. If k exceeds 1, the compensating vector locus with $k = 1$ should be shifted to the left; if k is less than 1, it should be shifted to the right. Thus, in practice, we only need to plot the compensating vector locus with $k = 1$ on a semi-transparent graph sheet; the values of the free parameters Ω_s and n for each value of k can be read by placing the transparent graph sheet on the compensating chart in such a way that the compensating vector locus lies in the proper position corresponding to the value of k. The compensating chart to be used in this procedure is that shown in Figs. III, IV, or V, or in the chart obtained by rotating the compensating chart of Fig. VI through an angle of 180°, depending on the specified value of the damping coefficient γ_0.

(2) SYNTHESIS OF S3-3

The transfer function of the compensating network S3-3 is

$$F_c(s) = k\frac{1+\frac{s}{\omega_s}}{1+\frac{s}{n\omega_s}} \tag{9.2}$$

as shown in Table 6.5. This network is mainly used to obtain a larger compensating region than that of a lead network with two degrees of freedom, or to improve the accuracy of the approximation of the specified response by the dominant component.

Consider a compensating vector locus (a) shown in Fig. 9.4. This compensating vector locus lies outside the compensating limit of the lead network with two degrees of freedom. In this case, compensation can be achieved by using a lead network with three degrees of freedom. Thus, if we give a value less than 1 to gain constant k of the compensating transfer function (9.2), then the compensating vector locus (a) is shifted to the right along the horizontal axis and we obtain the compensating vector locus (b) shown in Fig. 9.4. Therefore, we can henceforth synthesise the compensating network S3-3 by applying the same procedure as in the synthesis of the lead network S2-3 with two degrees of freedom.

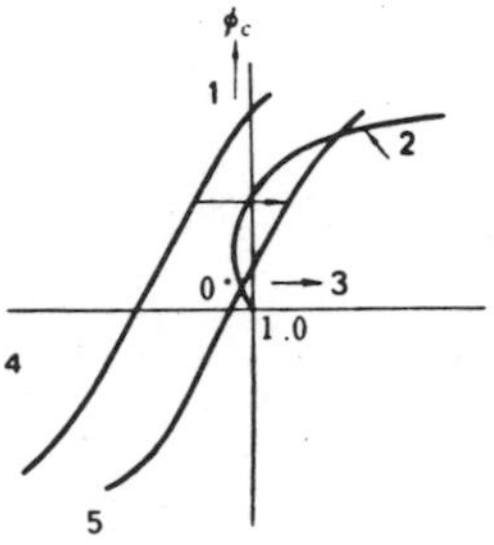

1 - *phase angle*; 2 - *compensating limit of* S2-3; 3 - g_c (*logarithmic scaling*); 4 - *case of* k = 1; 5 - *case of* k < 1

Fig. 9.4 Determination of the value of k

Suppose that we obtain the pole-zero configuration and root locus shown in Fig. 9.5, when a system to be synthesised is compensated by the lead network with two degrees of freedom. That is, the open-loop transfer function has a real root r_1 that is closer to the origin than are the specified pair of dominant roots r_0 and r_0^*. Then, the effect of r_1 on the transient response is quite large, and hence r_0 and r_0^* are no longer the dominant roots of the synthesised system with the compensation. This undesirable situation can be remedied by superimposing the second pole to the right of the given open-loop transfer function and the zero of the compensating transfer function. We shall discuss the synthesis of the lead network with three degrees of freedom with which we can achieve such compensation.

First ω_s in equation (9.2) is determined by the above condition. Thus, it is sufficient to determine the values of k and n. It is clear that the specified roots are the dominant roots of the synthesised system with this compensation.

For example, suppose that the compensating vector locus is the curve shown in Fig. 9.7. We determine the necessary value of the damped angular frequency ω_0, and from this and the determined value of ω_s we compute Ω_{s0}:

$$\Omega_{s0}=\frac{\omega_s}{\omega_0} \tag{9.3}$$

We then plot the Ω_{s0}-curve. We draw a horizontal line passing through the point ω_0 on the compensating vector locus, and we find the point of intersection of this horizontal line and the Ω_{s0}-curve. The desired value of n is the value of n at the point of intersection. The desired value of k is the ratio of the horizontal coordinate of ω_0 to the horizontal coordinate of this point of intersection. The procedure for finding these values is simple if we use the compensating charts.

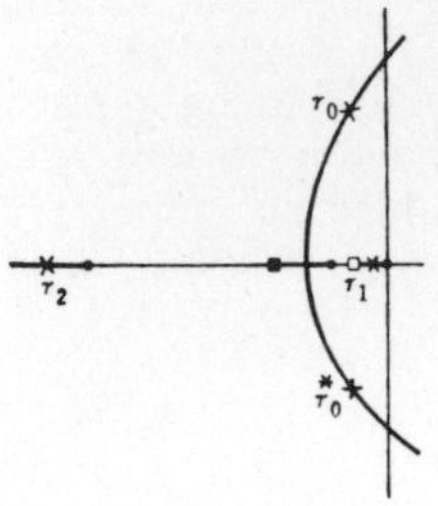

• : *pole of given open-loop transfer function*
▪ : *pole of compensating transfer function*
□ : *zero of compensating transfer function*

Fig. 9.5 Root locus with a root closer to the origin than the specified roots

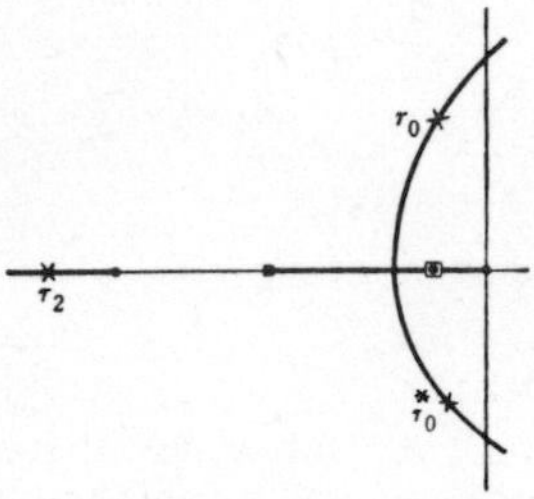

• : *pole of given open-loop transfer function*
▪ : *pole of compensating transfer function*
□ : *zero of compensating transfer function*

Fig. 9.6 Root locus with a root closer to the origin than the specified roots is eliminated

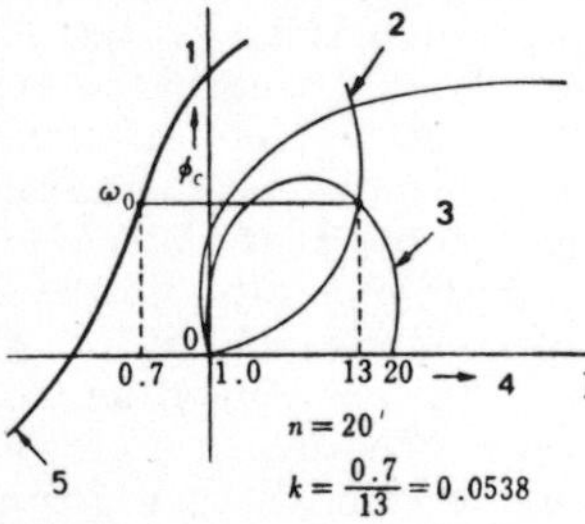

1 - *phase angle*; 2 - Ω_{so} *curve*; 3 - n-*curve*; 4 - g_c (*logarithmic scaling*); 5 - *compensating vector locus* (k = 1)

Fig. 9.7 Synthesis such that no roots are closer to the origin than are the specified roots is eliminated

(3) SYNTHESIS OF S3-1

As shown in Table 6.5, the transfer function $F_0(s)$ of the network S3-1 (a lead-lag network) is

$$F_0(s) = \frac{\left(1+\frac{s}{\omega_{s1}}\right)\left(1+\frac{s}{\omega_{s2}}\right)}{\left(1+\frac{s}{n\omega_{s1}}\right)\left(1+\frac{ns}{\omega_{s2}}\right)} \tag{9.4}$$

and relations between the network constants, the free parameters ω_{s1} and ω_{s2}, and n are as follows:

$$\left.\begin{aligned} \omega_{s1} &= \frac{1}{C_1R_1} \\ \omega_{s2} &= \frac{1}{C_2R_2} \\ (n-1)\left(\frac{1}{\omega_{s2}} - \frac{1}{n\omega_{s1}}\right) &= R_1C_2 \end{aligned}\right\} \quad (9.5)$$

where the inequalities

$$\omega_{s1}>0,\ \omega_{s2}>0,\ \text{and}\ n\omega_{s1}>\omega_{s2}\ \text{when}\ n>1 \quad (9.6)$$

must hold in order to give positive values to R_1, R_2, C_1, and C_2.

The transfer function (9.4) is the product of the following two transfer functions:

$$F_{c1}(s) = \frac{1+\dfrac{s}{\omega_{s1}}}{1+\dfrac{s}{n\omega_{s1}}} \quad (9.7)$$

$$F_{c2}(s) = \frac{1+\dfrac{s}{\omega_{s2}}}{1+\dfrac{ns}{\omega_{s2}}} \quad (9.8)$$

Here, $F_{c1}(s)$ is the transfer function of a lead network with two degrees of freedom and $F_{c2}(s)$ the transfer function of a lag network also with two degrees of freedom. Therefore, the network S3-1 can be synthesised by the following procedure: we express its compensating vector $g_c \underline{/\phi_c}$ as the product of two compensating vectors and synthesise a lead network for one factor and a lag network for the other factor. Since the free parameter n in the transfer functions (9.7) and (9.8) are the same free parameter, the above factorisation of $g_c \underline{/\phi_c}$ should satisfy this condition.

Such a factorisation of the compensating vector can be carried out on the logarithmic plane in the following manner. Let $g_c \underline{/\phi_c} = Z_c$. Then, Z_c can be expressed as a vector quantity

$$Z_c = K_1 \ln g_c + j K_2 \phi_c \quad (9.9)$$

on the complex plane, where K_1 and K_2 are coefficients determining the scalings on the real and imaginary axes. Therefore, we need to seperate the vector Z_c as shown in Fig. 9.8, into two vectors Z_{c1} and Z_{c2} such that (1) Z_{c1} lies within the compensating limit of the lead network, (2) Z_{c2} lies within the compensating limit of the lag network, and (3) the value of n corresponding to Z_{c2} is such that the n-curve passes through the end point of the vector Z_{c1}. There is no easy direct method of carrying out such a separation of Z_c. We can use the property, however, that the n-curve in the compensating chart of the lead network S2-3 and the n-curve in the compensating chart of the lag network S2-4 are symmetric with respect to the origin for the same value of n (this property was mentioned in Section 8.3), to find the separation. As shown in Fig. 9.8, it is sufficient to find two vectors Z_{c1} and $-Z_{c2}$ such that $Z_{c1}-(-Z_{c2}) = Z_c$ and the end points of both vectors lie on the same n-curve. Note that $-Z_{c2}$ is the inverse phase vector of Z_{c2}. Consequently, if the compensating vector locus Z_c is plotted on the logarithmic plane, and if we can translate Z_c so that it is a chord of an n-curve that lies within the compensating limit of the lead network, then the values of all the free parameters can be found from the relative break angular frequencies Ω_s at the initial and end points of the chord and the value of n.

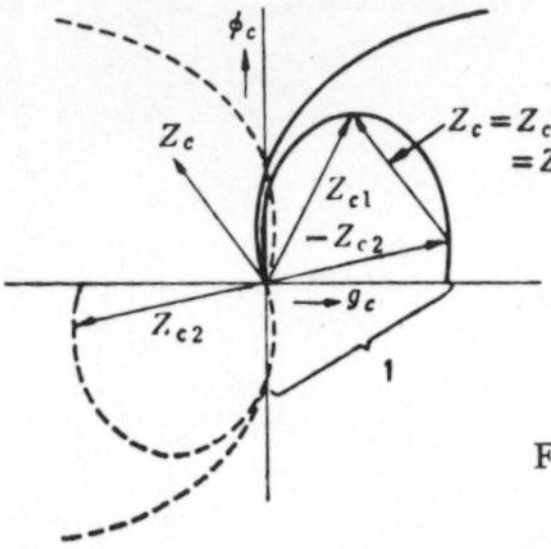

1 - n-*curves for the same value of* n

Fig. 9.8 Graphical illustration of the synthesis of the lead-lag network S3-1

The lead-lag network that we are considering has three degrees of freedom. Thus, we can assign an arbitrary value to one free parameter if we only require the synthesised automatic control system with the network S3-1 to have the specified roots. Here, we assume that the value of n is already given, and we shall discuss the actual procedure for finding the two free parameters ω_{s1} and ω_{s2} under this assumption.

(1) Plot the compensating vector locus on a semi-transparent sheet with logarithmic scaling.

(2) Determine, depending on the specified value of the damping coefficient γ_0, which compensating chart to use: Figs. III, IV, V, or VI in the Appendix.

(3) As shown in Fig. 9.9, place the transparent sheet on the selected compensating chart after turning the semi-transparent sheet over or after rotating it through an angle of 180° and choose an appropriate n-curve which encloses the compensating vector.

(4) Again rotate the semi-transparent sheet through an angle of 180° and place it on the compensating chart so that the end point of the compensating vector may coincide with the origin of the chart. Copy the chosen n-curve on the semi-transparent sheet (see Fig. 9.10).

(5) Place the semi-transparent sheet on the compensating chart with the origins superimposed and find the point of intersection of the n-curve on the chart and its copy* on the semi-transparent

*The purpose of copying the selected n-curve on the semi-transparent sheet is to find the point of intersection A. Therefore, it is sufficient to copy a part of the n-curve around this point.

sheet. Call the point of intersection A. Draw a line parallel to the compensating vector through the point A, and find the point of intersection of this line with the n-curve on the compensating chart. Call this point of intersection B (see Fig. 9.10).
(6) If the relative break angular frequencies at A and B are Ω_{s1} and Ω_{s2}, then the desired values of the free parameters ω_{s1} and ω_{s2} are

$$\omega_{s1}=\Omega_{s1}\omega_0 \quad \omega_{s2}=\Omega_{s2}\omega_0 n \tag{9.10}$$

We shall now discuss the compensating limit of the lead-lag network S3-1. The relation (9.5) must hold between the network constants of S3-1 and the values of the free parameters determined

1 - *reflection of the* n-*curve in the vertical axis*; 2 - *compensating limit* 3 - *the selected* n-*curve*; 4 - *reflection of compensating vector in the vertical axis*; 5 - g_c (*logarithmic scaling*) 6 - n-*curve rotated* 180°; 7 - *the value of* n *is determined so that the compensating vector lies in this domain* 8 - *compensating vector* $g_c \angle\phi_c$

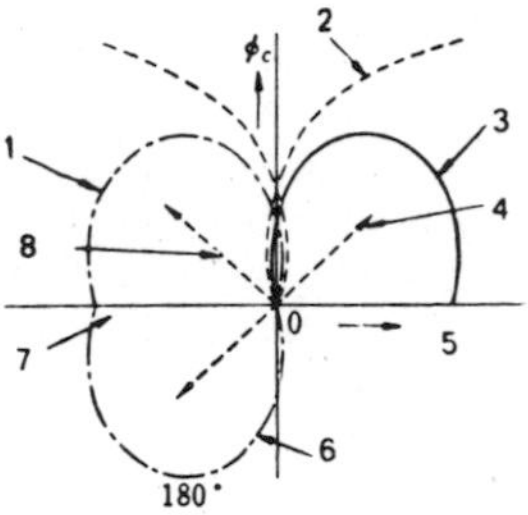

Fig. 9.9 Synthesis of S3-1 (first half of the procedure)

1 - *copy of* n-*curve*; 2 - *compensating limit*; 3 - n-*curve*; 4 - g_c (*logarithmic scaling*); 5 - ———: *curve on the semi-transparent sheet on which the compensating vector locus is plotted* 6 - - - - -, *curve on the compensating chart*

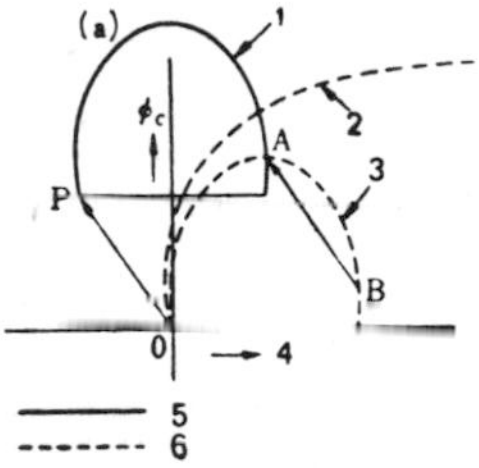

Fig. 9.10 Synthesis of S3-1 (second half of the procedure

by the above procedure. Since the network constants R_1, R_2, C_1, and C_2 are all positive numbers, the following conditions must hold:

$$\omega_{s1}>0, \ \omega_{s2}>0 \tag{9.11}$$

that is,

$$n\omega_{s1}>\omega_{s2} \text{ when } n>1 \tag{9.12}$$

Condition (9.11) holds whenever points A and B both lie above the horizontal axis (the region determined by $\phi_c > 0$) (see Fig. 9.10). Using equation (9.10), we can write condition (9.12) in the form

$$n\omega_0\Omega_{s1}>n\omega_0\Omega_{s2} \tag{9.13}$$

that is,

$$\Omega_{s1}>\Omega_{s2} \tag{9.14}$$

Consequently, condition (9.12) holds whenever Ω_{s1} at A is larger than Ω_{s2} at B. It is clear from observation of the compensating charts that the value of Ω_s at a point on an n-curve increases as the point moves along the n-curve in the counter-clockwise direction. Therefore, condition (9.12) holds if a point meets first A, then B, as the point moves along the n-curve in the counter-clockwise direction. For example, a system can be compensated by the lead-lag network shown in Fig. 9.11(a), but not by that shown in Fig. 9.11(b). For a given value of n, if point B coincides with P or if point A coincides with the origin, as shown in Fig. 9.12, it will be possible to synthesise a lead-lag network for the largest compensating vector. That is, if point B coincides with P then the end point of the corresponding compensating vector describes curve (b) of Fig. 9.12 when A moves from point P to the origin along the n-curve. Clearly, curve (b) is symmetric to curve (a) of Fig. 9.12 with respect to the vertical axis. If point A coincides with the origin 0, then the end point of the corresponding compensating vector describes curve (c) of Fig. 9.12 when B moves from the origin 0 to P along the n-curve. The curve (c) is then symmetrical to the n-curve, which is curve (a) of Fig. 9.12, with respect to the origin 0. Whenever the end point of a compensating vector lies in the region enclosed by these two curves (b) and (c), it is possible to synthesise a lead-lag network with positive network constants for this compensating vector by the above procedure. If we let n approach infinity, then the corresponding n-curve tends to the compensating limit of the lead network. Therefore, the compensating limit of the lead-lag network is the curve consisting of the compensating limit of the lag network and its reflection in the horizontal axis, as shown in Fig. 9.13. This compensating limit can be easily drawn by use of the scaling ruler.

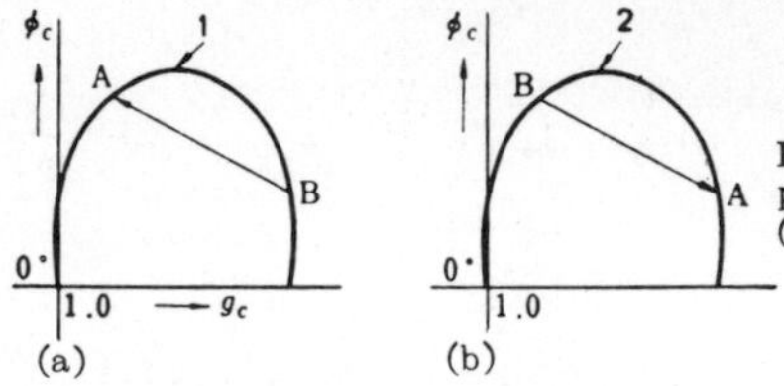

1 - n-*curve*; 2 - n-*curve*

Fig. 9.11 Graphical illustration of the possibility of compensation by S3-1 (a) case where compensation is possible; (b) where impossible

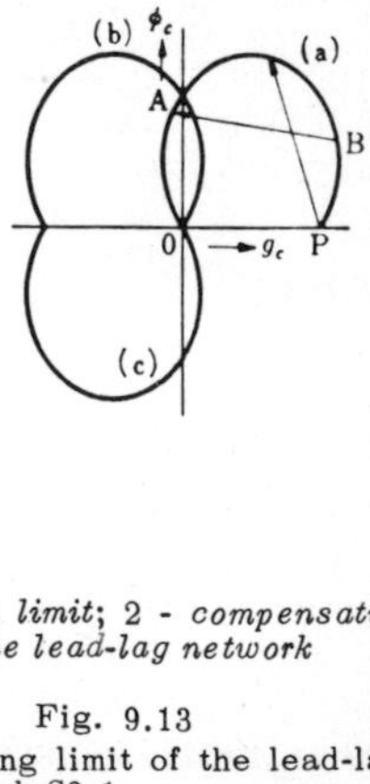

Fig. 9.12 Compensating region of S3-1

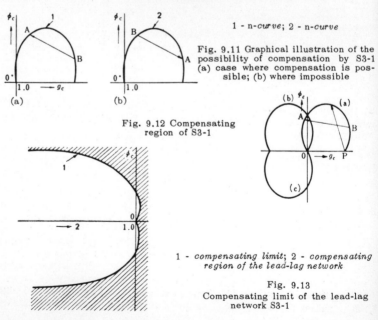

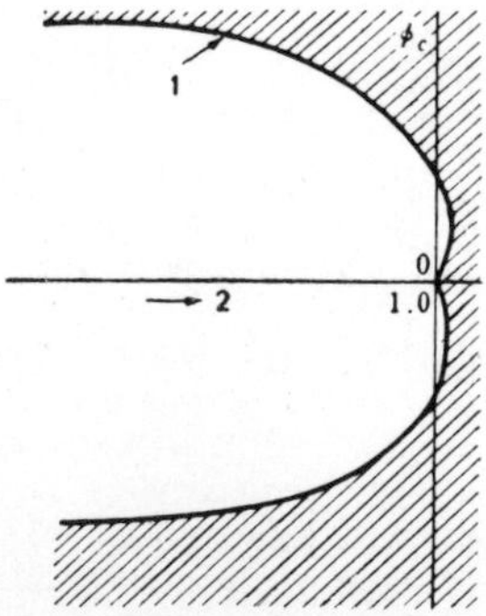

1 - *compensating limit*; 2 - *compensating region of the lead-lag network*

Fig. 9.13
Compensating limit of the lead-lag network S3-1

The advantage of using a network with three degrees of freedom is that in addition to letting the synthesised system have the specified roots, we can control another condition in the synthesis process. We shall give an example which shows this advantage.

Consider an automatic control system with the root locus shown in Fig. 9.14 and suppose that we obtain the pole-zero configuration and the root locus shown in Fig. 9.15 when this system is compensated by the lead-lag network with certain values of the free parameters. As shown in Fig. 9.15, there are two roots r_1 and $r_1{}^*$ which are closer to both the origin and the imaginary axis than are the specified roots r_0 and $r_0{}^*$; hence, the specified roots r_0 and $r_0{}^*$ may not be the dominant roots. To ensure that the specified roots become the dominant roots, it is sufficient to let a zero of the compensating transfer function coincide with the second pole (of the given open-loop transfer function) from the right in Fig. 9.15, so that the root locus of the given system will become Fig. 9.16. Specifically, we eliminate the pole of the given open-loop transfer function by giving a suitable value to the free parameter ω_{s1} (which is a zero of the compensating transfer function) and accomplish the desired synthesis by giving suitable values to the free parameters ω_{s2} and n. The actual procedure is as follows. (1) Let the value of ω_{s1} be equal to the second pole of the given open-loop transfer function from the right on the root locus plane.

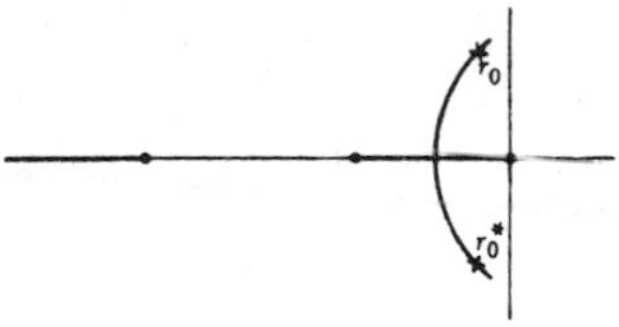

Fig. 9.14 Root locus of a given automatic control system

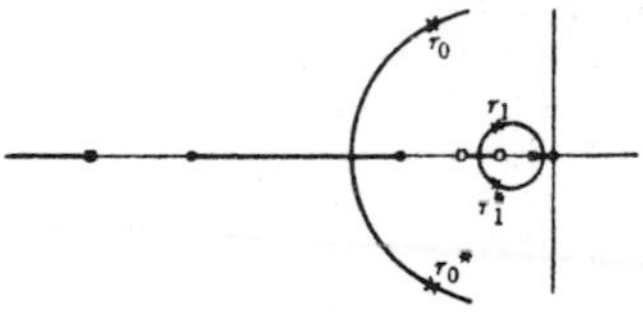

Fig. 9.15 Root locus with undesired roots r_1 and $r_1{}^*$ when the given system is compensated by the lead-lag network with certain values of the free parameters

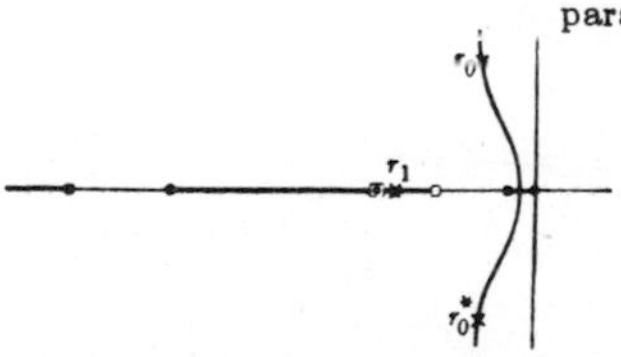

Fig. 9.16 Root locus when the unwanted roots in Fig. 9.15 are removed from the area of origin

(2) As shown in Fig. 9.17, plot the inverse vector OP of the compensating vector OP on a semi-transparent sheet where the vector OP has been plotted and place this semi-transparent sheet on the compensating chart in such a way that the end point P' coincides with the origin of the chart. Then copy onto the semi-transparent sheet the Ω_{s1}-curve corresponding to the value of Ω_{s1} determined by

$$\Omega_{s1}=\frac{\omega_{s1}}{\omega_0} \tag{9.15}$$

(3) After copying the Ω_{s1}-curve, place the semi-transparent sheet on the compensating chart again with the origins coinciding (see Fig. 9.17).

(4) For each value of n, find the intersecting points of the n-curve with the original Ω_{s1}-curve plotted on the compensating chart and with the copy of the Ω_{s1}-curve plotted on the semi-transparent sheet, and join these points with a straight line. The inclination of this line depends on the value of n. Choose a line that is parallel to the compensating vector **OP**.

(5) Read the value of n corresponding to the selected straight line and the relative break angular frequency at the point of intersection of the n-curve with the copy of Ω_{s1}-curve. If we denote the relative break angular frequency by Ω_{s2}, then the free parameter ω_{s2} is determined by

$$\omega_{s2}=\omega_0 n\Omega_{s2} \tag{9.16}$$

9.2. SYNTHESIS WITH SPECIFIED MAXIMUM ERROR

A transient response of an automatic control system to a unit step reference input is as shown in Fig. 9.18. The fundamental error $E_0(s)$, which is the response in the controlled variable to a disturbance shown in the block diagram of Fig. 9.19, is as shown in Fig. 9.20. The fundamental error is equal to 100% of the disturbance at $t = 0$ and becomes 0 at $t = t_0$; however, it continues to decrease for a while, taking negative values; then it approaches

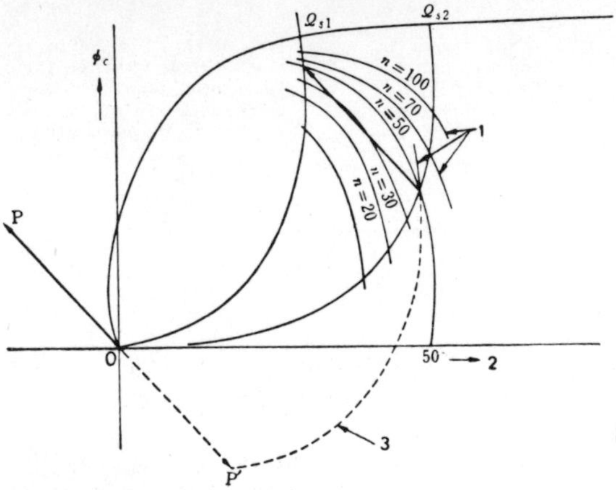

1 - n-*curves*; 2 - g_c (*logarithmic scaling*); 3 - *copy of* Ω_{s1}-*curve*

Fig. 9.17 Synthesis procedure for obtaining the root locus in Fig. 9.16, using the compensation network S3-1

0 again. That is, the fundamental error has a waveform. The relative maximum absolute value of the waveform is called the overshoot. This overshoot has essentially the same meaning as the overshoot shown in Fig. 9.18.

The absolute maximum value of the error response is not equal to the overshoot, as indicated in Fig. 9.20. That is, the largest error is attained at $t=0$, independently of the transfer function, and

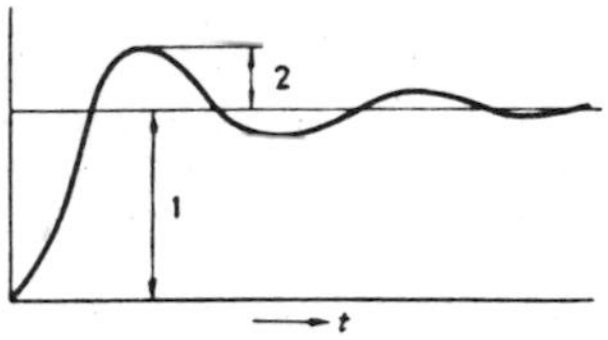

1 - *steady-state value*
2 - *overshoot*

Fig. 9.18 Transient response of an automatic control system for a unit step reference input

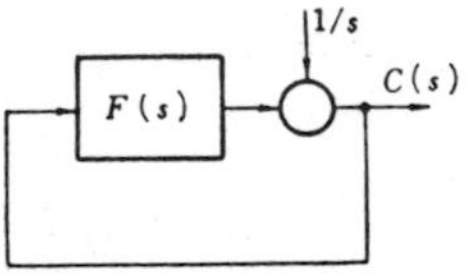

Fig. 9.19 Block diagram of error response to a disturbance

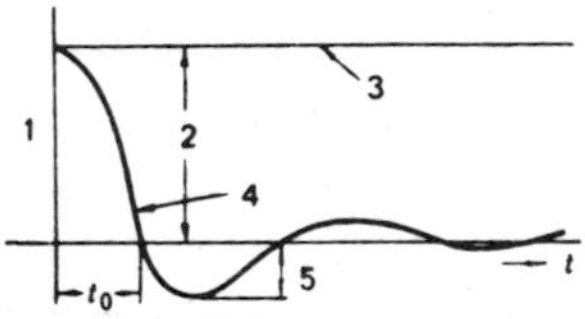

1 - *error*; 2 - *magnitude of disturbance*
3 - *disturbance*; 4 - *fundamental error response*; 5 - *overshoot*

Fig. 9.20 Fundamental error response of the system shown in Fig. 9.19

its magnitude is equal to the disturbance. On the other hand, if a unit step disturbance is applied between two forward transfer functions, as shown in Fig. 9.21, the error response is usually of the type shown in Fig. 9.22. Thus, the largest error is not necessarily attained at the instant $t = 0$ nor is its magnitude determined only by the disturbance in this case. However, the magnitude of the largest error is still greater than the overshoot. In any case, the largest value of the error response is called the maximum error. In the study of the theory, the magnitude of a maximum error is usually expressed in terms of the ratio of the maximum

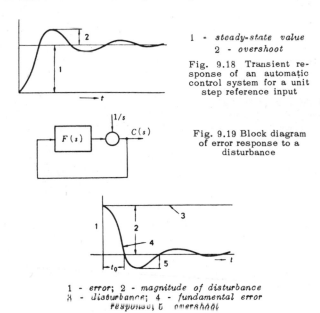

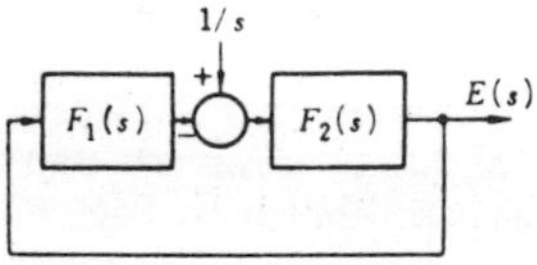

Fig. 9.21 Block diagram of a system where a disturbance is applied between two forward transfer functions

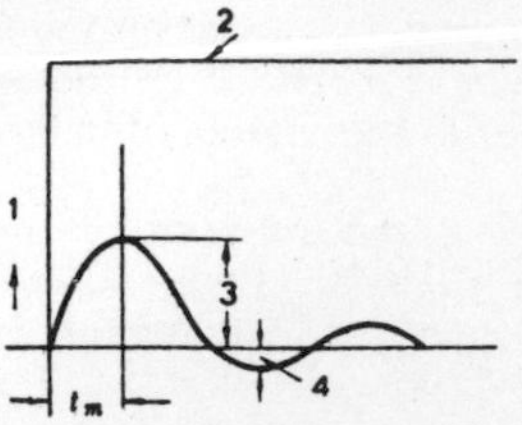

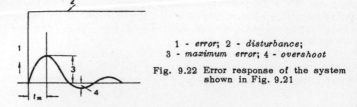

1 - *error*; 2 - *disturbance*;
3 - *maximum error*; 4 - *overshoot*

Fig. 9.22 Error response of the system shown in Fig. 9.21

error either to the change in the controlled variable for the disturbance when no other controlling factors are involved or to the variation ratio of the controlled system for the disturbance. For simplicity, we shall neglect the steady-state error in our discussions.

It is desirable to have a small maximum error in the transient response of an automatic control system. If a disturbance is applied between two forward transfer functions, as shown in Fig.

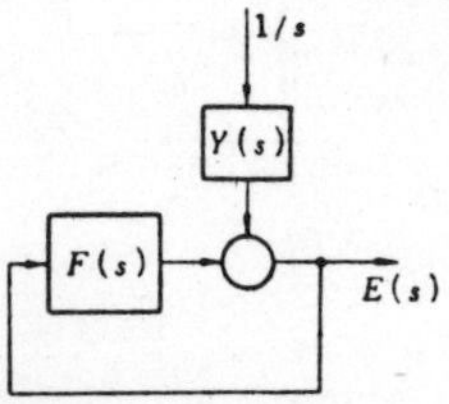

Fig. 9.23 Block diagram equivalent to that shown in Fig. 9.21

9.21, or through a disturbance transfer function $Y(s)$, as shown in Fig. 9.23, then it is possible to give a specified maximum error to the automatic control system by synthesising either the transfer function $F_2(s)$ or the disturbance transfer function $Y(s)$, whichever is appropriate. Often the value of the maximum error is specified, as in the synthesis of an automatic speed or voltage regulator. We shall discuss synthesis with such a requirement.

(1) RELATION BETWEEN MAXIMUM ERROR AND DISTURBANCE

Before discussing the synthesis process, we shall investigate the relation between a disturbance and a maximum error.

Disturbances have various waveforms, depending on their cause. However, a stepwise variation of the load is the major disturbance in an automatic regulating system and it has the greatest effect on the transient characteristics. Other disturbances affect the transient characteristics much more slowly than the load variation does, and their magnitudes are also negligible in general. Consequently, these disturbances are not the cause of the maximum error in most cases. Therefore, we shall take only the stepwise variation of a load as the disturbance.

When a disturbance is applied between two forward transfer functions, as shown in Fig. 9.21, the block diagram can be transformed into the equivalent block diagram shown in Fig. 9.23. Thus, we shall study the relation between a disturbance and the maximum error only for the block diagram in Fig. 9.23.

As mentioned in Section 2.9, the disturbance transfer function $Y(s)$ in Fig. 9.23 is of the form

$$Y(s)=\frac{Y_0}{1+sT_D} \tag{9.17}$$

where Y_0 is the steady-state variation ratio of the controlled system and T_D is the time constant of the disturbance. By use of expression (9.17), the block diagram in Fig. 9.23 can be again transformed equivalently into the block diagram shown in Fig. 9.24. Then, the error response is

$$E(s)=\frac{1}{s}\cdot\frac{Y_0}{1+sT_d}\cdot\frac{1}{1+F(s)} \tag{9.18}$$

If we interchange the transfer functions $Y_0/(1+sT_D)$ and $1/(1+F(s))$, we obtain the block diagram shown in Fig. 9.25. We recall that the output signal of the transfer function $1/(1+F(s)$ is called the fundamental error response. If we denote its t-representation by $E_o(s)$ and its t-representation by $e_o(t)$, we have

$$E_o(s)=\frac{1}{s}\cdot\frac{1}{1+F(s)} \tag{9.19}$$

$$e_o(t)=\mathcal{L}^{-1}E_o(s)=\mathcal{L}^{-1}\frac{1}{s}\ \frac{1}{1+F(s)} \tag{9.20}$$

Then, the error response $E(s)$ in the controlled variable can be regarded as the output signal of the disturbance transfer function for the input signal $E_o(s)$. For simplicity, we shall only consider the case of $Y_0=1$ in equation (9.17). The value of $E(s)$ in the case of $Y_0 \neq 1$ can easily be obtained by multiplying the value of $E(s)$ for $Y_0=1$ by Y_0. The waveform of the fundamental error $E_o(s)$ is as shown in Fig. 9.26. The maximum error is 100%, and it follows from what was said above that the waveform of $E_o(s)$ can be well

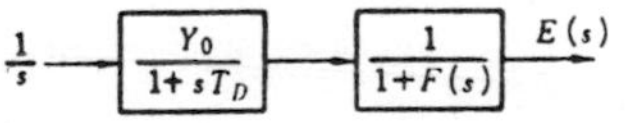

Fig. 9.24

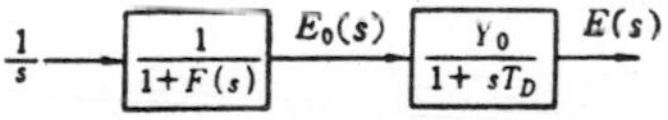

Fig. 9.25

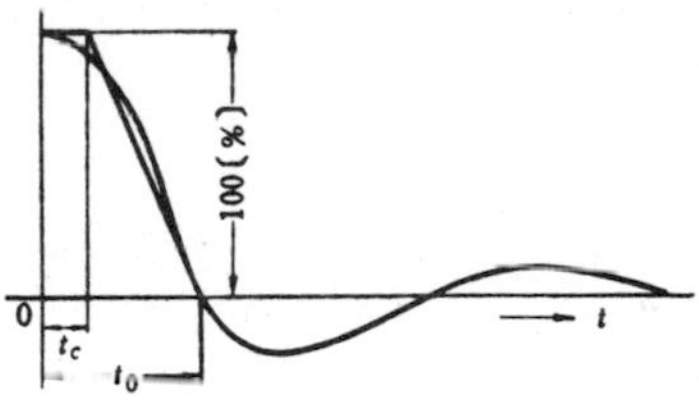

Fig. 9.26 Approximation of the waveform of a fundamental error response by a trapezoid

approximated by that of the dominant component of the error response for a well-synthesised control system. Therefore, the error response $E(s)$ in the controlled variable, and hence the maximum error, is approximately determined by the dominant roots and the time constant T_d of the disturbance.

In order to find the maximum error in a simple way, we approximate the waveform of the fundamental error response by a trapezoid, as shown in Fig. 9.26. In general, the maximum error is attained at the instant between 0 and t_0 at which the value of the fundamental error first vanishes. Accordingly, we only need the best approximation for the portion of the waveform corresponding to the time interval from $t = 0$ to $t = t_0$. Therefore, we need to find t_c for which the area of the trapezoid is equal to the area under the portion of the waveform of $E_0(s)$ corresponding to the time interval from $t = 0$ to $t = t_0$. For example, if the given system is a standard second-order system whose oscillation roots are

$$\left.\begin{aligned} r_0 &= -\alpha_0 + j\omega_0 = (-\gamma_0 + j)\omega_0 \\ r_0^* &= -\alpha_0 - j\omega_0 = (-\gamma_0 - j)\omega_0 \end{aligned}\right\} \tag{9.21}$$

then the values of t_0 and t_c are as follows:

$$t_0 = \frac{1}{\omega_0}\left(\frac{\pi}{2} + \tan^{-1}\gamma_0\right) \tag{9.22}$$

$$t_c = \frac{2\gamma_0}{1+\gamma_0^2}\,\frac{1}{\omega_0}\left\{2 + \frac{\sqrt{1+\gamma_0^2}}{\gamma_0}\,\epsilon^{-\gamma_0\left(\frac{\pi}{2} + \tan^{-1}\gamma_0\right)}\right\} - t_0 \tag{9.23}$$

We set

$$\tau_c = \frac{t_c}{t_0} \tag{9.24}$$

and get

$$\tau_c = \frac{2\gamma_0}{1+\gamma_0^2}\,\frac{1}{\frac{\pi}{2} + \tan^{-1}\gamma_0}\left\{2 + \frac{\sqrt{1+\gamma_0^2}}{\gamma_0}\,\epsilon^{-\gamma_0\left(\frac{\pi}{2} + \tan^{-1}\gamma_0\right)}\right\} - 1 \tag{9.25}$$

This constant τ_c is a value that is directly used in the synthesis. Table 9.1 shows the values of τ_c for various values of γ_0.

TABLE 9.1 VALUES OF τ_c

	value of $\tau_c = t_c/t_0$	
γ_0	standard second-order system	common higher-order system
0.3	0.177	0.21
0.4	0.145	0.17
0.5	0.105	0.13

For a system of order higher than second, the fundamental error response can also be well approximated by the dominant component error if the system is well synthesised. Therefore, the value of τ_c calculated for the standard second-order system can be used as the value for a higher-order system. However, a slight correction in the value of r_c for a higher-order system is desired, depending on the characteristics of the system, in order to improve the accuracy of the approximation by a trapezoid.

For example, consider an automatic control system that involves a dead time, as shown in the block diagram of Fig. 9.27(a). This block diagram can be equivalently transformed into the block diagram shown in Fig. 9.27(b). Clearly, the t-representation of the fundamental error response $E_0(s)$ represents the waveform shown in Fig. 9.27(c). Thus, the value of t_c here is the sum of the value of t_c for the standard second-order system and the dead time τ, and the value of t_0 here is the sum of the value of t_0 for the second-order system and τ. Here, the order of a system involving a dead time can be regarded as infinity, since the system has an infinite number of characteristic roots. Accordingly, the values of t_c and t_0 for a higher-order system of finite order are larger than those values for a standard second-order system, and accordingly, the value of $r_c = t_c/t_0$ for a higher-order system is also larger than the value for the standard second-order system. In fact, the value of r_c for a higher-order system can be obtained by increasing the value of r_c by an appropriate percentage less than 20 [%]. The values presented in Table 9.1 were obtained in this manner.

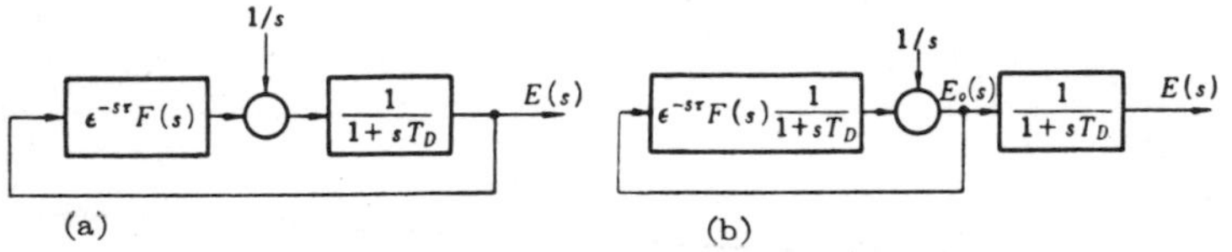

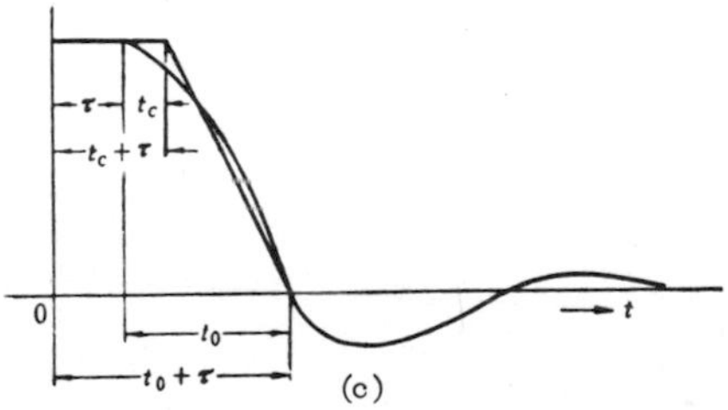

Fig. 9.27 Approximation of the fundamental error response where the control system involves a dead time: (a) block diagram of the system (b) equivalent block diagram (c) waveform of the fundamental error response

The approximation of the fundamental error response $e(t)$, shown in Fig. 9.26, obtained by using the t_0 and t_c calculated in the above manner, will be called the approximate fundamental error response and will be denoted by $e_{oa}(t)$. Then,

$$e_{oa}(t)=\begin{cases} 1 & (t_c \geqq t \geqq 0) \quad \text{(a)} \\ 1-\dfrac{t-t_c}{t_0-t_c} & (t_0 \geqq t \geqq t_c) \quad \text{(b)} \\ 0 & (t \geqq t_0) \quad \text{(c)} \end{cases} \tag{9.26}$$

If we denote by $E_{oa}(s)$ the s-representation of the approximate fundamental error response, then $E_{oa}(s)$ is expressed as

$$E_{oa}(s)=\frac{1}{s}-\frac{1}{s^2}\left(\frac{\epsilon^{-st_c}-\epsilon^{-st_o}}{t_0-t_c}\right) \tag{9.27}$$

If we denote by $E_a(s)$ the s-representation of the approximate error response in the controlled variable (that is, the output of the transfer function $1/(1 + s\,T_D)$ when the input is the approximate fundamental error response $E_{oa}(s)$ (as shown in Fig. 9.28), then

$$E_a(s)=\frac{E_{oa}(s)}{1+sT_d} \tag{9.28}$$

If we substitute equation (9.26) into this expression, we obtain

$$E_o(s)=\frac{1}{1+sT_d}\left\{\frac{1}{s}-\frac{1}{s^2}\;\frac{\epsilon^{-st_c}-\epsilon^{-st_o}}{t_0-t_c}\right\} \tag{9.29}$$

Therefore, the t-expression $e_a(t)$ of the approximate error response in the controlled variable can be calculated as follows:

$$e_a(t)=\mathcal{L}^{-1}E_a(s)$$

$$=\left\{\begin{array}{ll} 1-\epsilon^{-\frac{t}{T_d}} & (t_c>t>0)\ \text{(a)} \\ \dfrac{t_0+T_d}{t_0-t_c}-\dfrac{t}{t_0-t_c}-\epsilon^{-t/T_d}\left(1+\dfrac{T_d}{t_0-t_c}\epsilon^{t_c/T_d}\right) & (t_0>t>t_c)\ \text{(b)} \\ \epsilon^{-t/T_d}\left\{\dfrac{T_d}{t_0-t_c}(\epsilon^{t_0/T_d}-\epsilon^{t_c/T_d})-1\right\} & (t>t_0)\ \text{(c)} \end{array}\right\} \tag{9.30}$$

If we plot $e_a(t)$, we obtain Fig. 9.29. This shows that the approximate error response attains its maximum at a time t such that $t_0 > t > t_c$. This maximum value is the approximate value of the maximum error. In order to find this approximate maximum error, we set the derivative of the expression (9.30)(b) equal to zero. Then the time t_{ma} at which the approximate error response attains its maximum value is

$$t_{ma}=T_d\ln\left(\frac{t_0-t_c}{T_d}+\epsilon^{t_c/T_d}\right) \tag{9.31}$$

If we substitute this t_{ma} into the expression (9.30) (b), we get fo the maximum value e_{ma} of $e_a(t)$:

$$e_{ma}=\frac{t_c}{t_0-t_c}-\frac{T_d}{t_0-t_c}\ln\left(\frac{t_0-t_c}{T_d}+\epsilon^{\frac{t}{T_d}}\right) \tag{9.32}$$

This expression can be simplified by the substitutions

$$\frac{t_c}{t_0}=\tau_c \tag{9.33}$$

$$\frac{T_d}{t_0}=\tau_d \tag{9.34}$$

as follows:

$$e_{ma}=\frac{1}{1-\tau_c}-\frac{\tau_d}{1-\tau_c}\ln\left(\frac{1-\tau_c}{\tau_d}+\epsilon^{\tau_c/\tau_d}\right) \tag{9.35}$$

This last equation shows that the approximate value e_{ma} of the maximum value is determined by τ_d and τ_c. Fig. 9.30 shows

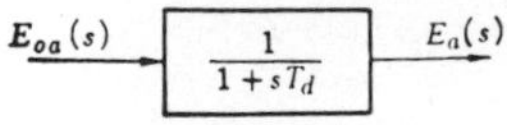

Fig. 9.28

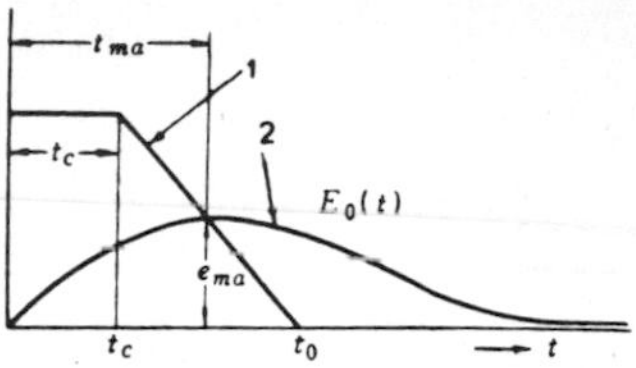

Fig. 9.29 Approximate fundamental error response and approximate error response

1 - *approximate fundamental error response*; 2 - *approximate error response*

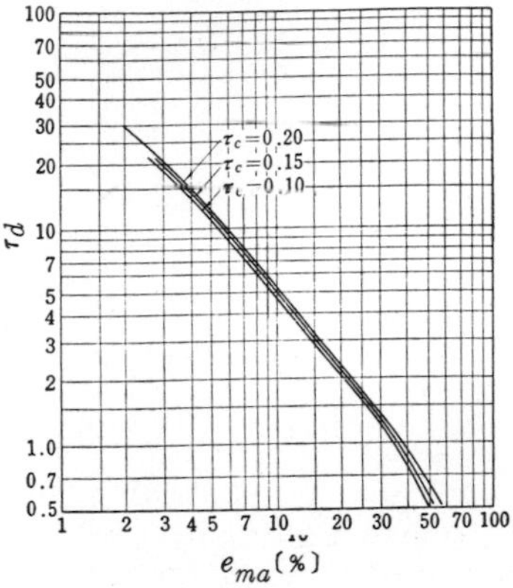

Fig. 9.30 Relation between the approximate maximum error e_{ma} and the relative time constant $r_d = T_d/t_0$ of the disturbance

the relation between e_{ma} and r_d for the values of r_c that are most commonly used in practical synthesis.

(2) PRACTICAL SYNTHESIS PROCEDURE

If we use the preceding results, we can find a time constant T_d of the disturbance that satisfies a specification in which the damping coefficient γ_0 of the dominant root, the damped angular frequency ω_0, and the maximum error e_m are given. It is also possible to find the damped angular frequency ω_0 of a dominant root which satisfies a specification in which the time constant of a disturbance and the maximum error are given.

If the maximum error e_m is specified as a percentage of the steady-state variation ratio of the controlled variable (that is, if the steady-state variation ratio of the controlled variable is 100 [%]), then the value of r_d corresponding to the approximate maximum error e_{ma} can be immediately read from Fig. 9.30. Here, the value of r_c is a number determined by equation (9.24) or equation (9.33), but we may select a suitable value for r_c from Table 9.1.

If a dominant root $r_0 = (-\gamma_0 + j)\omega_0$ is given, that is, if a damping coefficient γ_0 and a damped angular frequency ω_0 are given, then the value of t_0 can be calculated from equation (9.22):

$$t_0 = \frac{1}{\omega_0}\left(\frac{\pi}{2} + \tan^{-1}\gamma_0\right) \tag{9.36}$$

Since the time constant T_d of the disturbance, t_0 and r_d found from Fig. 9.30 are related by equation (9.34), we have

$$T_d = \tau_d t_0 = \frac{\tau_d}{\omega_0}\left(\frac{\pi}{2} + \tan^{-1}\gamma_0\right) \tag{9.37}$$

$$= \frac{\tau_d}{\omega_0} D \tag{9.38}$$

where D is given by

$$D = \frac{\pi}{2} + \tan^{-1}\gamma_0 \tag{9.39}$$

Table 9.2 shows the calculated values of D for $\gamma_0 = 0.3, 0.4,$ and 0.5.

TABLE 9.2
CALCULATED
VALUES OF D

γ_0	$D = \frac{\pi}{2} + \tan^{-1}\gamma_0$
0.3	1.862
0.4	1.950
0.5	2.034

We now discuss how to find the damped angular frequency ω_0 when the time constant T_D of the disturbance and the maximum error e_m are specified. The value of t_0 can be calculated from equation (9.34):

$$t_0 = \frac{T_d}{\tau_d} \tag{9.40}$$

Substituting this value into equation (9.22), we obtain

$$\omega_0 = \frac{\tau_d}{T_d}\left(\frac{\pi}{2} + \tan^{-1}\gamma_0\right) = \frac{\tau_d}{T_d} D \tag{9.41}$$

Here we can use a value from Table 9.1 for D.

The above discussions show that if any two of the three quantities maximum error e_m, damped angular frequency ω_0, and time constant T_d of the disturbance are given, we can always find the third. In actual synthesis, the maximum instant error e_m is specified according to the operational conditions required for the automatic control system, while the damped angular frequency ω_0 should be as large as possible. Often the time constant T_d of a disturbance is specified, but we are sometimes forced to use a larger time constant in order to satisfy other requirements. If this is the case, the time constant Td should be increased as little as possible, in view of the response velocity and cost. Accordingly, in practice we need to find a synthesis such that the damped angular frequency is as large as possible and the required increment in the time constant of the disturbance is as small as possible.

The procedure of such a synthesis is as follows:

(a) Selection of γ_0 and r_c. Choose suitable values from Tables 6.2 and 9.1 for the damping coefficient γ_0 and r_c, respectively, depending on the order and type of automatic control system being synthesised.

(b) Determination of τ_d. Read the value of τ_d from Fig. 9.30 for the chosen value of τ_c and the specified value of the approximate maximum instant error e_{ma}.
(c) Calculation of $\omega_0 T_d$. Using the determined value of τ_c and Table 9.2, calculate the value of $\omega_0 T_d$ from the equation

$$\omega_0 T_d = D\tau_d \tag{9.42}$$

(d) Construction of the compensating vector locus. Calculate the value of the compensating vector for various values of ω_0 and plot the compensating vector locus on a semi-transparent graph sheet with logarithmic scaling. If T_d is included as one of the time constants of the open-loop transfer function, T_d may be replaced by $D\tau_d/\omega_0$ for the above calculation.
(e) Selection of compensating network, determination of the allowable maximum value of ω_0*, and selection of the degree of freedom of the compensating network. Follow the procedure discussed in the previous sections.
(f) Determination of T_d. Determine the value of T_d from equation (9.37). That is,

$$T_d = \frac{\tau_d}{\omega_0} D$$

(g) Determination of the network constants of the compensating network. Follow the procedure discussed in previous sections.

9.3 EXAMPLE OF SYNTHESIS (SYNTHESIS OF VELOCITY REGULATOR)

We shall present an example of synthesis of an automatic control system by the procedures discussed in this and the preceding chapter.

(1) SPECIFICATION AND CONSTRUCTION OF AN AUTOMATIC CONTROL SYSTEM TO BE SYNTHESISED

(a) Type of automatic control system. Velocity regulator (which regulates rotational frequency).
(b) Construction of the regulator. Specified characteristics and system constants of the regulator. Construction of the regulator is shown in Fig. 9.31. Specified values of the system constants of the regulator are shown in Table 9.3.

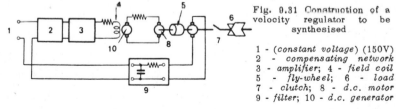

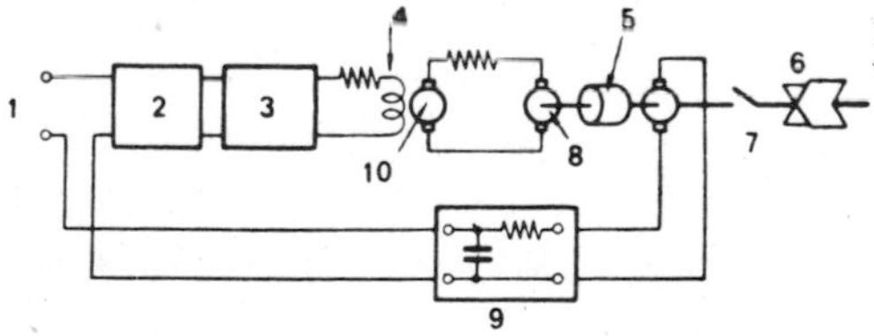

Fig. 9.31 Construction of a velocity regulator to be synthesised

1 - (*constant voltage*) (150V)
2 - *compensating network*
3 - *amplifier*; 4 - *field coil*
5 - *fly-wheel*; 6 - *load*
7 - *clutch*; 8 - *d.c. motor*
9 - *filter*; 10 - *d.c. generator*

*Since the value of $D\tau_d$ is determined by the specified maximum error e_m, the time constant T_d of the disturbance automatically becomes as small as possible (by virtue of equation (9.42)) when we assign to ω_0 as large as value as possible.

TABLE 9.3 SPECIFIED VALUES OF SYSTEM CONSTANTS

Rated rotational frequency of motor	N_0 = 1500 [rpm]
Velocity variation ratio of electrically driven generator (in case of 100 [%] load variation)	Y_0 = 10 [%]
Time constant of generator (without fly-wheel)	T_m = 0.4 [s]
Moment of inertia of rotating part of generator	GD^2 = 1 [kg - m²] where J = 4 [kg - m²]
Resistance of field coil of generator	R_f = 10 [Ω]
Inductance of field coil of generator	L_f = 0.8 [H]
Amplification coefficient of generator	R_c = 50 [V/A]
Ratio of rotational frequency of motor to voltage	N_m = 150 [rpm/V]
Ratio of voltage to rotational frequency of tachometer generator	N_T = 0.1 [V/rpm]
Time constant of filter	T_3 = 0.03 [s]

(c) Specified characteristic.

The output rotational frequency should be maintained at the constant value 1500 [rpm].

The disturbance should be 100% of load variation.

The steady-state velocity variation ratio should be 0.02 [%] (in case of 100 [%] of load variation).

The allowable maximum instant change of the velocity should be 0.5 [%] of the rated rotational frequency of the motor or equivalently 7.5 [rpm].

The damping coefficient γ_0 should be 0.4.

The response velocity should be as large as possible.

The moment of inertia of a fly-wheel should be the smallest value for which other required characteristics are satisfied.

(d) Constants which should be determined by synthesis.

Amplification coefficient K_0 of amplifier.

Moment of inertia J_F of fly-wheel or the constant GD^2.

Damped angular frequency ω_0.

Network constants of compensating network.

(2) PRELIMINARY CALCULATIONS

(a) Block diagram. If we construct the block diagram of the system shown in Fig. 9.31 with the specified constants given in Table 9.3, we obtain Fig. 9.32. Some details of the calculations to find the numerical values used in the block diagram are omitted here. The transfer function of the compensating network (which is the compensating transfer function), the amplification coefficient of the amplifier, and the time constant of the fly-wheel are denoted by terms $F_c(s)$, K_0, and T_F, respectively. These are the constants whose values are to be determined in the synthesis so as to satisfy

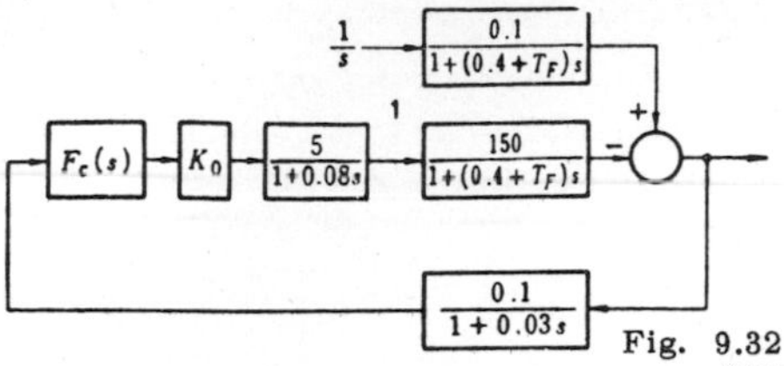

1 - *voltage*

Fig. 9.32 Block diagram of the velocity regulator shown in Fig. 9.32

the required characteristic of the velocity regulator.
(b) Time constant of disturbance. If we denote by T_m the time constant of the rotating part of the motor, then the time constant T_d of the disturbance is

$$T_d = T_m + T_F \tag{9.43}$$

$$= 0.4 + T_F \tag{9.44}$$

(c) Maximum error e_m. If Y_0 is the steady-state variation ratio of the generator and Y_m is the specified allowable maximum value of the instant change in the velocity of the generator, then the maximum error e_m is

$$e_m = \frac{Y_m}{Y_0} = \frac{0.5[\%]}{10\ [\%]} = 5.0\ [\%] \tag{9.45}$$

(3) SYNTHESIS OF THE STEADY-STATE CHARACTERISTIC

(a) Determination of the amplification coefficient K_0 of the amplifier. According to equation (6.15), the gain constant A of the open-loop transfer of the velocity regulator is

$$A = \frac{Y_0}{\eta} - 1 \tag{9.46}$$

where Y_0 (= steady-state variation ratio of the generator) = 10 [%] and η (= specified steady-state variation of velocity regulator) = 0.02 [%]. Therefore, we obtain

$$A = \frac{10}{0.02} - 1 = 499 \tag{9.47}$$

If A_0 is the gain constant of the part given in the block diagram of Fig. 9.32, then

$$\omega_0 T_d = 1.95 \times 12.0 = 23.4$$

If we let the gain constant of the compensating transfer function be 1, then the amplification coefficient K_0 is

$$K_0 = \frac{A}{A_0} = \frac{499}{75} = 6.65 \tag{9.48}$$

(4) SYNTHESIS OF TRANSIENT CHARACTERISTICS

(a) Determination of τ_d. Since $\gamma_0 = 0.4$ and the velocity regulator is a third-order system without zeros, we choose $\tau_c = 0.2$. Reading the value of τ_d for $e_{ma} = 5$ [%] and $\tau_c = 0.2$ from Fig. 9.30, we obtain

$$\tau_d = 12.0 \tag{9.49}$$

(b) Calculation of $\omega_0 T_d$. From equation (9.42),

$$A_0 = 5 \times 150 \times 0.1 = 75$$

On the other hand, we have $D = 1.95$ from Table 9.2 and $\tau_d = 12.0$ from equation (9.49). Therefore,

$$\omega_0 T_d = 1.95 \times 12.0 = 23.4 \tag{9.50}$$

and we have

$$T_d = \frac{23.4}{\omega_0} \tag{9.51}$$

(c) Compensating vector. The open-loop transfer function $F_0(s)$ of the velocity regulator without the compensating network is

$$F_0(s) = \frac{499}{(1+T_d s)(1+0.08\,s)(1+0.03\,s)} \tag{9.52}$$

Therefore, the compensating vector $g_c\underline{/\phi_c}$ is

$$g_c\underline{/\phi_c} = \frac{\underline{/-180^\circ}}{499}(1+T_d r_0)(1+0.08 r_0)(1+0.03\,r_0) \tag{9.53}$$

Here r_0 is the dominant root of the velocity regulator, and $r_0 = (-0.4 + j)\,\omega_0$. If we substitute this expression for r_0 and equation (9.51) into equation (9.53), the compensating vector is calculated as follows:

$$\begin{aligned} g_c\underline{/\phi_c} &= \frac{\underline{/-180^\circ}}{499}\{1+23.4(-0.4+j)\}\{1+0.08(-0.4+j)\omega_0\} \\ &\quad \{1+0.03(-0.4+j)\omega_0\} \\ &= \frac{\underline{/-180^\circ}}{499}(1-0.4\times 23.4+j\,23.4)(1-0.4\times 0.08\,\omega_0+j\,0.08\,\omega_0) \\ &\quad (1-0.4\times 0.03\,\omega_0+j\,0.03\,\omega_0) \\ &= 4.99\times 10^{-2}\underline{/-70.0^\circ}(1-0.032\,\omega_0+j\,0.08\,\omega_0) \\ &\quad (1-0.012\,\omega_0+j\,0.03\,\omega_0) \end{aligned} \tag{9.54}$$

(d) Range of ω_0. It is clear from equation (9.44) that the time constant T_d takes its minimum value 0.4 where $T_F = 0$. From equation (9.50), the value of ω_0 is then

$$\omega_0 = \frac{23.4}{T_D} = \frac{23.4}{0.4} = 58.6 \text{ [rad/s]} \tag{9.55}$$

Therefore, the value of ω_0 must be less than or equal to 58.6 [rad/sec].

(e) Compensating vector locus. The compensating vector locus could be plotted from the values of g_c/ϕ_c calculated for various values of ω_0 by using equation (9.54). To eliminate the laborious calculations, however, we take the following procedure. Calculate the value of g_c/ϕ_c for ω_0 = 58.6 [rad/sec] (which is the maximum value of ω_0):

$$
\begin{aligned}
|g_c/\phi_c|_{\omega_0=58.6} &= 4.99\times10^{-2}\underline{/-70.4^\circ}(1-0.032\times58.6+j0.08\times58.6)\\
&\quad(1-0.012\times58.6+j0.03\times58.6)\\
&=4.99\times10^{-2}\underline{/-70.4^\circ}(-0.871+j4.68)(0.297+j1.755)\\
&=4.99\times10^{-2}\underline{/-70.4^\circ}\times4.75\underline{/100.4^\circ}\times1.762\underline{/80.5^\circ}\\
&=0.42\underline{/110.5^\circ}
\end{aligned} \tag{9.56}
$$

and plot the value on the compensating locus plane. Then, we obtain Figs. 9.33. Comparing this point with the compensating limits of the various series networks introduced previously, we note that the desired compensation cannot be achieved by using any one of those networks. It may be possible to achieve the desired compensation if we use more than two of those networks in cascade. We shall, however, examine the possibility of achieving the desired compensation with one network by taking a smaller value of ω_0 than its maximum. For this purpose, we calculate the value of the network for ω_0 = 30 [rad/sec]:

$$
\begin{aligned}
g_c/\phi_c &= 4.99\times10^{-2}\underline{/-70.4^\circ}(1-0.032\times30+j0.08\times30)\\
&\quad(1-0.012\times30+j0.03\times30)\\
&=4.99\times10^{-2}\underline{/-70.4^\circ}(-0.04+j2.4)(0.64+j0.9)\\
&=4.99\times10^{-2}\underline{/-70.4^\circ}\times2.40\underline{/90^\circ}\times1.11\underline{/54.6^\circ}\\
&=0.133\underline{/74.2^\circ}
\end{aligned} \tag{9.57}
$$

Plotting this value on the compensating vector locus plane, we note that this point is within the compensating limit of the lead-lag network S3-1 with three degrees of freedom. It is also within the network S2-5. However, we cannot use network S2-5 in this case, because the gain constant of this network is less than 1 and it will deteriorate the steady-state characteristics of the velocity regulator when it is used as the compensating network. Therefore, we choose the lead-lag network S3-1. It can be seen from Fig. 9.33 that we can use a larger value of ω_0 than 30 [rad/sec] for this compensating network. Thus, we again examine the possibility of having ω_0 = 40 [rad/sec]. For ω_0 = 40 [rad/sec], the value of the compensating vector is

$$
\begin{aligned}
|g_c/\phi_c|_{\omega_0=40} &= 4.99\times10^{-2}\underline{/-70.4^\circ}(1-0.032\times40+j0.08\times40)\\
&\quad(1-0.012\times40+j0.03\times40)\\
&=4.99\times10^{-2}\underline{/-70.4^\circ}(-0.28+j3.2)(0.52+j1.2)
\end{aligned} \tag{9.58}
$$

$$=4.99\times10^{-2}\underline{/-70.4^\circ}\times3.21\underline{/95.0^\circ}\times1.30\underline{/66.6^\circ}$$

$$=0.21\underline{/91.2^\circ}$$

Plotting this value on the compensating vector plane, we see, as shown in Fig. 9.33, that the desired compensation can be achieved with the network S3-1 for ω_0 = 40 [rad/sec]. It is theoretically possible to achieve the desired compensation with the network S3-1 even if we use a slightly larger value of ω_0 than 40 [rad/sec]. In practice, however, a difficulty often arises in the actual construction of the network itself when the endpoint of the compensating vector is very close to its compensating limit. Thus, we choose ω_0 = 40 [rad/sec].

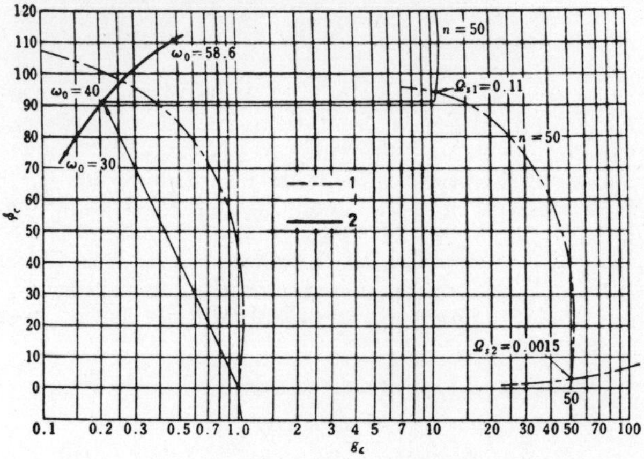

1 - — — —: *curves on the compensating chart*
2 - ————: *curve on the compensating vector plane*

Fig. 9.33 Use of the compensating chart

(f) Determination of the values of the free parameters. To determine the suitable values of the free parameters of the compensating network, we follow the procedure illustrated in Table 6 in the Appendix, as follows:

(1) Turn the compensating vector plane over and place it on Table IV (γ_0 = 0.4) of the Appendix. Then choose a suitable value of n. In this case, we find

$$n=50 \tag{9.59}$$

(2) Slide the compensating vector plane in such a way that the end point of the compensating vector coincides with the origin of the compensating chart, and copy the n-curve corresponding to n = 50 on to the compensating vector plane.

(3) Move the compensating vector plane in such a way that its origin coincides with the origin of the compensating chart, and find

the point of intersection of the original (n = 50)-curve and its copy on the compensating vector. Read the value of Ω_s corresponding to the point of intersection and denote it by Ω_{s1}. In this case, we have

$$\Omega_{s1}=0.11 \tag{9.60}$$

(4) Moving the compensating vector plane so that the end point of the compensating vector coincides with the origin of the compensating chart, read the value of Ω_s corresponding to the point of intersection, and denote it by Ω_{s2}. In this case, we have

$$\Omega_{s2}=0.015 \tag{9.61}$$

(5) Then, the free parameters ω_{s1} and $n\omega_{s1}$, which are related to the lead property of the network S3-1, are calculated as follows:

$$\omega_{s1}=\omega_0\Omega_{s1}=40\times0.11=4.40 \ : \text{(numerator)} \tag{9.62}$$

$$n\omega_{s1}=n\omega_0\Omega_{s1}=50\times40\times0.11=220 \ : \text{(denominator)} \tag{9.63}$$

The free parameters ω_{s2} and ω_{s2}/n, which are related to the lag property, are also calculated as follows:

$$\omega_{s2}=n\omega_0=50\times40\times0.0015=3.00 \ : \text{(numerator)} \tag{9.64}$$

$$\omega_{s2}/n=\omega_0\Omega_{s2}=40\times0.0015=0.06 \ : \text{(denominator)} \tag{9.65}$$

(6) Therefore, the compensating transfer function is

$$F_0(s)=\frac{\left(1+\frac{s}{4.40}\right)\left(1+\frac{s}{3.00}\right)}{\left(1+\frac{s}{220}\right)\left(1+\frac{s}{0.06}\right)}=\frac{(1+0.228)(1+0.333\,s)}{(1+4.55\times10^{-3}s)(1+16.6\,s)} \tag{9.66}$$

(7) Since ω_0 = 40 [rad/sec], the time constant T_d of the disturbance can be calculated from equation (9.51):

$$T_d=\frac{23.4}{40}=0.585 \ [\text{s}] \tag{9.67}$$

(g) Examination of dominant root. If we compensate the velocity regulator with the above network, the open-loop transfer function $F(s)$ is $F(s) = F_0(s)\ F_c(s)$

$$=\frac{499(1+0.228)(1+0.333\,s)}{(1+0.585\,s)(1+0.08\,s)(1+0.03\,s)(1+0.00455\,s)(1+16.6\,s)} \tag{9.68}$$

Accordingly, the reciprocal $1/B_0$ of the residue of the dominant root is calculated from equation (5.85) as follows:

$$1/B_0=5-2+\frac{1}{1+0.228\,r_0}+\frac{1}{1+0.333\,r_0}-\frac{1}{1+0.585\,r_0}-\frac{1}{1+0.08\,r_0}$$
$$-\frac{1}{1+0.03\,r_0}-\frac{1}{1+0.00455\,r_0}-\frac{1}{1+16.65\,r_0} \tag{9.69}$$

Substituting the dominant root $r_0 = -16 + j40$ into tho above equation, we have

$$1/B_0=3+\frac{1}{-2.65+j9.11}+\frac{1}{-4.33+j13.3}-\frac{1}{-8.36+j23.4}$$
$$-\frac{1}{-0.28+j3.2}-\frac{1}{0.52+j1.2}-\frac{1}{0.927+j0.182} \quad (9.70)$$
$$-\frac{1}{-265+j665}$$

The last term in this equation is small relative to the others, and hence it is negligible. Thus, $1/B_0$ can be approximated as

$$\frac{1}{B_0}\doteqdot 3+\frac{1}{9.49}\angle{-106.2^\circ}+\frac{1}{14.0}\angle{-108.0^\circ}-\frac{1}{24.9}\angle{-109.6^\circ}$$
$$-\frac{1}{32}\angle{-95.0^\circ}-\frac{1}{1.307}\angle{-66.6^\circ}-\frac{1}{0.945}\angle{11.0^\circ}$$
$$=3-0.105\angle{73.8^\circ}-0.0715\angle{72.0^\circ}+0.0402\angle{70.4^\circ}+0.312 \quad (9.71)$$
$$\angle{85.0^\circ}-0.765\angle{-66.6^\circ}-1.06\angle{-11.0^\circ}$$
$$=3-0.0296-0.0221+0.0135+0.0278-0.305-1.04$$
$$+j(-0.101-0.0680+0.0379+0.311+0.702+0.202)$$
$$=1.65+j1.084$$

This value of $1/B_0$ satisfies the residue condition for $r_0 = -16 + j40$ to be the dominant root. Therefore, we take the root

$$r_0=-16+j40 \quad (9.72)$$

as the dominant root. It is then clear that the transfer function given by equation (9.66) and the time constant T_d of the disturbance given by equation (9.67) are suitable.

(h) Determination of system constants.

(i) The time constant T_F of the fly-wheel attached to the rotating part of the motor is

$$T_F=T_d-T_m=0.585-0.4=0.185 \text{ [s]} \quad (9.73)$$

Since the moment of inertia of the rotating part with the fly-wheel is 4 [kg-m^2] and the time constant of the rotating part without the fly-wheel is 0.4, the moment of inertia J_F of the fly-wheel is

$$J_F=4\times\frac{0.185}{0.4}=1.85 \text{ [kg-m}^2\text{]} \quad (9.74)$$

and hence we have

$$GD_F^2=\frac{J_F}{4}=0.463 \text{ [kg-m}^2\text{]} \quad (9.75)$$

(8) Calculation of network constants of the network S3-1. From the relations between the network constants of S3-1 and the free parameters, the network constants are calculated as follows:

$$R_1C_1=\frac{1}{\omega_{s1}}=\frac{1}{4.40}=0.228 \text{ [s]} \quad (9.76)$$

$$R_2C_2 = \frac{1}{\omega_{s2}} = \frac{1}{3.00} = 0.333\ \text{[s]} \tag{9.77}$$

$$\begin{aligned} R_1C_2 &= (n-1)\left(\frac{1}{\omega_{s1}} - \frac{1}{n\omega_{s2}}\right) \\ &= (50-1)\left(\frac{1}{4.40} - \frac{1}{50\times 3.00}\right) = 10.82\ \text{[s]} \end{aligned} \tag{9.78}$$

If we let $C_2 = 10$ [μF], we obtain

$$R_1 = \frac{10.82}{10}\times 10^6 = 1.08\times 10^6 = 1.08\ [\text{M}\Omega] \tag{9.79}$$

$$C_1 = \frac{0.228}{1.08}\times 10^{-6} = 0.211\times 10^{-6} = 0.211\ [\mu\text{F}] \tag{9.80}$$

$$R_2 = \frac{0.333}{10}\times 10^6 = 0.0333\times 10^6 = 33.3\ [\text{k}\Omega] \tag{9.81}$$

Therefore, the synthesised compensating network is as shown in Fig. 9.34.

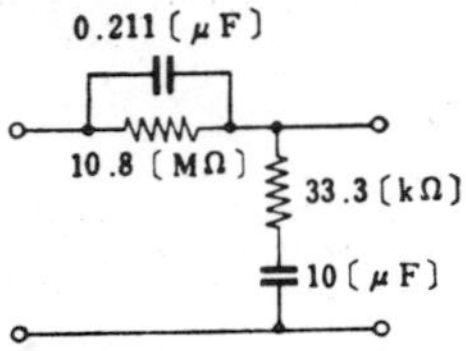

Fig. 9.34 Synthesised compensating network

(J) Examination of the synthesised velocity regulator. The block diagram of the velocity regulator synthesised by the above procedure is shown in Fig. 9.35, and its root locus is shown in Fig. 9.36. Fig. 9.36 shows that there is a root near a pole beside the dominant root. However, this root has no significant effect on the characteristics of the velocity regulator, since it is also close to a zero. Fig. 9.37 shows the response of the synthesised velocity regulator calculated by an analogue computer.

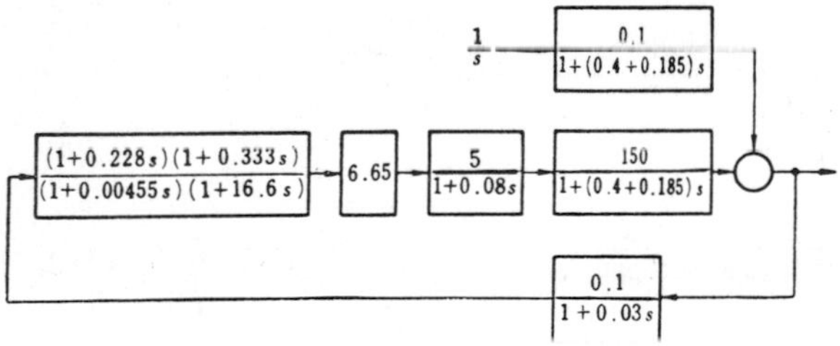

Fig. 9.35 Block diagram of the synthesised velocity regulator

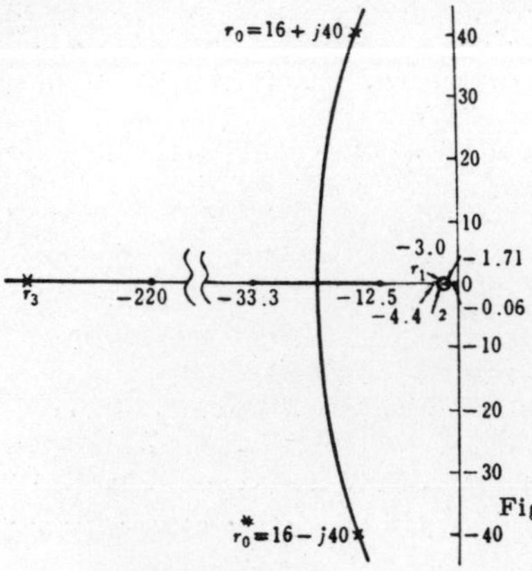

Fig. 9.36 Root locus of the synthesised velocity regulator

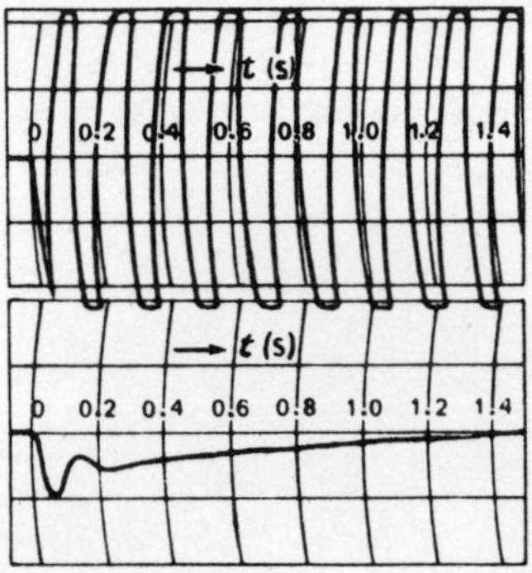

(a)

(a) - response before compensation (when loaded); (b) - response after compensation (when loaded)

(b)

Fig. 9.37 Response of the synthesized velocity regulator calculated by analogue computer

EXERCISE PROBLEMS

(1) Suppose that the transfer function $F_c(s)$ of the lead-lag network shown in the diagram is

$$F_c(s)=\frac{\left(1+\frac{s}{\omega_{s1}}\right)\left(1+\frac{s}{\omega_{s2}}\right)}{\left(1+\frac{s}{n\omega_{s1}}\right)\left(1+\frac{ns}{\omega_{s2}}\right)}$$

Find the values of ω_{s1}, ω_{s2}, and n.

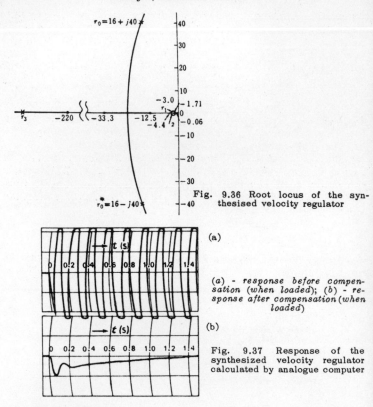

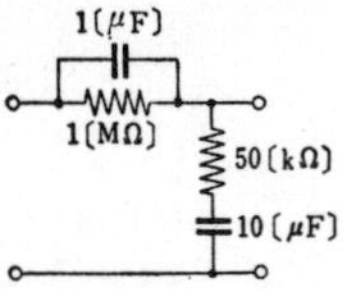

(2) Given an automatic control system whose transfer function $F_o(s)$ is

$$F_0(s)=\frac{30}{s\left(1+\frac{s}{4}\right)\left(1+\frac{s}{16}\right)}$$

we wish to make the response velocity as large as possible by suitable series compensation. Determine the type of compensating network and find its network constants and free parameters. We assume that $\gamma_0 = 0.5$.

(3) Given an automatic control system whose transfer function $F_0(s)$ is

$$F_0(s)=\frac{500}{(1+0.8\,s)(1+0.5\,s)(1+0.05\,s)}$$

synthesise a system from the given transfer function by using a lead-lag compensating network that will make the response velocity as large as possible. We assume that $\gamma_0 = 0.4$.

(4) Suppose that the allowable maximum velocity change of the motor is specified to be 0.3% of the rated rotational frequency of the motor in the example of Section 9.3 and that all other items in the specification are the same as in that example. Synthesise the velocity regulator that meets this specification.

10

Nonlinear Automatic Control

10.1 OUTLINE OF NONLINEAR AUTOMATIC CONTROL

We have discussed only linear automatic control systems in the previous chapters. For linear automatic control, the law of superposition always holds. More specifically, if the input signal is multiplied by n, so is the output signal. This property is called linearity. When an automatic control contains elements, such as a saturation element or a relay mechanism, whose network constants depend on the magnitude of the input, the system does not have the above property. Such an automatic control system is called a nonlinear automatic control system.

Every practical automatic control system has nonlinear characteristics to some degree. In a strict sense, it can be said that every practical automatic control system is a nonlinear automatic control system. Analysis of nonlinear characteristics is extremely complicated in general, and the results of the analysis have little generality. Synthesis of a nonlinear automatic control system is also more complicated. Accordingly, we usually approximate a nonlinear automatic control system with a suitable linear automatic control system, if possible, and we analyse or synthesise the approximate system instead of dealing with the nonlinear system itself. In practice, if the nonlinear characteristics of an automatic control system are not significant, the nonlinear system can be approximated by a linear automatic control system, and the approximate system has sufficiently satisfactory characteristics for practical purposes. Therefore, we need nonlinear analysis and synthesis only when the nonlinear characteristics are so significant that the nonlinear system cannot be approximated by a linear one.

Significant nonlinear characteristics arise in the following situations:

(1) When a controlled system with a limited range of control or an element with a limited operation is used in an automatic control system for economic or other reasons, its output signal corresponding to an input signal with magnitude larger than a certain value has the characteristics shown in Fig. 10.1. A controlled system or an element shows the same characteristics when a device that limits the magnitudes of their output signals is used to avoid damage due to excessive magnitudes of their output signals. The nonlinear characteristic shown in Fig. 10.1 is called saturation.

Since an element having saturation characteristics responds linearly to an input signal with small magnitude, we only need to treat it as a nonlinear element for the input range for which the output is saturated. Saturation can be relatively easily analysed or synthesised in most cases.

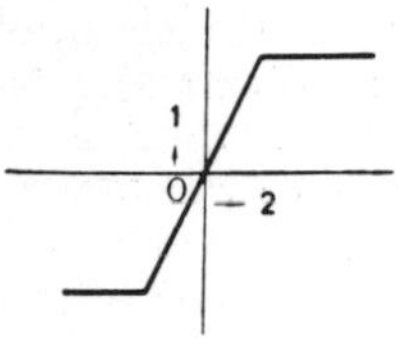

1 - *output signal*; 2 - *input signal*

(2) Hysteresis and dead band are undesired nonlinear characteristics, since they deteriorate the characteristics of an automatic control system. If they cannot be removed, we need to treat the automatic control system as a nonlinear system. Their characteristics are shown in Fig. 10.2 (a) and (b) respectively. These nonlinear characteristics have a considerable effect on both the transient and the steady-state characteristics. Thus, we need a careful examination of these nonlinear characteristics in each automatic control system.

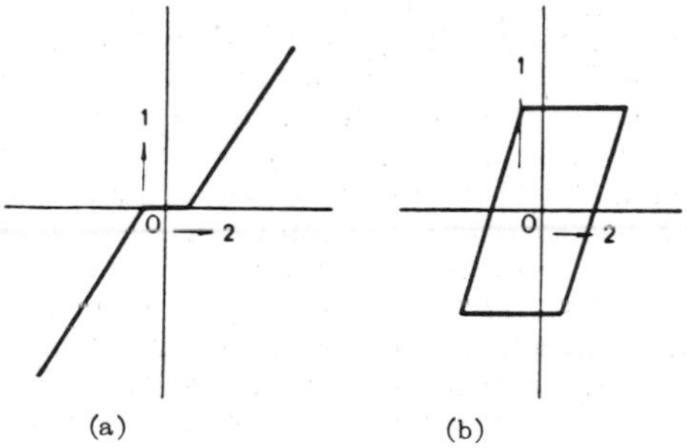

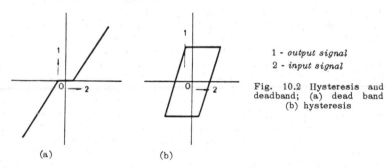

1 - *output signal*
2 - *input signal*

Fig. 10.2 Hysteresis and deadband; (a) dead band (b) hysteresis

(3) Often when a relay or some other type of switch is used in an automatic control system to simplify the structure of the system or to reduce the weight, the automatic control system will have the nonlinear characteristics shown in Fig. 10.3 (a) or (b). The former is a combination of saturation and dead band, and is caused by the relay having a threshold of operation. The latter is the special hysteresis of a relay.

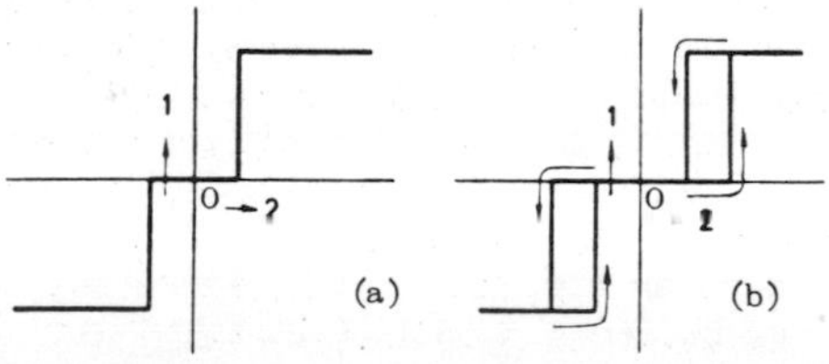

1 - *output*; 2 - *input*

Fig. 10.3 Characteristics of a relay; (a) ideal characteristic (b) hysteresis of relay

(4) Some nonlinear characteristics are purposely used on occasion in an automatic control system in order to improve the characteristics of the system. In this case, different nonlinear characteristics are used in different ways, depending on the purpose. Therefore, we need to examine the nonlinear characteristics in each case.

As a means of analysing or synthesising nonlinear characteristics of automatic control systems, we have the following four methods:
(a) The differential equation method. In this method, we divide a nonlinear response into several regions so that each region can be approximated by a linear response, and each approximated region is calculated by means of a differential equation. In general, this method involves complicated procedures and calculations and is not suited for the synthesis of nonlinear characteristics.
(b) The phase plane method. This method is effective when the order of the differential equation of a nonlinear automatic control system is low. However, it is not practical for a higher-order nonlinear system. It is also unsuitable for synthesis.
(c) The frequency response method. This method is applicable to a nonlinear automatic control system that satisfies certain conditions. It is the most convenient method in practice, since it is quite similar to the frequency response method for the linear case as far as the necessary conditions are satisfied. We shall deal primarily with this method in what follows.
(d) The analogue-computer method. Since a computer is used for calculations in this method, it is clearly the most convenient method for analysis. It is a particularly useful method for nonlinear analysis, since nonlinear analysis involves many laborious calculations. However, we still need a theoretical examination by another method together with this computer method to carry out nonlinear synthesis.

In any case, the treatment of nonlinear characteristics involves more complicated and laborious computations than those required for the treatment of linear characteristics. As mentioned before, however, we only need deal with nonlinear characteristics in most cases where automatic control systems have a simple structure. In fact, most of the nonlinear automatic control systems which we treat in practical cases consist of one nonlinear element and some other linear elements. Thus, we shall mainly discuss such nonlinear automatic control systems in what follows.

10.2. STABILITY CRITERION BASED ON FREQUENCY RESPONSE METHOD

The frequency response method developed in the previous chapters are applicable only to linear automatic control systems, not to nonlinear ones. However, if a nonlinear system meets certain requirements, a similar method is applicable to the nonlinear system.

For example, consider a nonlinear automatic control system consisting of a nonlinear controlling element (N) and a linear controlled system (L) as shown in Fig. 10.4. If the input signal to the nonlinear controlling element (N), which is the error signal, has a sinusoidal waveform, then the output signal of (N) has a distorted sinusoidal waveform as shown in Fig. 10.4. When this distorted sinusoidal wave passes through the controlled system which has a low-pass filter characteristic, the high harmonics of the distorted sinusoidal waveform are mostly filtered out and the controlled variable is a sinusoidal wave consisting of the output signal to the fundamental component of the distorted waveform. Consequently, this nonlinear system has very similar characteristics when the error signal has a sinusoidal waveform. Thus, we can formulate the frequency response of the nonlinear system by taking the ratio of the output signal to the input signal, where the input and output signal are expressed in vector quantities.

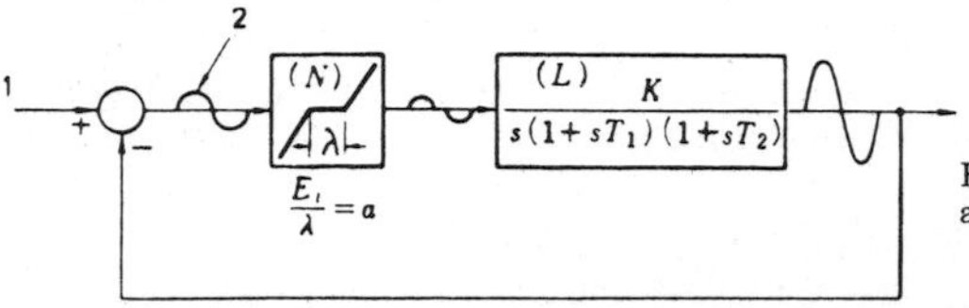

Fig. 10.4 Example of a non-linear automatic control system

1 - *reference input*; 2 - *error signal* (*which is the input signal to the nonlinear element*)

If we plot the frequency response as in the linear case, we obtain the vector locus shown in Fig. 10.5. As shown in this figure, the frequency-response vector locus of a nonlinear system is a different curve for a different magnitude of the error signal, while that of a linear system is one curve regardless of the magnitude of the error signal. This is the essential difference between the frequency-response vector locus of a nonlinear system and that of a linear system. The reason for this is as follows. If the nonlinear element has a dead band characteristic, as shown in Fig. 10.5, the level of the output signal of the nonlinear element is zero for any error signal with level less than the band width 2λ of the dead band. When the input signal has a level greater than 2λ, the level of the output signal is greater than zero, and it increases nonlinearly as the level of the error signal, as shown in Fig. 10.6. In Fig. 10.6, the amplitude of the error signal (which is the input signal), is expressed in terms of its ratio to the band width 2 instead of its actual value. If we apply the Nyquist stability criterion for a linear system to the frequency response vector locus in Fig. 10.5, we find the following. (1) Though the vector locus is different for different levels of the input signal every vector locus cuts across the real axis to the right of the point $-1 + j\,0$ (when the frequency increases). Therefore, the nonlinear system is stable. (2) The resonance value M_p decreases and the attentuation of the transient response slows down as the level of the error signal (which is the input signal) decreases.

Consider a nonlinear system obtained by multiplying by 3 the gain constant K of the linear part (L) in the preceding nonlinear automatic control system. Then, the frequency-response vector locus of this system is the family of curves shown in Fig. 10.7. Observing Fig. 10.7, we note that this nonlinear automatic control system is stable for the input level $a = E_i / \lambda$ less than 10 and unstable for a larger than 10. It seems that the degree of the instability increases as a increases. In practice, however, as soon as the error signal level a exceeds the value 10, the nonlinear system becomes unstable, and then the level of the error signal gradually increases. Accordingly, the degree of instability increases, and the vector locus moves to the left, and finally the error signal level reaches $a = \infty$. That is, once the error signal level becomes greater than 10, the nonlinear system becomes unstable. Consequently, if the error signal level a becomes larger than 10 even momentarily (because of some disturbance during the stable operation of the nonlinear system with a less than 10, the nonlinear system becomes unstable and never becomes stable again automatically. Thus, a nonlinear system with a frequency response vector locus of the type shown in Fig. 10.7 becomes unstable easily and is not suitable for practical use, whereas a

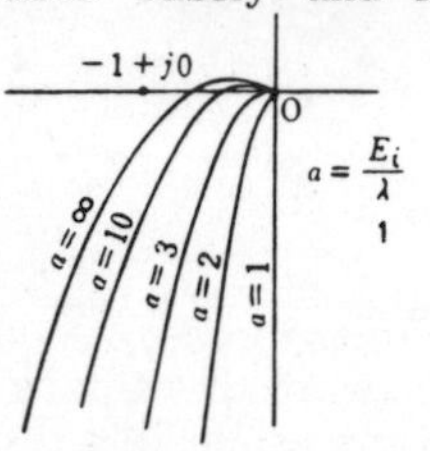

1 - *(relative input signal)*

Fig. 10.5 Frequency response vector locus of the nonlinear system shown in Fig. 10.4 (This nonlinear system is stable for all levels of the error signal)

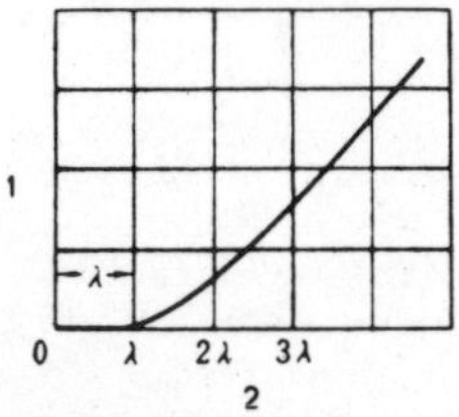

1 - *output signal*; 2 - *amplitude of input signal*

Fig. 10.6 Signal-transfer characteristics of a nonlinear element

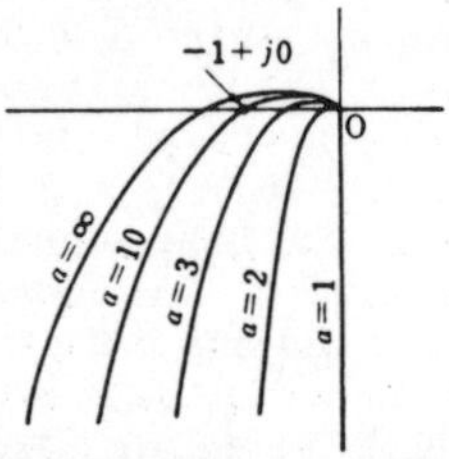

Fig. 10.7 Another example of a frequency response vector locus of a nonlinear system easily becomes unstable

nonlinear system with frequency response vector locus of the type shown in Fig. 10.5 is always stable and is suitable for practical use.

The stability of a nonlinear automatic control system can be examined by observing its frequency response vector locus, as mentioned above. It is cumbersome, however, to construct the frequency response vector locus of a nonlinear automatic control system, since we need to plot a family of curves for different values of the error signal level. Thus, we shall develop an approach to eliminate this inconvenience. Since the controlled system (L) is linear, its frequency response vector locus is a curve that is independent of the error signal level. Consequently, the fact that the frequency response vector locus is a different curve for a different error signal level (as shown in Figs. 10.5 and 10.7) is caused by the nonlinear element (N). Thus, we shall find the signal-transfer characteristic* of a nonlinear element. In the expression for the signal-transfer characteristic, we need to use a sinusoidal waveform as the input signal to the nonlinear element and the fundamental component of the distorted sinusoidal waveform (which is the output of the nonlinear element) as the output signal.

As shown in Fig. 10.4, the signal transfer characteristic of a nonlinear element, which is the relation between the sinusoidal input waveform and the fundamental component of the distorted sinusoidal output waveform, is independent of the frequency when the nonlinear element has a dead band characteristic; the level of the fundamental component of the distorted sinusoidal waveform is completely determined by the level of the sinusoidal input waveform, as shown in Fig. 10.6. Thus, we define the transfer function of a nonlinear element to be the ratio of the fundamental component of the output signal to the input signal, and we denote it by $G_N(a)$ where $a = E_i / \lambda$, λ is the half-band-width, and E_i is the input signal. On the other hand, the frequency response $G_L(j\omega)$ of the linear controlled system depends on the frequency of the input signal. Then,

$$F(j\omega) = G_N(a) \cdot G_L(j\omega) \tag{10.1}$$

In the stability criterion already introduced, we determined the stability of the nonlinear automatic control system by the position of the vector locus of the open-loop frequency response $F(j\omega)$ with respect to the point $-1 + j0$. If we use the vector locus of $F(j\omega)/K$ (where K is a constant) instead of the vector locus of $F(j\omega)$, we can determine the stability of the same nonlinear automatic control system by observing the position of the vector locus with respect to the point $-1/K + j0$ instead of the point $-1 + j0$. Using this result, we can determine the stability of the nonlinear automatic control system by observing the position of the vector locus of

$$\frac{F(j\omega)}{G_N(a)} = G_L(j\omega) \tag{10.2}$$

with respect to the point $-1/G_N(a) + j0$. Here, the point $-1/G_N(a) + j0$ varies its position depending on the error signal level a. Thus, the point $-1/G_N(a) + j0$ draws a locus as a varies. Fig. 10.8 shows the frequency response vector locus of the linear controlled system (L) (in Fig. 10.4) and the locus of the point $-1/G_N(a) + j0$ which are plotted on the same plane. It is equivalent to the frequency response vector locus shown in Fig. 10.5. Fig. 10.9 shows the frequency response vector locus of the linear element

*This characteristic is represented by the ratio of the sinusiodal output signal to the sinusiodal input signal expressed in vector quantities. This ratio of vectors is called the describing function and has a similar property to the frequency response. In the above example, its value is independent of frequency.

and the locus of the point $-1/G_N(a) + j0$ in the case in which the time constant K of the linear controlled system is multiplied by 3, and it is equivalent to the frequency response vector locus shown in Fig. 10.7.

In Fig. 10.8, the point $-1/G_N(a) + j0$ is always located to the left of the vector locus of $G_L(j\omega)$ for all values of the error

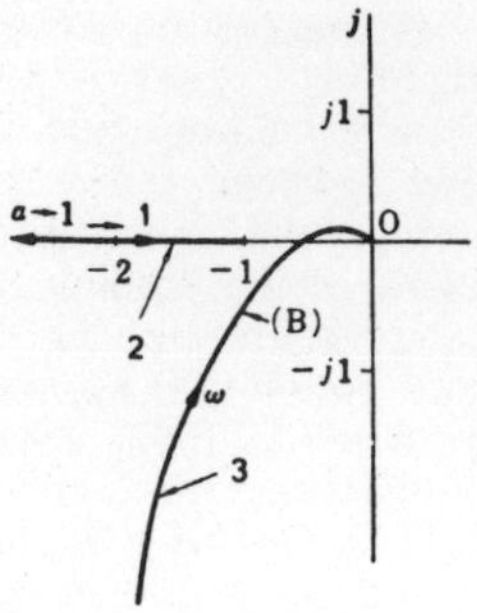

1 - *direction in which* a *increases*
2 - *locus of the point* $-1/(G_N(a)) + j0$
3 - *vector locus of* $G_L(j\omega)$

Fig. 10.8 Frequency response vector locus of the nonlinear system (See Fig. 10.4), where the frequency response vector locus of the linear controlled system and the locus of the point $- G_N(a) + jo$ are plotted separately

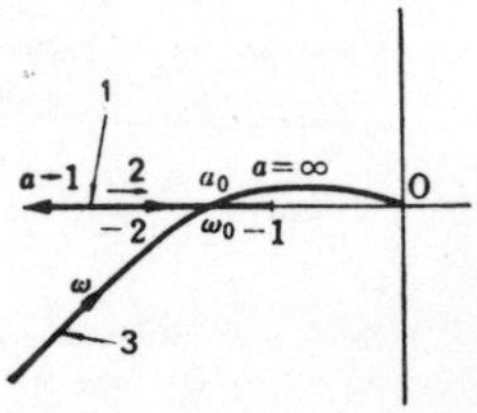

1 - *locus of the point* $-1/(G_N(a)) + j0$
2 - *direction in which* a *increases*
3 - *vector locus of* $G_L(j\omega)$

Fig. 10.9 Equivalent frequency response vector locus of the nonlinear system obtained by multiplying by 3 the time constant of the linear controlled system in Fig. 10.4

signal level, and hence this nonlinear system is stable independently of the error signal level. In Fig. 10.9, the two loci intersect. If the amplitude of the error signal is a_0 at the point of intersection and the corresponding angular frequency is ω_0, it seems from a theoretical view that the nonlinear system continuously oscillates with constant error level a_0 and constant angular frequency ω_0. In reality, however, it behaves differently. That is, if for some reason the error signal level becomes less than a_0 at some instant during the oscillation with constant amplitude, the nonlinear system will start becoming stable and the error signal will then decrease with time. Consequently, the stability increases with time, and finally the oscillation disappears. On the other hand, if the error signal level becomes larger than a_0 at some instant during the oscillation with constant amplitude, the nonlinear system will start becoming unstable and the error signal level will then increase. Consequently, the instability increases with time, and finally the error amplitude tends to infinity. Specifically, when a increases, the point $-1/G_N(a) + j0$ will cross the boundary from the stable into the unstable region at $a = a_0$. The behaviour of the nonlinear system at $a = a_0$ is extremely unstable. Thus, such a point of intersection is called an unstable point of intersection.

We shall now discuss an intersection of a different type. Assume that the nonlinear element (N) has the saturation characteristics shown in Fig. 10.10 instead of the dead band characteristic in the nonlinear system shown in Fig. 10.4. Then, the output signal of the nonlinear element (N) is the distorted sinusoidal waveform shown in Fig. 10.11 (b) if the input signal has a level larger than λ. The signal transfer characteristic (which is the describing function) of (N) is as shown in Fig. 10.12. The locus of $-1/G_N(a) + j0$ (where $a = E_i/\lambda$ is the curve shown in Fig. 10.13 (a). This nonlinear automatic control system is unstable for an error signal level less than a_0. It is stable, however, for an error signal level greater than a_0, and the error signal level decreases with time. Consequently, for an error signal level larger than a_0, the nonlinear system maintains a stable oscillation (called a limit cycle) with a constant error amplitude a_0 and a frequency ω_0 which corresponds to the point of intersection of the locus of $-1/G_N(a) + j0$ and the vector locus of $G_L(j\omega)$. Such a point of intersection is called a stable point of intersection.

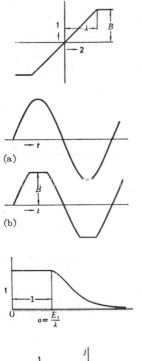

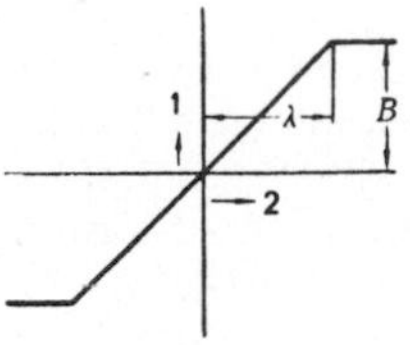

1 - *output signal*; 2 - *input signal*

Fig. 10.10 Saturation characteristic

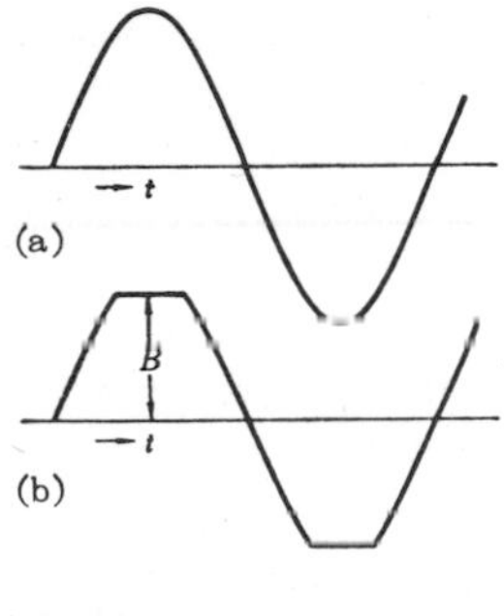

Fig. 10.11 Relation between input and output signals of nonlinear elements a saturation characteristic: (a) input signal; (b) output signal

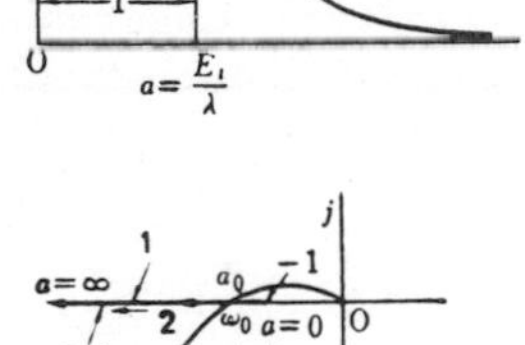

1 - *amplification factor*

Fig. 10.12 Signal transfer characteristics of a nonlinear element with saturation

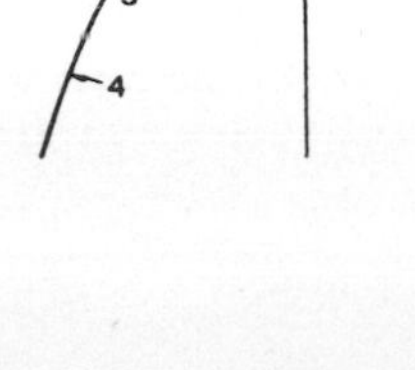

1 - *locus of the point* $-1/(G_N(a)) + j0$
2 - *direction of increasing* a; 3 - *direction of increasing* ω; 4 - *vector locus of* $G_L(j\omega)$

Fig. 10.13 Frequency response vector locus of a nonlinear automatic control system with a saturation element

A limit cycle is rather desirable for a nonlinear system unless its amplitude is larger than a desired value, because it is useful in practice to reduce or remove the static error caused by Coulomb friction or other causes and to increase the linearity of the nonlinear system.

As shown in Fig. 10.9, when a increases, the point $-1/G_N(a) + j0$ crosses the boundary from the unstable region to the stable region at a stable point of intersection. This, together with the previous examination of an unstable point of intersection, indicates that we can determine whether a point of intersection is stable or not by observing the direction of increasing a.

10.3. DESCRIBING FUNCTIONS

The expression $G_N(a)$, which represents the signal transfer characteristic of a nonlinear element, is called the describing function. The describing function is similar to the frequency response of a linear element, but it differs from the frequency response, since it is a function of the input signal level in general. As already mentioned, the describing function is found by the following procedure: we first expand the output waveform (which is a distorted sinusoidal waveform) in a Fourier series, find the amplitude and the phase angle of the fundamental component, then express the fundamental component in vector representation, and finally divide this vector representation by the vector representation of the input signal, to obtain the describing function. The describing function is clearly a vector quantity.

As an example, we shall find the describing function of the nonlinear element shown in Fig. 10.4. We assume that the nonlinear element has a dead band characteristic, as shown in Fig. 10.14. That is, the width of the dead band is 2λ, and the curve of the output signal for an input signal larger than λ is a line with slope 1. The output waveform for the sinusoidal input wave is shown in Fig. 10.15. That is, if the input signal waveform is

$$e_i = E_i \sin\theta \qquad \theta = \omega t \tag{10.3}$$

the corresponding output signal e_o takes the value

$$e_o = E_i \sin\theta - \lambda \tag{10.4}$$

in the interval from θ_1 to θ_2, and $e_o = 0$ in the intervals from 0 to θ_1 and from θ_2 to π, where

$$\theta_1 = \sin^{-1}\frac{\lambda}{E_i} \tag{10.5}$$

$$\theta_2 = \pi - \theta_1 \tag{10.6}$$

The general method of calculating the fundamental component of the output waveform by the Fourier expansion of the output signal is as follows: we calculate the amplitude A_1 of the sine wave and the amplitude B_1 of the cosine wave, which appear in the fundamental component as

$$A_1 = \frac{1}{\pi} \int_0^{2\pi} e_o \sin \theta d\theta \tag{10.7}$$

$$B_1 = \frac{1}{\pi} \int_0^{2\pi} e_o \cos \theta d\theta \tag{10.8}$$

Then we compute the amplitude C_1 of the fundamental component and the phase angle ϕ_1:

$$C_1 = \sqrt{A_1^2 + B_1^2} \tag{10.9}$$

$$\phi_1 = \tan^{-1} \frac{B_1}{A_1} \tag{10.10}$$

We can, however, use a simplified method in this example, since the output waveform shown in Fig. 10.15 is symmetric with respect to the origin. Specifically, the symmetry of the output waveform implies that no cosine waveforms are contained in the fundamental component, and hence $B_1 = 0$. Consequently, we have $C_1 = A_1$. Again from symmetry, we can calculate the amplitude A_1 of the sine wave from the equation

$$A_1 = \frac{2}{\pi} \int_0^{\pi} e_o \sin \theta d\theta \tag{10.11}$$

If we substitute the expression for e_o given by equation (10.4) into equation (10.11), the latter equation can be written

$$A_1 = \frac{2}{\pi} \int_{\theta_1}^{\pi-\theta_1} (E_i \sin \theta - \lambda) \sin \theta d\theta \tag{10.12}$$

$$= \frac{2}{\pi} \left[E_i \int_{\theta_1}^{\pi-\theta_1} \sin^2 \theta d\theta - \lambda \int_{\theta_1}^{\pi-\theta_1} \sin \theta d\theta \right] \tag{10.13}$$

$$= \frac{2}{\pi} \left[\frac{E_i}{2} \int_{\theta_1}^{\pi-\theta_1} (1 - \cos 2\theta) d\theta + \lambda \left| \cos \theta \right|_{\theta_1}^{\pi-\theta_1} \right] \tag{10.14}$$

Here, we used $\theta_2 = \pi - \theta_1$ and θ_1 as the upper and the lower limits of integration instead of 0 and π since e_o is 0 in the intervals from 0 to θ_1 and from θ_2 to π. The integral in the expression (10.14) is

$$\begin{aligned} \int_{\theta_1}^{\pi-\theta_1} (1 - \cos 2\theta) d\theta &= \pi - 2\theta_1 - \frac{1}{2} \{\sin(2\pi - 2\theta_1) - \sin 2\theta_1\} \\ &= \pi - 2\theta_1 - \sin 2\theta_1 \end{aligned} \tag{10.15}$$

and the second term is

$$\left| \cos \theta \right|_{\theta_1}^{\pi-\theta_1} = \cos(\pi - \theta_1) - \cos \theta_1 = -2 \cos \theta_1 \tag{10.16}$$

Therefore, substitution of the expressions (10.15) and (10.16) into equation (10.14) yields

$$A_1 = \frac{2}{\pi} \left[\frac{E_i}{2} (\pi - 2\theta_1 - \sin 2\theta_1) - 2\lambda \cos \theta_1 \right] \tag{10.17}$$

Since we have

$$=2\frac{\lambda}{E_i}\cos\theta_1 \tag{10.18}$$

from equation (10.5), A_1 can be evaluated as

$$A_1=\frac{2}{\pi}\left[\frac{E_i}{2}(\pi-2\theta_1)-\lambda\cos\theta_1\right] \tag{10.19}$$

$$=E_i-\frac{2}{\pi}(E_i\theta_1+\lambda\cos\theta_1) \tag{10.20}$$

$$=E_i-\frac{2}{\pi}(E_i\theta_1+\lambda\sqrt{1-(\sin\theta_1)^2}) \tag{10.21}$$

Substituting equation (10.5) into this, we finally obtain

$$A_1=E_i-\frac{2}{\pi}\left(E_i\sin^{-1}\frac{\lambda}{E_i}+\lambda\sqrt{1-\left(\frac{\lambda}{E_i}\right)^2}\right) \tag{10.22}$$

Indeed the curve shown in Fig. 10.6 expresses the relation between E_i and A_1 given by this equation.

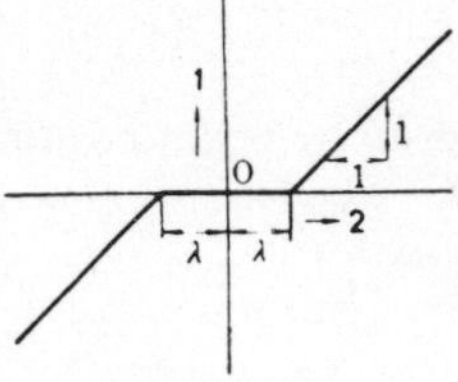

1 - *input*; 2 - *output*

Fig. 10.14 Dead band characteristic

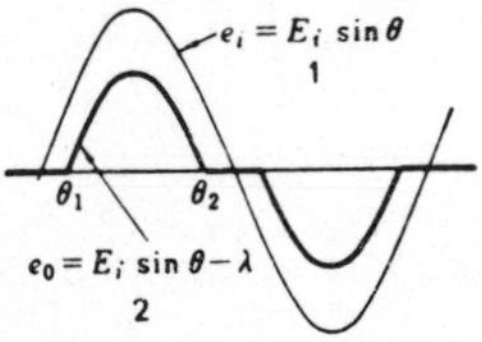

1 - *input signal*; 2 - *output signal*

Fig. 10.15 Relation between input and output waveform of a nonlinear element with dead band characteristics

If we use the value of A_1 calculated in the above, the fundamental component of the output waveform of the nonlinear element for the sinusoidal input waveform $E_i \sin\omega t$ is

$$\left\{E_i-\frac{2}{\pi}\left(E_i\sin^{-1}\frac{\lambda}{E_i}+\lambda\sqrt{1-\left(\frac{\lambda}{E_i}\right)^2}\right\}\sin\omega t \tag{10.23}$$

for $E_i > \lambda$ and is equal to 0 for $E_i \leqq \lambda$. Since the vector representation of the output waveform and the input waveform are $A_1\underline{/0}$ and $E_i\underline{/0}$ respectively, the describing function is

$$\frac{A_1\underline{/0}}{E_i\underline{/0}}=\left\{1-\frac{2}{\pi}\left(\sin^{-1}\frac{\lambda}{E_i}+\frac{\lambda}{E_i}\sqrt{1-\left(\frac{\lambda}{E_i}\right)^2}\right)\right\}\underline{/0} \tag{10.24}$$

The expression (10.24) is a function of E_i/λ. If we set $E_i/\lambda = a$, it becomes a function of a. If we denote this function by $G_N(a)$, we have

$$G_N(a)=\left\{1-\frac{2}{\pi}\left(\sin^{-1}\frac{1}{a}+\frac{1}{a}\sqrt{1-\frac{1}{a^2}}\right)\right\}\underline{/0} \tag{10.25}$$

for $a > 1$, and $G_N(a) = 0$ for $0 < a < 1$. The function $G_N(a)$ is the describing function of the nonlinear element having a dead band characteristic.

Describing functions of other nonlinear elements can be obtained by similar methods. We shall however, omit details of the calculations, and we present the describing functions of only a few nonlinear elements.

Figure 10.16 shows a simplified relay characteristic. If the width of the hysteresis is $2h$, the amplitude of the output signal is B, and if the amplitude of the input signal is E_i, then the describing function $G_N(E_i)$ is

$$G_N(E_i)=\frac{4B}{\pi E_i}\underline{/-\sin^{-1}\frac{h}{E_i}} \tag{10.26}$$

For example, if $B = 10$ and $h = 5$, then from equation (10.26) the describing function $G_N(E_i)$ is

$$G_N(E_i)=\frac{40}{\pi E_i}\underline{/-\sin^{-1}\frac{5}{E_i}} \tag{10.27}$$

Plotting the locus of the point $-1/G_N(E_i) + j0$, which is used

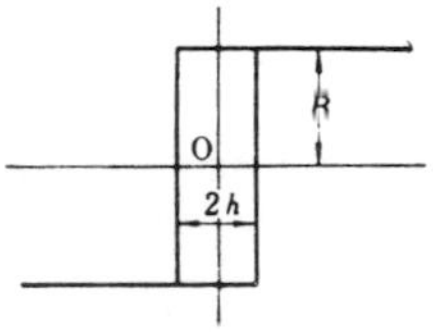

Fig. 10.16 Simplified relay characteristics

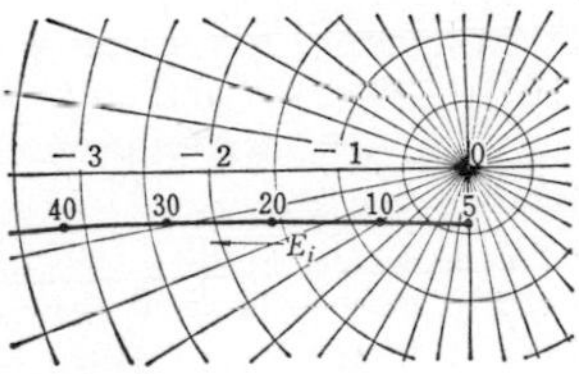

Fig. 10.17 Example of the locus of the point $-1/G_N(Ei)$ + $j0$ for a simplified relay

to determine the stability of a nonlinear system containing a relay, we obtain the curve shown in Fig. 10.17.

The signal transfer characteristics of a relay with dead band characteristics are shown in Fig. 10.18. The describing function $G_N(a)$ of this relay is as follows:

$$G_N(a) = -\frac{4B}{\pi a}\left\{\sin\frac{1}{2}\left(\cos^{-1}\frac{1-\alpha}{2a} + \cos^{-1}\frac{1+\alpha}{2a}\right)\right\} \Big/ -\frac{1}{2}\sin^{-1}\frac{1+\alpha}{2a} - \sin^{-1}\frac{1-\alpha}{2a} \tag{10.28}$$

for $a > (1 + \alpha)/2$, while

$$G_N(a) = 0 \tag{10.29}$$

for $a < (1 + \alpha)/2$, where $a = E_i / \lambda$ and $\alpha = h / \lambda$.

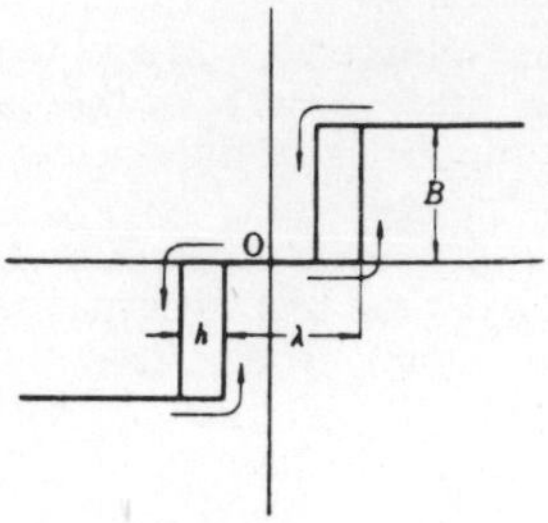

Fig. 10.18 Relay characteristics with a deadband

10.4. SAMPLED DATA CONTROL

In all the automatic control systems that we have discussed, the errors were continuously detected and the controlled variables were continuously measured. It is not necessary, however, to detect the error in every instance when an automatic control system has a slow response. If an automatic control system contains an element which operates discontinuously, it is called a sampled data control system.

A sampled data control system is generally used in the following cases: when continuous measurement of the controlled variables or continuous control is impossible, when continuous control is disadvantageous, when a computer that takes time for computation, such as a digital computer, is used as an element, and when one controller is required to control many systems.

Construction of a sampled data control system is shown in Fig. 10.19. A sampler is a device that produces a signal as a series of pulses, such as the one shown in Fig. 10.20 (a) from a continuous signal such as that in Fig. 10.20 (b) by closing the switch periodically with an extremely small switch-closed time duration. The envelope of the pulses in the pulse series is equal to the continuous signal. The conversion of the continuous signal in Fig. 10.20 (a) into the series of pulses in Fig. 10.20 (b) itself is called sampling, and the duration between successive switch closures is called the sampling period. The holder in Fig. 10.19 is an element that converts the series of pulses in Fig. 10.21 (a) into the step signal shown in Fig. 10.21 (b), which is convenient for controlling the system.

The behaviour of a sampled data control system is quite similar to that of a continuous automatic control system when the sampling period is sufficiently small in comparison with the rate of the variation in the error signal. It can then be approximated by a continuous automatic control system. However, if the sampling period is relatively large, the transient response of a sampled data control system is different from that of a continuous control system, and hence the sampled data control system cannot be approximated by a continuous control system. Consequently, we need a new method for the analysis of sampled data control systems. The Laplace transform can be used in the new method. In general, however, the Laplace transform of a sampled signal turns out to be an infinite series, and the calculation is naturally complicated. To remove this disadvantage, we introduce the Z-transformation. If we use the Z-transformation, the new method for the analysis of a sampled data control system becomes similar to the usual method for the analysis of a continuous control system.

The sampled signal obtained from the continuous signal $f(t)$ in Fig. 10.22 (a) by sampling with sampling period T is the pulse series shown in Fig. 10.22 (b). If we denote this sampled signal by $f^*(t)$, the amplitude of the nth pulse of $f^*(t)$ is $f(nT)$ and occurs at the time nT measured from $t = 0$. Thus, the nth pulse is expressed by

$$f(nT)\delta(t-nT) \tag{10.30}$$

The Laplace transform of the nth pulse is

$$\mathcal{L}f(nT)\delta(t-nT)=f(nT)\epsilon^{-snT} \tag{10.31}$$

Therefore the Laplace transform of the pulse series $f^*(t)$ is

$$\mathcal{L}f^*(t)=\sum_{n=0}^{\infty}f(nT)\epsilon^{-snT} \tag{10.32}$$

We set

$$\epsilon^{sT}=z \tag{10.33}$$

so that the Laplace transform in equation (10.32) becomes a function of z. If we denote this function by $F^*(z)$, we have

$$F^*(z)=\sum_{n=0}^{\infty}f(nT)z^{-n}$$

The function $F^*(z)$ is called the Z-transform of $f(t)$ and is denoted by

$$F^*(z)=Zf(t) \tag{10.34}$$

as in the case of the Laplace transform. The waveform represented by $F^*(z)$ is called the waveform of the z-representation of $f^*(t)$.

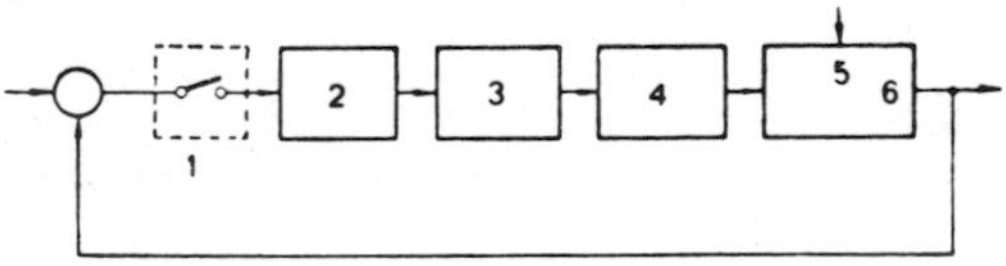

1 - *sampler*; 2 - *controller*; 3 - *holder*; 4 - *manipulating unit*; 5 - *disturbance*; 6 - *controlled system*

Fig. 10.19 Construction of a sampled data control system

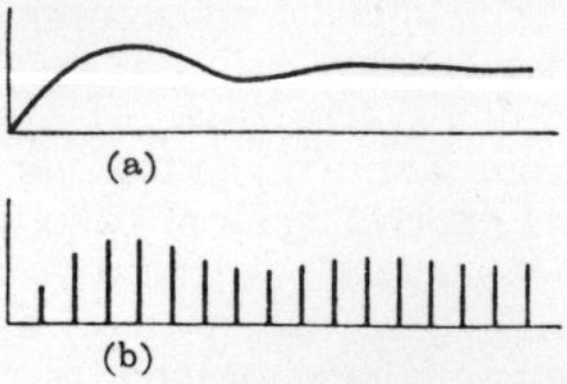

Fig. 10.20 Signal transfer characteristic of sampler

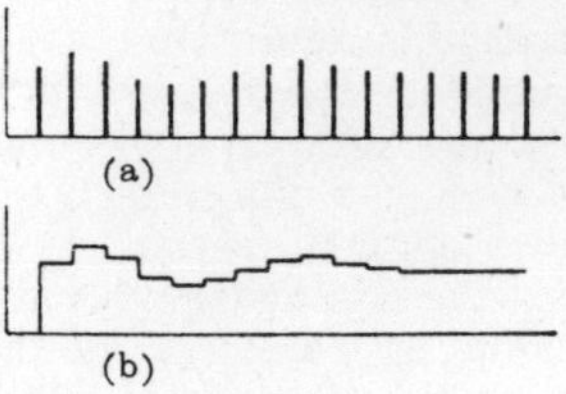

Fig. 10.21 Signal transfer characteristics of holder

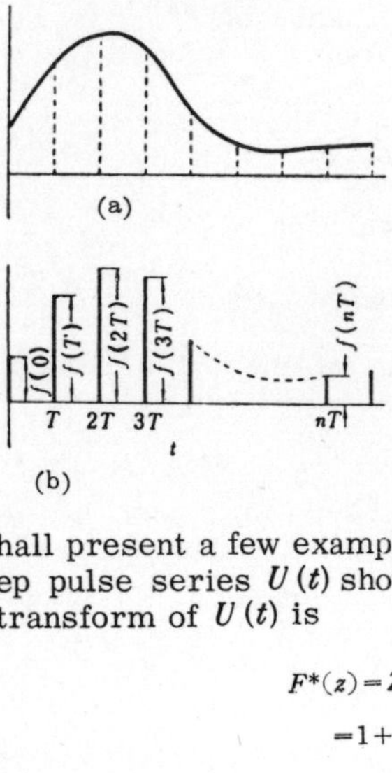

Fig. 10.22 Sampling: (a) continuous signal; (b) sampled signal $f^*(t)$

We shall present a few examples of Z-transforms. Consider the unit step pulse series $U(t)$ shown in Fig. 10.23. Since $f(nT) = 1$, the Z-transform of $U(t)$ is

$$F^*(z) = Z\,U(t) = \sum z^{-n} \tag{10.35}$$

$$= 1 + \frac{1}{z} + \frac{1}{z^2} + \frac{1}{z^3} + \cdots\cdots$$

$$= \frac{1}{1 - \frac{1}{z}}$$

$$= \frac{z}{z-1} \tag{10.36}$$

The Z-transform of $\epsilon^{-at} U(t)$ is calculated as follows:

$$Z\epsilon^{at}\,U(t) = \sum_{n=0}^{\infty} \epsilon^{-anT} z^{-n} \tag{10.37}$$

$$= 1 + \frac{\epsilon^{-aT}}{z} + \frac{(\epsilon^{-aT})^2}{z^2} + \cdots\cdots$$

$$= \frac{1}{1 - \frac{\epsilon^{-aT}}{z}}$$

$$= \frac{z}{z - \epsilon^{-aT}} \tag{10.38}$$

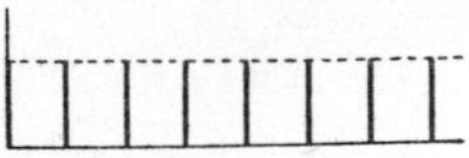

Fig. 10.23 Unit step pulse series

The transformation by which we can find the amplitude of each pulse $f(nT)$ from a given waveform of the z-representation $F^*(z)$ is called the inverse Z-transformation. It is denoted by

$$Z^{-1}F^*(z)=f(nT) \tag{10.39}$$

As is clear from the preceding discussion, we can find the inverse z-transform of $F^*(z)$ by expanding $F^*(z)$ in a power series: That is, if we expand $F^*(z)$ as

$$F^*(z)=1+\frac{A_1}{z}+\frac{A_2}{z^2}+\frac{A_3}{z^3}+\cdots\cdots+\frac{A_n}{z^n}+\cdots\cdots \tag{10.40}$$

the amplitude $f(nT)$ of the nth pulse is

$$f(nT)=A_n \tag{10.41}$$

According to the theory of complex functions, the inverse z-transform of $F^*(z)$ can be calculated from the equation

$$Z^{-1}F^*(z)=\frac{1}{2\pi j}\int_{-j\infty}^{+j\infty}F^*(z)z^{n-1}dz \tag{10.42}$$

The Z-transforms and the inverse Z-transforms of some simple transfer functions are shown in Table 10.1.

TABLE 10.1 Z-TRANSFORMS

transfer function $F(s)$	waveform of t-representation $F(nt)$	waveform of z-representation $F^*(z)$
$\frac{1}{s}$	1	$\frac{z}{z-1}$
$\frac{1}{s+a}$	ϵ^{-naT}	$\frac{z}{z-\epsilon^{-aT}}$
$\frac{a}{s(s+a)}$	$1-\epsilon^{-naT}$	$\frac{z}{z-1}-\frac{z}{z-\epsilon^{-aT}}$
$\frac{b\ \ a}{(s+a)(s+b)}$	$\epsilon^{-naT}-\epsilon^{-nbT}$	$\frac{z}{z-\epsilon^{-aT}}-\frac{z}{z-\epsilon^{-bT}}$

10.5 SAMPLED TRANSFER FUNCTIONS

Let $F_1^*(z)$ be the z-representation of a pulse series which is applied to a network as an input signal and let $F_0^*(z)$ be the z-representation of the pulse series obtained by sampling from the output signal of the network. Then, the function $G^*(z)$ defined by

$$\frac{F_o^*(z)}{F_1^*(z)} = G^*(z) \tag{10.43}$$

is called the sampled transfer function.

Let us investigate the properties of the sampled transfer function. As an example, consider the network shown in Fig. 10.24, and suppose that the z-representation of the input signal to the network is $F_1{}^*(z)$, that the t-representation of the corresponding output signal is $f_o(t)$, and that the z-representation of the series of pulses obtained by sampling is $F_o{}^*(z)$. If $f_1(t)$ is the input signal before sampling, the n th pulse of the sampled input signal is $f_1(nT)\,\delta(t - nT)$, and its Laplace transform is

$$f_1(nT)\epsilon^{-snT} \tag{10.44}$$

If we denote by $F_{on}(s)$ the output signal of the transfer function $G(s)$ for the n th pulse given by equation (10.44), we have

$$F_{on}(s) = G(s)f_1(nT)\epsilon^{-snT} = f_1(nT)G(s)\epsilon^{-snT}$$

The t-representation $f_{on}(t)$ of the output signal of $G(s)$ for the nth pulse is then found by applying the inverse Laplace transformation to the output signal $F_{on}(s)$ as follows:

$$\begin{aligned} f_{on}(t) &= \mathcal{L}^{-1} f_1(nT)G(s)\epsilon^{-snT} \\ &= f_1(nT)g(t-nT) \end{aligned} \tag{10.45}$$

where $g(t)$ is the impulse response of $G(s)$, i.e. $\mathcal{L}^{-1}G(s) = g(t)$. Applying the Z-transformation to the expression (10.45), we obtain the series of pulses

$$F^*_{on}(z) = \sum_{m=1}^{\infty} |f_1(nT)g(t-nT)|_{t=mT} \cdot \epsilon^{-smT} \tag{10.46}$$

Since $F^*_{on}(z)$ is the z-representation of the series of pulses obtained by sampling the output signal of $G(s)$ for the nth pulse of the input pulse series, the z-representation $F_o^*(z)$ of the output signal corresponding to the input signal $F_1{}^*(z)$ will be obtained by taking the sum of $F^*_{on}(z)$ over the range from n = 1 to $n = \infty$:

$$F_o^*(z) = \sum_{n=1}^{\infty} F^*_{on}(z) = \sum_{n=1}^{\infty} \sum_{m=1}^{\infty} (f_1(nT)g(mT-nT)\epsilon^{-smT} \tag{10.47}$$

If we set $m - n = l$, then $m = n + l$, and hence equation (10.47) can be written as follows:

$$F_o^*(s) = \sum_{n=1}^{\infty} \sum_{l=1-n}^{\infty} (f_1(nT)g(lT)\epsilon^{-s(l+n)T}) \tag{10.48}$$

$$= \sum_{n=1}^{\infty} \cdot \sum_{l=1-n}^{\infty} [f_1(nT)\epsilon^{-snT} \cdot g(lT)\epsilon^{-slT}]$$

$$= \sum_{n=1}^{\infty} f_1(nT)\epsilon^{-snT} \sum_{l=1-n}^{\infty} g(lT)\epsilon^{-slT} \tag{10.49}$$

$$= \sum_{n=1}^{\infty} f_1(nT)\epsilon^{-snT}\left(\sum_{l=-n}^{0} g(lT)\epsilon^{-slT} + \sum_{l=1}^{\infty} g(lT)\epsilon^{-slT}\right) \tag{10.50}$$

Here $g(t) = 0$ for $t < 0$, since $g(t)$ is the impulse response of $G(s)$, and hence $g(lT)$ is 0 for a negative value of l. Consequently, equation (10.50) can be simplified to

$$F_o^*(s) = \sum_{n=1}^{\infty} f_1(nT)\epsilon^{-sT} \sum_{l=1}^{\infty} g(lT)\epsilon^{-slT} \tag{10.51}$$

$$= F_1^*(s) \sum_{l=1}^{\infty} g(lT)\epsilon^{-slT} \tag{10.52}$$

Therefore, the sampled transfer function $G^*(z)$ is

$$G^*(z) = \frac{F_o^*(z)}{F_1^*(z)} = \sum_{l=1}^{\infty} g(lT)\epsilon^{-slT} \tag{10.53}$$

$$= Zg(t)$$

$$= Z\mathcal{L}^{-1}G(s) \tag{10.54}$$

The latter expression shows that the sampled transfer function is the z-representation of the impulse response of the transfer function.

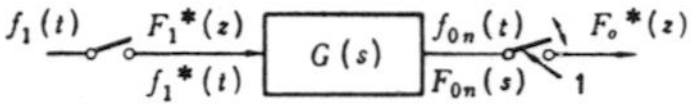

1 - *sampler*

Fig. 10.24 Calculation of sampled transfer function

10.6. ANALYSIS OF A SAMPLED DATA CONTROL SYSTEM

If we use the Z-transforms of waveforms, and if we use the sampled transfer functions to express signal transfer characteristics, most analyses or calculations of the characteristics of sampled data control systems can be carried out by the procedures used in the analyses of continuous control systems. We shall not discuss all the details of the procedures but only certain of them, which are different from those for continuous control systems.

As shown in Fig. 10.19, a holder is usually used after the sampler in a sampled data control system. In fact, a holder is a special element which is used only in a sampled data control system. Thus, we shall find the transfer function of a holder.

Suppose that the series of pulses shown in Fig. 10.25 (a) is an input signal to a holder and that the series of pulses $e_i(t)$ is expressed by the equations

$$e_i(t) = f(0)\delta(t) + f(T)\delta(t-T) + f(2T)\delta(t-2T) + f(3T)\delta(t-3T) \tag{10.55}$$

$$+ \cdots\cdots + f(nT)\delta(t-nT) + \cdots\cdots$$

$$= \sum_{0}^{\infty} f(nT)\delta(t-nT) \tag{10.56}$$

Then, the corresponding output signal $e_o(t)$ of the holder has the waveform shown in Fig. 10.25 (b), i.e.,

$$e_o(t) = f(0)\,1(t) + \{f(T) - f(a)\}\,1(t-T) + \{f(2\,T) - f(T)\}\,1(t-2\,T)$$
$$\{f(3\,T) - f(2\,T)\}\,1(t-3\,T) + \cdots\cdots + [f(nT) - \{f(n-1)T\}]\,1(t-nT)$$
$$+\cdots\cdots \tag{10.57}$$

Therefore, the transfer function of the holder is the ratio of the Laplace transform of $e_i(t)$ to that of $e_o(t)$. The Laplace of equation (10.55) is

$$\mathcal{L}e_i(t) = E_i(s) = f(0) + f(T)\epsilon^{-sT} + f(2\,T)\epsilon^{-2sT} + \cdots\cdots$$
$$+ f(nT)\epsilon^{-nsT} + \cdots\cdots \tag{10.58}$$

$$= \sum_{n=0}^{\infty} f(nT)\epsilon^{-nsT} \tag{10.59}$$

and the Laplace transform of equation (10.57) is

$$\mathcal{L}e_o(t) = E_o(s) = \frac{f(0)}{s} + \{f(T) - f(0)\}\frac{\epsilon^{-sT}}{s} + \{f(2\,T) - f(T)\}$$
$$\frac{\epsilon^{-2sT}}{s} + \{f(3\,T) - f(2\,T)\}\frac{\epsilon^{-3sT}}{s} + \cdots\cdots$$
$$+ \{f(nT) - f([n-1]T)\}\frac{\epsilon^{-nsT}}{s} + \cdots \tag{10.60}$$

$$= \frac{1}{s}\{f(0)(1-\epsilon^{-sT}) + f(T)(\epsilon^{-sT} - \epsilon^{-2sT}) + f(2T)(\epsilon^{-2sT} - \epsilon^{-3sT})$$
$$+ \cdots\cdots + f nT(\epsilon^{-nsT} - \epsilon^{-(n+1)sT}) + \cdots\cdots\} \tag{10.61}$$

$$= \frac{1}{s}\{f(0)(1-\epsilon^{-sT}) + f(T)\epsilon^{-sT}(1-\epsilon^{-sT}) + f(2\,T)\epsilon^{-2sT}(1-\epsilon^{-sT})$$
$$+ \cdots\cdots + f(nT)\epsilon^{-nsT}(1-\epsilon^{-sT}) + \cdots\cdots \tag{10.62}$$

$$= \frac{1-\epsilon^{-sT}}{s}\{f(0) + f(T)\epsilon^{-sT} + f(2\,T)\epsilon^{-2sT} + \cdots\cdots$$
$$+ f(nT\epsilon)^{-nsT} + \cdots\cdots = \frac{1-\epsilon^{-sT}}{s}\sum_{n=0}^{\infty} f(nT)\epsilon^{-nsT} \tag{10.63}$$

Denoting the transfer function of the holder by $G_h(s)$, we get, from equations (10.59) and (10.63),

$$G_h(s) = \frac{E_o(s)}{E_i(s)} = \frac{1-\epsilon^{-sT}}{s} \tag{10.64}$$

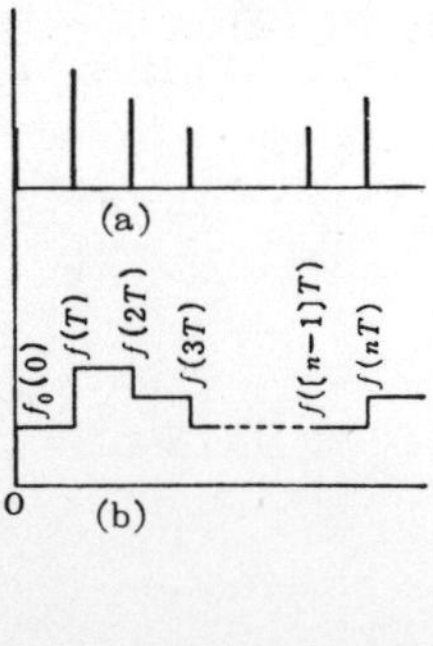

Fig. 10.25 Relation between input and output signals of holder: (a) input pulse series; (b) output signal

It has been shown that if we use a sampled transfer function instead of the usual transfer function, then a sampled data control system can be analysed by almost the same procedure as in the case of a continuous control system. It has also been shown that for a given transfer function the corresponding sampled transfer function is obtained by merely replacing the variable s by z in the given transfer function, where

$$z=\epsilon^{sT} \tag{10.65}$$

In order to apply the Nyquist stability criterion to a continuous control system, we substitute $s = j\omega$ into the open-loop transfer function and plot the locus of the resulting open-loop transfer function as ω varies from $-\infty$ to $+\infty$. Thus, in order to apply the Nyquist stability criterion to a sampled data control system, it is sufficient to substitute $s = j\omega$ into equation (10.65) so that we obtain

$$z=\epsilon^{j\omega T} \tag{10.66}$$

and to plot the locus of the expression resulting from the substitution of equation (10.66) into the open-loop sampled transfer function of the sampled data system as ω varies from $-\infty$ to $+\infty$. When ω varies from $-\infty$ to $+\infty$, the point z traces the unit circle with centre at the origin on the z-plane, as shown in Fig. 10.26. Therefore, stability of a sampled data control system can be determined by applying the Nyquist stability criterion to the locus of the open-loop pulse transfer function constructed by varying z on the unit circle.

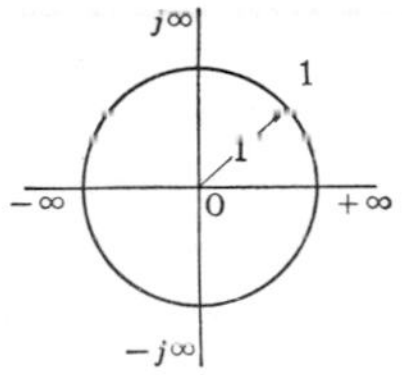

1 - *The* z-*plane*

Fig. 10.26 The stability limit plotted on the z-plane

The root locus (see Section 5.3) of a sampled data control system can also be constructed by plotting the poles and zeros of the open-loop pulse transfer function on the z-plane and by following the same procedure as used in the continuous control case. However, we cannot estimate the response waveform of a sampled data control system from the locations of its characteristic roots on the z-plane by following the same procedure as in the continuous control case. This can easily be seen from the fact that the imaginary axis of the s-plane corresponds to the unit circle on the z-plane.

Appendix

1. Appendix Tables 1-7 summarise the synthesis of compensating networks. Appendix Figures I-VI show the compensating charts that are most frequently used in actual synthesis.
2. When we use an Appendix table or a compensating chart in an Appendix figure for a synthesis, we also need a compensating vector locus plotted on a semi-transparent sheet with the same logarithmic scaling as used in the compensating chart.

Table 1

Network number and type	Compensating transf. function	Compensation formula	Pole-zero configuration
S 2-1 (Proportional + differentiating network)	$k\left(1+\frac{s}{\omega_s}\right)$	$\omega_s=\omega_0(\gamma_0+\cos\phi_c)$ $k=g_c(\cos\phi_c+\gamma_0\sin\phi_c)$	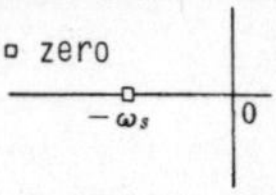

Compensating network	Calculation of network constants	Compensating limit of network	Compensating chart to be used
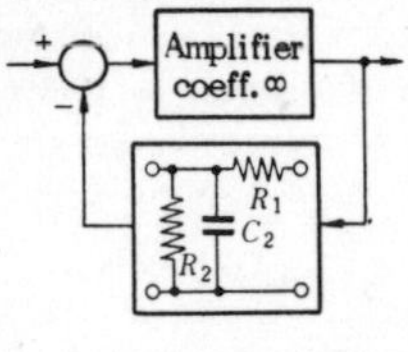	$R_1=\frac{1}{c_1}\ \frac{k}{\omega_s}$ $R_2=\frac{1}{c_2}\ \frac{k}{(k-1)\omega_s}$	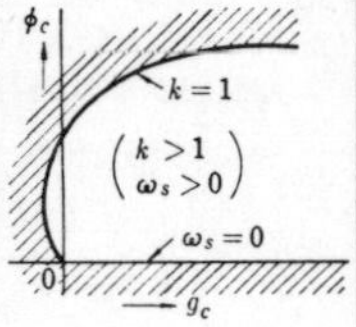	Figure I

Procedure for using compensating chart

1. Determine origin of compensating chart depending on specified value of γ_0
2. Place compensating vector locus plane on compensating chart so that their origins coincide.
3. Read value of k for point on compensating vector locus corresponding to desired value of ω_0
4. Draw a horizontal line through point on compensating vector locus corresponding to desired value of ω_0 and through point of intersection of this horizontal line and the Ω_s -curve corresponding to specified value of γ_0 Read the value of Ω_s corresponding to the point of intersection.
5. Compute value of ω_s from this value of Ω_s by using equation = $\omega_s=\Omega_s\omega_0$

S 2-1

Table 2

Network number and type	Compensating transf. function	Compensating formula	Pole-zero configuration
S 2-2 Proportional + integrating network	$k\left(1+\frac{\omega_s}{s}\right)$	$\omega_s=\frac{\omega_0(1+\gamma_0^2)}{\gamma_0-\cot\phi_c}$ $k=g_c(\cos\phi_c-\gamma_0\sin\phi_c)$	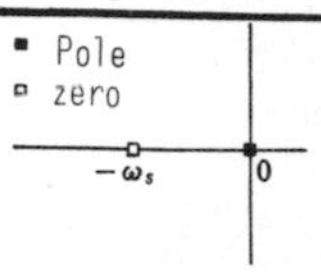

Compensating network	Calculation of network constants	Compensating limit of network	Compens. chart to be used
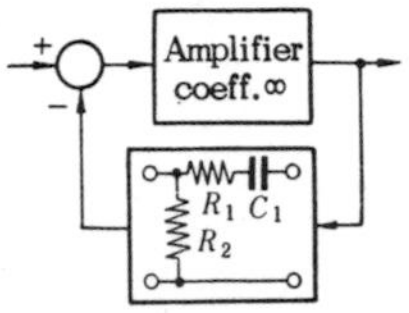	$R_1=\frac{1}{c_1}\ \frac{k-1}{k\omega_s}$ $R_2=\frac{1}{C_2}\ \frac{k}{\omega_s}$	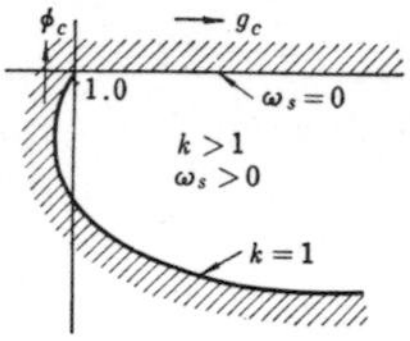	Figure 11

Procedure for using compensating chart

1. Determine origin of compensating chart depending on specified value of γ_0
2. Place compensating vector locus on compensating chart so that their origins coincide.
3. Read value of k for point on compensating vector locus corresponding to desired value ω_0
4. Draw a horizontal line through point on compensating vector locus corresponding to desired value of ω_0 ; find the point of intersection of horizontal line and the Ω_s curve corresponding to specified value of γ_0 . Read the value of Ω_s corresponding to point of intersection.
5. Compute value of ω_s from this value of Ω_s by using equation $\omega_s=\Omega_s\omega_0$

S 2-2

Table 3

Network number and type	Compensat. transfer function	Compensating formula	Pole-zero configuration
S 2-3 Lead network	$\dfrac{1+\dfrac{s}{\omega_s}}{1+\dfrac{s}{n\omega_s}}$	$\omega_s=\dfrac{\omega_c(1+\gamma_0^2)\sin\phi_c}{g_c-\cos\phi_c+\gamma_0\sin\phi_c}$ $n=\dfrac{g_c-\cos\phi_c+\gamma_0\sin\phi_c}{\cos\phi_c+\gamma_0\sin\phi_c-1/g_c}$	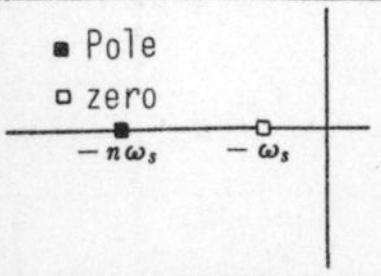

Compensating network	Calculation of network constants	Compensating limit of network	Compens. chart to be used
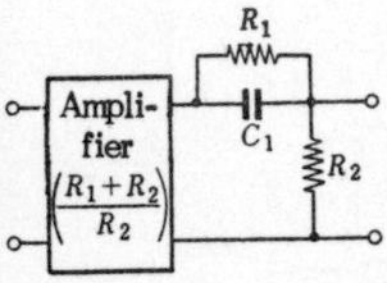	$R_1=\dfrac{1}{C_1}\cdot\dfrac{1}{\omega_s}$ $R_2=\dfrac{1}{C_1}\cdot\dfrac{1}{(n-1)\omega_s}$	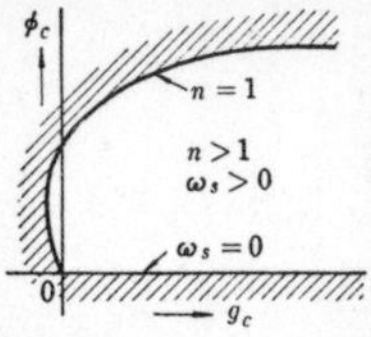	Fig. III (when $\gamma_0=0.3$) Fig. IV (when $\gamma_0=0.5$) Fig. V (when $\gamma_0=0.5$) Fig. VI (when $\gamma_0=0.6$)

Procedure for using compensating chart

1. Place compensating vector locus plane on compensating chart.
2. Read value of n and value of Ω_s for point on compensating vector locus corresponding to desired value of ω_0
3. Compute value of ω_s from this value of Ω_s by using equation $\omega_s=\Omega_s\omega_0$

S 2-3

Table 4

Network number and type	Compensat. transfer function	Compensating formula	Pole-zero configuration
S 2-4 Lag network	$\dfrac{1+\dfrac{s}{\omega_s}}{1+\dfrac{ns}{\omega_s}}$	$\omega_s=\dfrac{\omega_0(1+\gamma_0^2)\sin\phi_c}{g_c-\cos\phi_c+\gamma_0\sin\phi_c}$ $n=\dfrac{\cos\phi_c+\gamma_0\sin\phi_c-1/g_c}{g_c-\cos\phi_c+\gamma_0\sin\phi_c}$	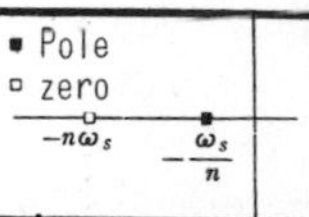

Compensating network	Calculation of network constants	Compensating limit of network	Compensating chart to be used
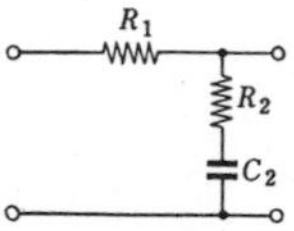	$R_1=\dfrac{1}{C_2}\cdot\dfrac{n-1}{\omega_s}$ $R_2=\dfrac{1}{C_2}\cdot\dfrac{1}{\omega_s}$	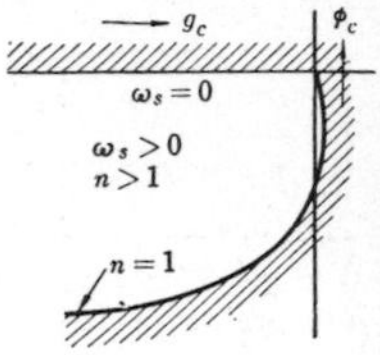	Fig. III (when $\gamma_0=0.3$) Fig. IV (when $\gamma_0=0.4$) Fig. V (when $\gamma_0=0.5$) Fig. VI (when $\gamma_0=0.6$)

Procedure for using compensating chart

1. Rotate compensating vector locus plane by 180°, and place it on compensating chart.
2. Read value of n and value of Ω_s for point on compensating vector locus corresponding to desired value of ω_0
3. Compute value of ω_s from this value of Ω_s by using equation $\omega_s=\Omega_s\omega_0 n$

S 2-4

Table 5

Network number and type	Compensating transfer function	Compensating formula	Pole-zero configuration
S 2-5 Lead network	$\frac{1}{n}\cdot\frac{1+\frac{s}{\omega_s}}{1+\frac{s}{n\omega_s}}$	$\omega_s=\frac{\omega_0(\cos\phi_c+\gamma_0\sin\phi_c-g_c)}{\sin\phi_c}$ $n=\frac{1/g_c-\cos\phi_c+\gamma_0\sin\phi_c}{\cos\phi_c+\gamma_0\sin\phi_c-g_c}$	■ Pole □ zero 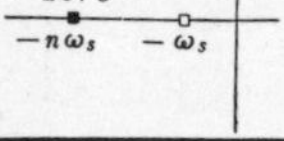

Compensating network	Calculation of network constants	Compensating limit of network	Compensating chart to be used
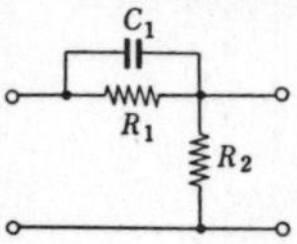	$R_1=\frac{1}{C_1}\cdot\frac{1}{\omega_s}$ $n=\frac{R_1}{R_2}+1$	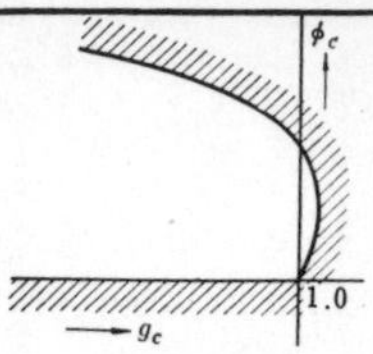	Fig. III (when $\gamma_0=0.3$) Fig. IV (when $\gamma_0=0.4$) Fig. V (when $\gamma_0=0.5$) Fig. VI (when $\gamma_0=0.6$)

Procedure for using compensating chart

1. Turn over compensating vector locus plane, and place it on compensating chart.
2. Read value of n and value of Ω_s for point on vector locus corresponding to desired value of ω_0
3. Compute value of ω_s from these values of n and Ω_s by using equation

$$\omega_s=\frac{\omega_0(1+\gamma_0^2)}{n^2\Omega_s}$$

S 2-5

Table 6

Network number and type	Compensating transfer function	Compensating formula	Pole-zero configuration
S 3-1 Lead-lag network	$\dfrac{\left(1+\dfrac{s}{\omega_{s1}}\right)\left(1+\dfrac{s}{\omega_{s2}}\right)}{\left(1+\dfrac{s}{n\omega_{s1}}\right)\left(1+\dfrac{ns}{\omega_{s2}}\right)}$	Compensating chart necessary	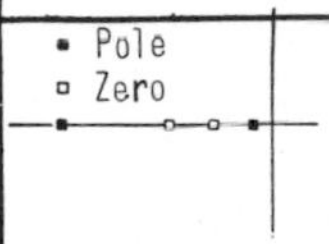

Compensating network	Calculation of network constants	Compensating limit of network	Compensating chart to be used
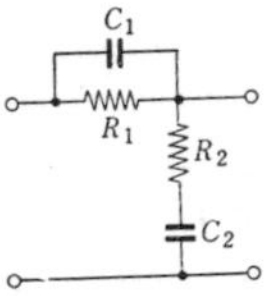	$R_1=\dfrac{1}{C_1}\cdot\dfrac{1}{\omega_{s1}}$ $R_2=\dfrac{1}{C_1}\dfrac{n}{(n-1)(n\omega_{s1}-\omega_{s2})}$ $C_2=C_1(n-1)\left(\dfrac{\omega_{s1}}{\omega_{s2}}-\dfrac{1}{n}\right)$	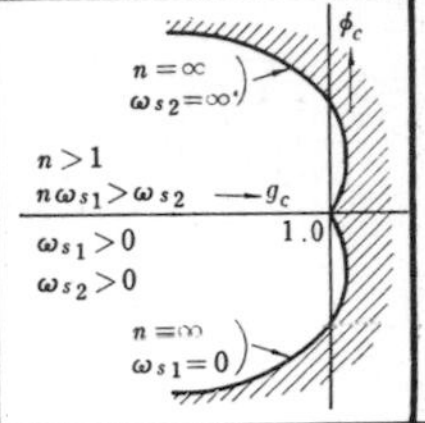	Fig. III (when $\gamma_0=0.3$) Fig. IV (when $\gamma_0=0.4$) Fig. V (when $\gamma_0=0.5$) Fig. VI (when $\gamma_0=0.6$)

Procedure for using compensating chart.

1. Rotate compensating vector locus plane 180°, about y-axis or about an axis perpendicular to it and place on compensating chart. Select a suitable n-curve that encloses point on compensating vector corresponding to desired value of ω_0

2. Place compensating vector locus plane on compensating chart so that origin of chart coincides with point on compensating vector locus corresponding to desired value of ω_0; copy selected n-curve on to compensating vector locus plane.

3. Slide compensating vector locus plane so that its origin coincides with origin of compensating chart; find point of intersection A of n-curve on chart and its copy on compensating vector locus. Read values of Ω_s corresponding to point A and denote it by Ω_{s1}

4. Again slide the compensating vector locus plane on compensating chart so that it will take position described in step 2 and read value of Ω_s corresponding to A. Denote this value by Ω_{s2}

5. Using Ω_{s1} and Ω_{s2}, compute values of ω_{s1}, and ω_{s2} from equations $\omega_{s1}=\Omega_{s1}\omega_0$

$$\omega_{s2}=\Omega_{s2}\omega_0 n$$

S 3-1

Table 7

Network number and type	Compensating transfer function	Compensating formula	Pole-zero configuration
P 2-1 Differentiating network and damping transformers	$\dfrac{k\dfrac{s}{\omega_s}}{1+\dfrac{s}{\omega_s}}$	$\omega_s=\dfrac{\omega_0(1+\gamma_0^2)}{\gamma_0+\cos\phi_c}$ $k=\dfrac{g_c}{\cos\phi_c+\gamma_0\sin\phi_c}$	—

Compensating network	Calculation of network constants	Compensating limit of compensating network	Compensating chart to be used
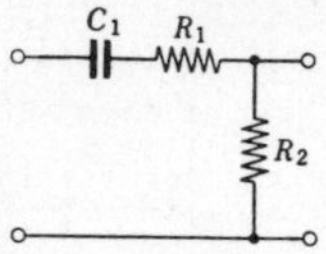	$R_1=\dfrac{1}{C_1}\;\dfrac{1-k}{\omega_s}$ $R_2=\dfrac{1}{C_1}\;\dfrac{k}{\omega_s}$	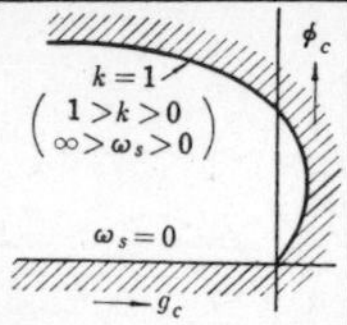	Fig. 11.
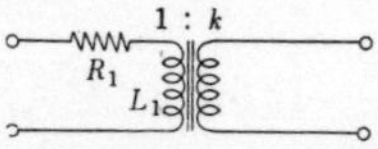	$R_1=L_1\omega_s$ k: Turns ratio	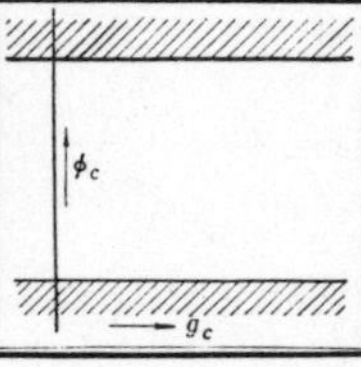	
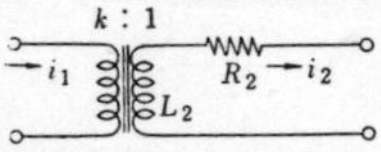	$R_2=L_2\omega_s$ n: Turns ratio		

Procedure for using compensating chart

1. Determine origin of compensating chart depending on specified value of γ_0
2. Rotate compensating vector locus plane through an angle of 180°; rotate it through 180° about y axis or axis perpendicular to it, and place it on compensating chart so that origins coincide.
3. Read the value of k for point on compensating vector locus corresponding to desired value of ω_0, and denote it by k'.
4. Draw a horizontal line through point on compensating vector locus and find point of intersection of horizontal line and Ω_s curve corresponding to specified value of γ_0. Read value of Ω_s corresponding to point of intersection.
5. Compute value of ω_s and k from these values of Ω_s and k' by using equations: $\omega_s=\Omega_s\omega_0$

$$k=\frac{1}{k'}$$

P2-1

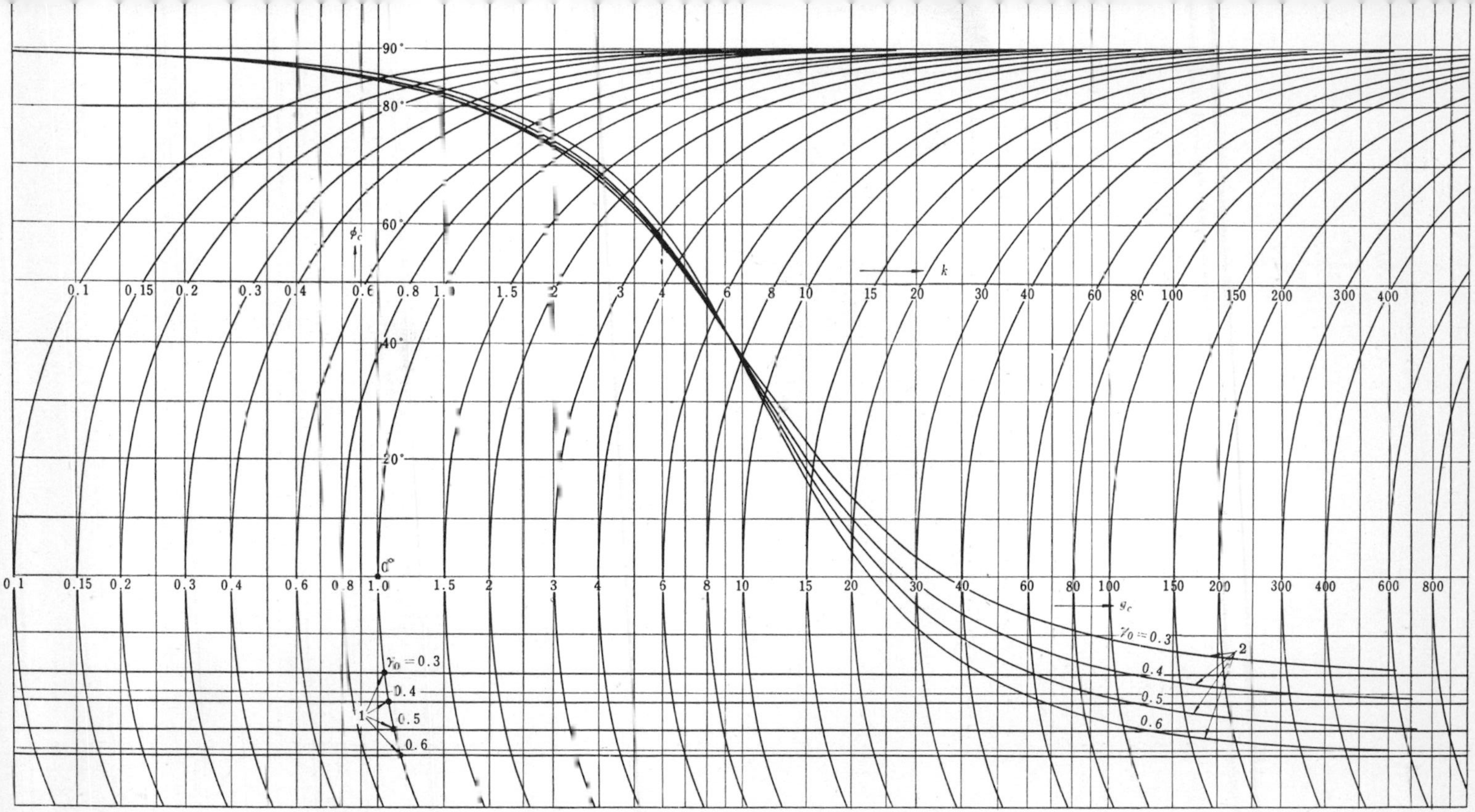

Fig. I

Compensating chart of $F_c(s) = k\ (1 + s/\omega_s)$ *and* $k/(1 + s/\omega_s)$

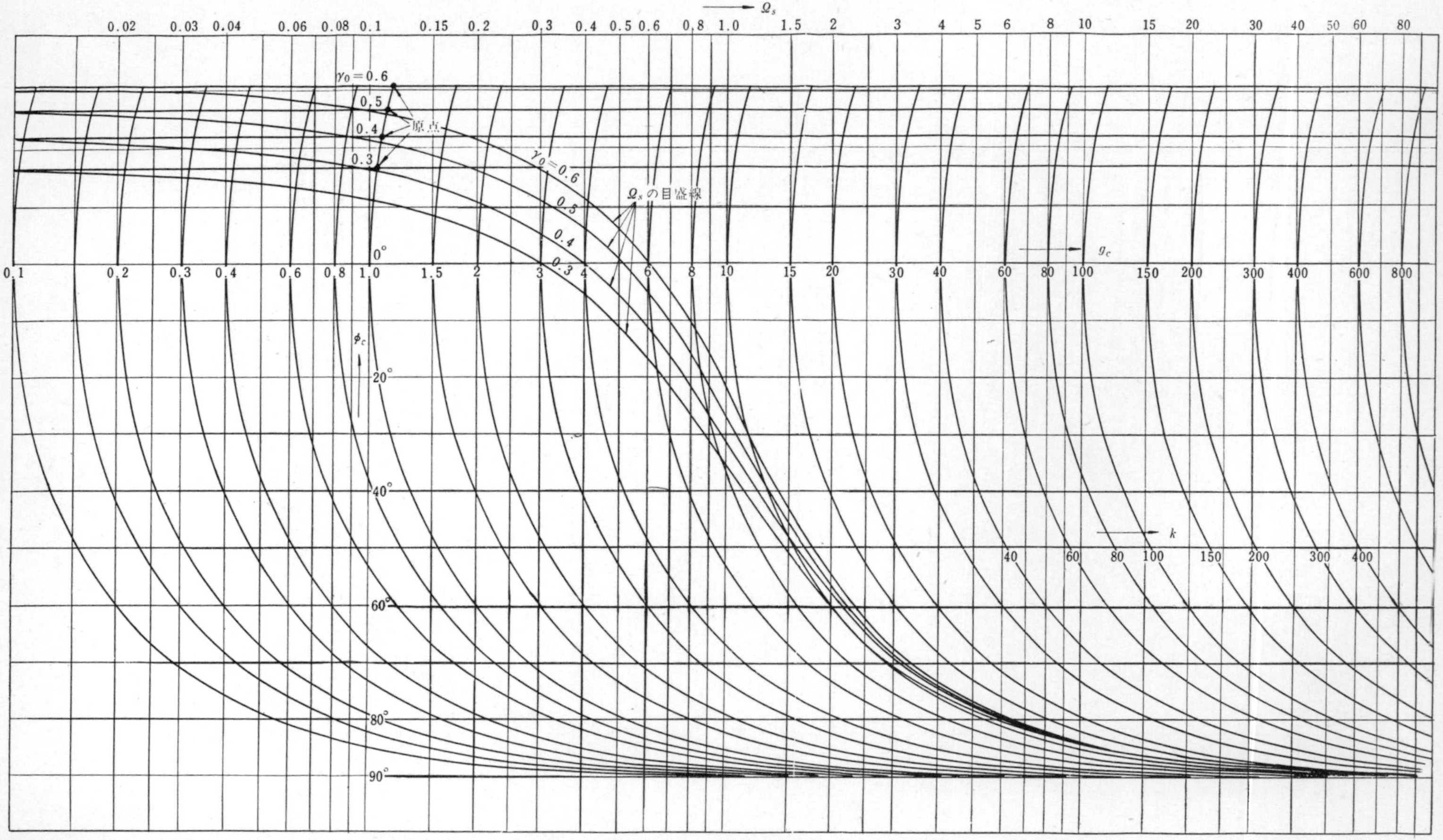

Fig. II Compensating chart of $F_c(s)=k\left(1+\frac{\omega_s}{\ldots}\right)$ and sk/ω_s …

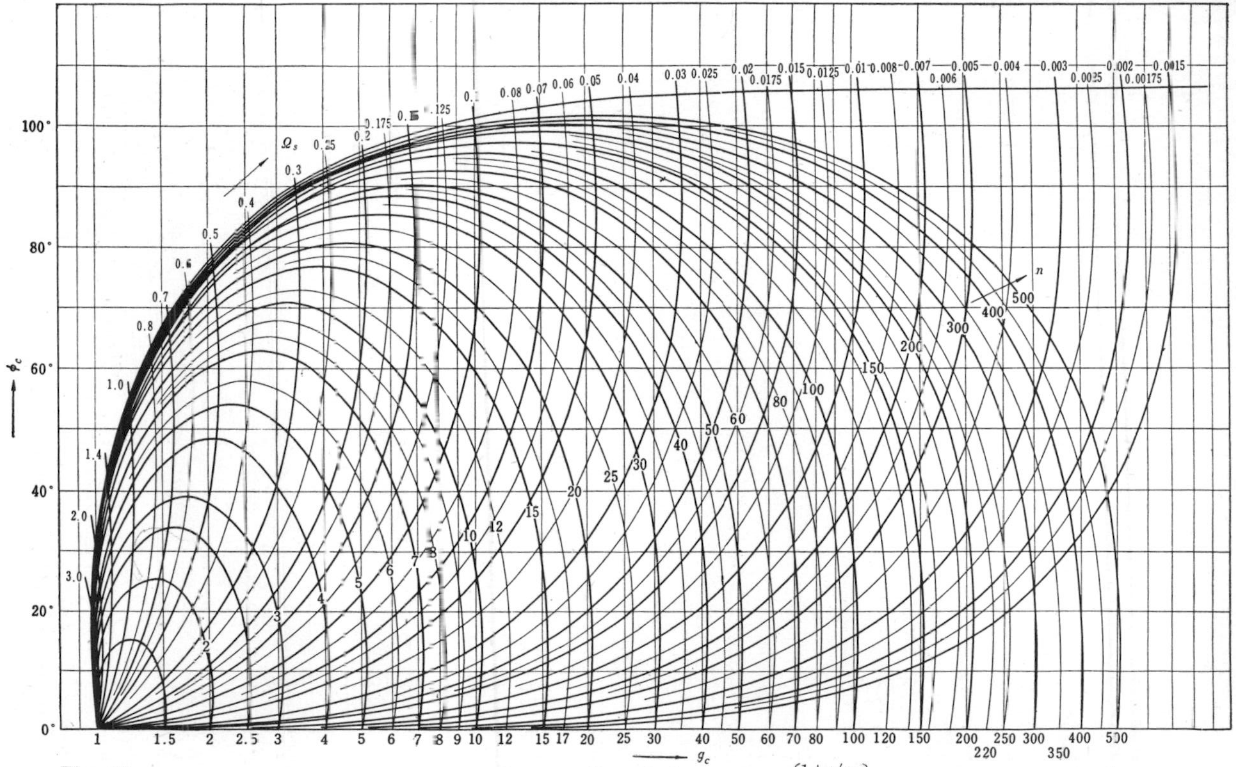

Fig. III

Compensating chart of $F_c(s) = \frac{(1+s/\omega_s)}{(1+s/n\cdot\omega_s)}$ $(\gamma_0=0.3)$

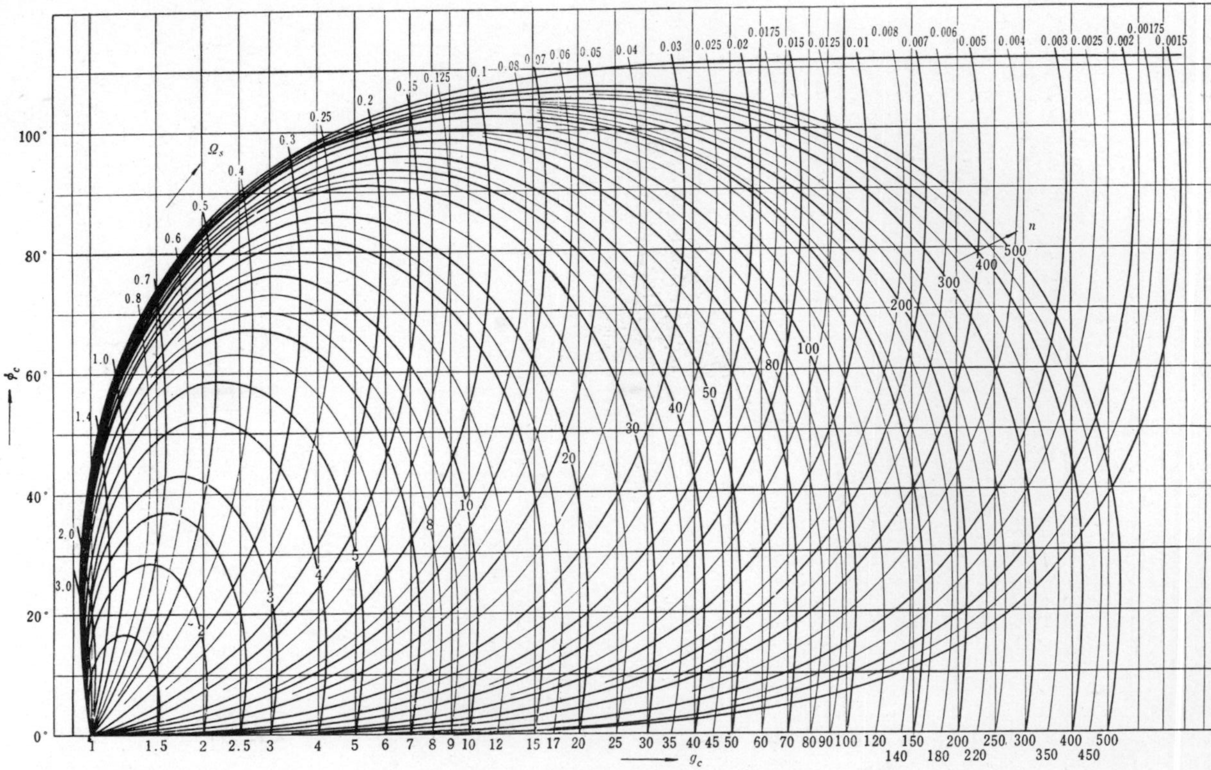

Fig. IV *Compensating chart of* $F_c(s)=\frac{(1+s/\omega_s)}{(1+s/n\cdot\omega_s)}$ $(\gamma_0=0.4)$

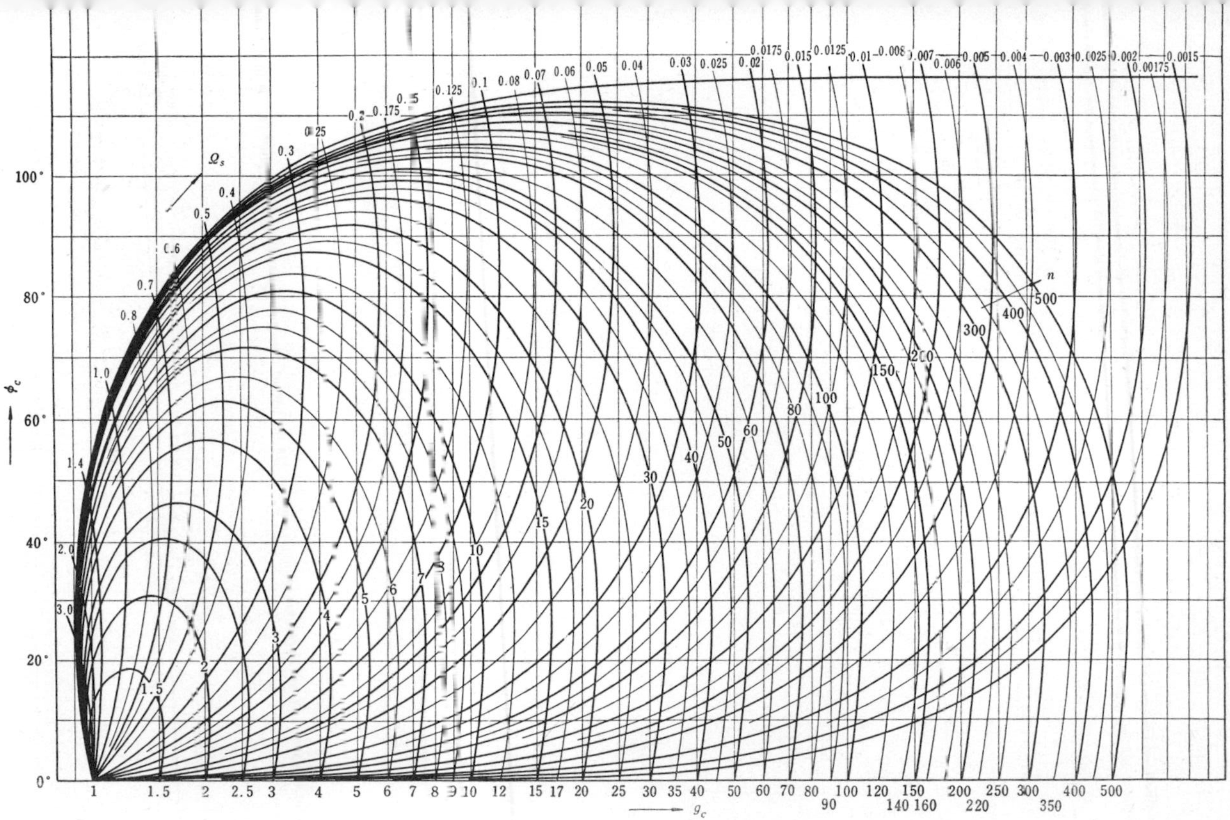

Fig. V *Compensating charts of* $F_c(s)=\dfrac{(1+s/\omega_s)}{(1+s/n\cdot\omega_s)}$ $(\gamma_0=0.5)$

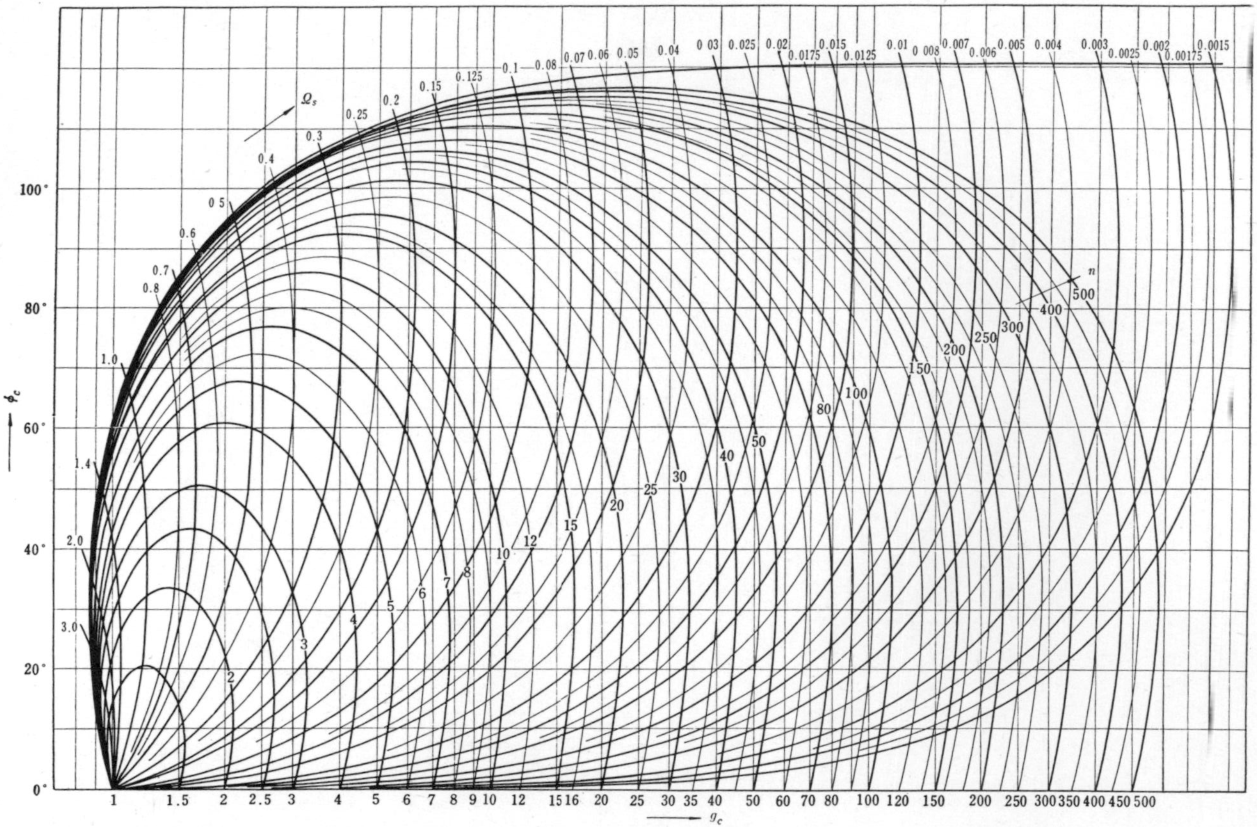

ϕ_c
100°
80°
60°
40°
20°
0°
g_c
1 1.5 2 2.5 3 4 5 6 7 8 9 10 12 15 16 20 25 30 35 40 50 60 70 80 100 120 150 200 250 300 350 400 450 500
Ω_s
3.0 2.0 1.4 1.0 0.8 0.7 0.6 0.5 0.4 0.3 0.25 0.2 0.15 0.125 0.1 0.08 0.07 0.06 0.05 0.04 0.03 0.025 0.02 0.0175 0.015 0.0125 0.01 0.008 0.007 0.006 0.005 0.004 0.003 0.0025 0.002 0.00175 0.0015
n
2 3 4 5 6 7 8 10 12 15 20 25 30 40 50 80 100 150 200 250 300 400 500

$(1+s/\omega_s)$

ANSWERS TO PROBLEMS

Chapter II

Signal Transmission and its representation

1 (a) $\frac{e_0}{e_i}=\frac{R}{R+j\omega L}$, $\frac{e_0}{e_i}=\frac{R}{R+\alpha L+j\omega L}$

(b) $\frac{j\omega CR}{1+j\omega CR}$, $\frac{j\omega CR}{1+\alpha CR+j\omega CR}$

(2)

	When $e_i=50\,\epsilon^{(-15+j30)t}$	When $e_i=50\,\epsilon^{j30t}$	When $e_i=50\,\epsilon^{(15+j30)t}$
(a)	$(35.2-j\,48.4)\epsilon^{(-15+j30)t}$	$154\epsilon^{j30t}$	$(35.2+j\,48.4)\epsilon^{(15+j30)t}$
(b)	$(300-j\,189)\epsilon^{(-15+j30)t}$	$(24.2-j\,56.1)\epsilon^{j30t}$	$(15.6-j\,25.6)\epsilon^{(15+j30)t}$
(c)	$(-7.80-j\,18.2)\epsilon^{(-15+j30)t}$	$(1.74-j\,16.4)\epsilon^{j30t}$	$(5.80-j\,10.5)\epsilon^{(15+j30)t}$

(3)

	Transfer function	Constants of transfer functions
(a)	$\frac{1+sT_1}{1+sT_2}$	$T_1=C_2R_2$, $T_2=C_2(R_1+R_2)$
(b)	$k\frac{1+sT_1}{1+sT_2}$	$k=\frac{R_2}{R_1+R_2}$, $T_1=C_1R_1$, $T_2=C_1\frac{R_1R_2}{R_1+R_2}$
(c)	$\frac{skT}{1+sT}$	$k=\frac{R_2}{R_1+R_2}$, $T=C_1(R_1+R_2)$
(d)	$\frac{(1+sT_1)(1+sT_2)}{1+s(T_1+T_2+C_2R_1)+s^2T_1T_2}$	$T_1=C_1R_1$, $T_2=C_2R_2$

(4) $\frac{0.152}{1+0.359\,s}$ $\left[\frac{\text{rad}}{\text{s}}/\text{V}\right]$

(5) $\frac{7.5}{(1+0.16\,s)(1+0.833\,s)}$, $R_f=7.0$ [Ω]

(6) $\frac{k}{\frac{\tau_1}{\omega_1}+sJ}$, Time constant $T=J\frac{\omega_1}{\tau_1}$

(7) $\frac{k}{s\left(1+s\frac{m}{D}\right)}$

(8) (i) $\frac{1}{2}(\epsilon^{-t}-\epsilon^{-5t})\mathit{1}$ (ii) $(\epsilon^{-4t}+\epsilon^{-6t})\mathit{1}$ (iii) $\frac{1}{36}(6t+1-9\epsilon^{-2t}+8\epsilon^{-3t})\mathit{1}$

(iv) $(4\epsilon^{-4t}-2\epsilon^{-2t}+\epsilon^{-t})\mathit{1}$ (v) $\frac{1}{36}\{4-9\epsilon^{-t}+(6t+5)\epsilon^{-3t}\}\mathit{1}$

(vi) $\mathit{1}(t-0.5)$ (vii) $\{0.25\,\epsilon^{-t}\cos(2t-53°)-0.15\,\epsilon^{-5t}\}\mathit{1}$

(viii) $1.5\,\epsilon^{-0.5t}\mathit{1}(t-1)$

(9) (i) $\frac{s}{s^2+\omega^2}$ (ii) $\frac{s\sin\phi+\omega\cos\phi}{s^2+\omega^2}$ (iii) $\frac{s^2}{s^2+\omega^2}$ (iv) $\frac{5\,\epsilon^{-st}}{s+3}$

(10) (a) $\frac{1}{s}(1-\epsilon^{-sT})$ (b) $\frac{\frac{3\pi}{T}}{s^2+\left(\frac{\pi}{T}\right)^2}(1+\epsilon^{-sT})$

(c) $\frac{1}{s}(3-\epsilon^{-sT_1}-\epsilon^{-sT_2}-\epsilon^{-sT_3})$ (d) $\frac{2}{s}\left(\frac{1}{sT}+1-\frac{1}{1-\epsilon^{-sT}}\right)$

(11) (i) $\left(sL+R+\frac{1}{sC}\right)I(s)=\frac{1}{s}$ (ii) $(s^2M+sD+K)X(s)=\frac{F_0 s}{s^2+\omega_0^2}$

(iii) $(3s^2+8s+5)\Theta(s)=\frac{10}{s}$ (iv) $\left(5s+6+\frac{12}{s}\right)X(s)=\frac{1}{(s+3)^2}$

(12) When the switch is being closed, we have

$$E\left\{\frac{R_3}{R_1+R_3}+K(1-\epsilon^{-\frac{t}{T}})1\right\},\qquad \text{where}\quad K=\frac{R_1^2R_3}{(R_1+R_3)(R_1R_2+R_1R_3+R_2R_3)},$$

$$T=\frac{L_1(R_1+R_2)}{R_1R_2+R_1R_3+R_2R_3}$$

When the switch is being opened, we have

$$E\left\{\frac{R_3(R_1+R_2)}{R_1R_2+R_1R_3+R_2R_3}-K(1-\epsilon^{-\frac{t}{T}})1\right\},\qquad \text{where}\quad K=\frac{R_1^2R_3}{(R_1+R_3)(R_1R_2+R_1R_3+R_2R_3)}$$

$$T=\frac{L_1}{R_1+R_3}$$

(13) When the switch is being closed, the forward transfer function is

$$\frac{R_oR_l}{(R_oR_l+R_iR_l+R_iR_o)}\cdot\frac{1+s\frac{L_o}{R_o}}{1+s\frac{L_o(R_l+R_i)}{(R_oR_l+R_iR_l+R_oR_i)}}$$

and the disturbance transfer function is

$$\frac{R_oR_i}{R_oR_l+R_iR_l+R_iR_o}\cdot\frac{1+s\frac{L_o}{R_o}}{1+s\frac{L_o(R_l+R_i)}{R_oR_l+R_iR_l+R_oR_i}}$$

When the switch is being opened, the forward transfer function is

$$\frac{R_0}{R_i+R_0}\cdot\frac{1+s\frac{L_0}{R_0}}{1+s\frac{L_0}{R_i+R_0}}$$

and the disturbance transfer function is

$$\frac{R_0^2R_i}{(R_iR_0+R_iR_l+R_0R_l)(R_i+R_0)}\cdot\frac{1+s\frac{L_0}{R_0}}{1+s\frac{L_0}{R_i+R_0}}$$

(14) When the switch is being closed, the forward transfer function is

$$\frac{R_l}{R_i+R_l}\cdot\frac{1+s\frac{JR_m}{N^2}}{1+s\frac{J}{N^2}\cdot\frac{R_lR_i+R_lR_m+R_iR_m}{R_i+R_m}}$$

and the disturbance transfer function is

$$\frac{R_i}{R_i+R_l}\cdot\frac{1+s\frac{JR_m}{N^2}}{1+s\frac{J}{N^2}\cdot\frac{R_lR_i+R_lR_m+R_iR_m}{R_i+R_m}}$$

When the switch is being opened, the forward transfer function is

$$\frac{1+s\dfrac{JR_m}{N^2}}{1+s\dfrac{J(R_i+R_m)}{N^2}}$$

and the disturbance transfer function is

$$\frac{R_i}{R_i+R_l}\cdot\frac{1+s\dfrac{JR_m}{N^2}}{1+s\dfrac{J(R_i+R_m)}{N^2}}$$

(15) $T=\dfrac{T_1}{Q_2}\left\{Q_1+(Q_2-Q_1)\epsilon^{-\frac{Q_2}{hV}t}\right\}1$

(16) The transfer function of the controlled system is

$$\frac{NN_T}{DR_i+N^2}\cdot\frac{1}{1+s\dfrac{DL_i+JR_i}{DR_i+N^2}+s^2\dfrac{L_iJ}{DR_i+N^2}}$$

and the disturbance transfer function is

$$\frac{R_iN_T\left(1+s\dfrac{L_i}{R_i}\right)}{DR_i+N^2}\cdot\frac{1}{1+s\dfrac{DL_i+JR_i}{DR_i+N^2}+s^2\dfrac{L_iJ}{DR_i+N^2}}$$

(17) (1) $\dfrac{F_1F_2}{1+F_1F_2+F_1F_3}$ (2) $\dfrac{F_1F_2F_3F_4}{1+F_3F_2+F_4F_3+F_1F_2F_3F_4}$

(18) (1) The open loop transfer function is $F_1(s)F_2(s)$ and the disturbance transfer function is $Y(s)F_2(s)$.

(2) The open loop transfer function is $F_1(s)F_2(s)/\{1+F_2(s)\}$ and the disturbance transfer function is $Y(s)/\{1+F_2(s)\}$.

(3) The open loop transfer function is $F_1(s)F_2(s)/\{1+F_2(s)\}$ $F_3(s)$ and the disturbance function is $F_2(s)/\{1+F_2(s)F_3(s)\}$

Chapter III.

Characteristics of automatic control systems and their analysis

(1) (2) 17.8 (3) 0.199[%]

(4) (1) $1+sCR$ (2) $1+\dfrac{1}{sCR}$ (3) $1+\dfrac{R_1}{R_2}\left(1+\dfrac{C_1}{C_2}\right)+sC_1R_1+\dfrac{1}{sC_2R_2}$

(5) (1) $\dfrac{R_2}{R_1}(1+sC_1R_1)$ (2) $\dfrac{R_2}{R_1}\left(1+\dfrac{1}{sC_2R_2}\right)$ (3) $\dfrac{R_2}{R_1}(1+sC_1R_1)\left(1+\dfrac{1}{sC_2R_2}\right)$

(6) (a) 90.9 [Ω] (b) 199 [Ω]

(7) 0.816 [V], $R_e=16.3$ [Ω] (7) $9(1-\epsilon^{-5t})1$ [cm]

(8) $\omega_n=\sqrt{\dfrac{k_1A}{(1+n)m}}$ $\zeta=\dfrac{D}{2}\sqrt{\dfrac{1+n}{k_1Am}}$

(9) $\dfrac{l_2}{l_1}\cdot\dfrac{1}{1+\dfrac{A}{k}\left(1+\dfrac{l_2}{l_1}\right)s}$

(10) (i) The transient response waveform starts with the value 0 at $t = 0$ and increases with a certain slope.

(ii) The transient response waveform starts with a nonzero value at $t = 0$ and increases with a certain slope.

(iii) The transient response waveform starts with the value 0 at $t = 0$, remains flat for a while, and then increases gradually.

(11) The fundamental error response is the expression (3·76), where

$$\omega_n=\sqrt{\frac{Ak_pk_0}{DL_f}},\quad \zeta=\frac{R_f}{2}\sqrt{\frac{D}{Ak_pk_0L_f}}$$

(12) $2.24(\epsilon^{-1.38t}-\epsilon^{-3.62t})\mathbf{1}$

(14) The automatic control system is in the critically damped state at $T = 0.695$ [sec].

Chapter IV

Frequency response of automatic control systems

(1) - (4)

(5) $\dfrac{10}{(1+0.5\,s)(1+0.05\,s)}$

(6) Stable. $M_p = 1.6$

(7) Stable

(8) $\phi_m = 6°$. 1/1.65 time.

(9) $k < 4$.

Chapter V.

Characteristic roots of automatic control systems

(1) (i) $1.22\,\epsilon^{-0.5t}\cos(t-48.4°)+0.166\,\epsilon^{-3t}$

(ii) $2.22\,\epsilon^{-t}\cos(t-96.0°)+1.25\,\epsilon^{-2t}+0.00617\,\epsilon^{-10t}$

(2) $1.81\,\epsilon^{-0.5t}\cos(t+30.3°)-0.57\,\epsilon^{-3t}$

(3) (a) 0 (b) KT_1/T_2

(4) (i) The roots r_1 and r_2 are dominant roots.

(ii) The roots r_1 and r_2 are not dominant roots.

(5) The roots are the dominant roots.

(6) The roots are the dominant roots.

(7)

(8) (i) 11.25 (ii) 39 (iii) 1.57 (iv) 0.0595 と 0.54

(9) (i) $-1\pm j6$ (ii) $-0.8\pm j9.3$

(10) $\{1-1.072\,\epsilon^{-0.4t}\cos(1.35\,t-16°)-0.14\,\epsilon^{-10.6t}\}\,1$

Chapter VI.

Synthesis of automatic control systems

(1) $\phi_m=43°,\ M_p=1.35$ (2) $K=1.65$ (3) $\omega_0=10$ [rad/s]

(4) $A\geqq 9.6$ (5) $l=9.43$ [cm] (6) $\frac{i_d}{i_l}=\frac{i_r\eta}{I_0}$. $i_d=0.4$ [mA]

(7) $K\left(1+\frac{l_2}{l_1}\right)$ (8) $F(s)=K\left(1+\frac{1}{sT}\right)$ (9) $\frac{1+sD_2k_2}{1+sD_2(k_1+k_2)}$

(11) $F(s)=\frac{l_2}{Kl_1}\left(1+\frac{l_1'}{l_2'}\right)\left(\frac{1+sk_1D}{1+sk_1D(1+l_1'/l_2')}\right)$

(12) $F_0(s)=\frac{1+0.1\,s}{s(1+0.5\,s)(1+0.1s)+1}$

Chapter VIII.

Synthesis of the transient characteristics from the root configuration

(1) (i) See Section 8.3 (ii) See Section 8.4 (iii) See Section 8.6
(iv) See Section 8.2

(2) (1) $\Omega_s>0,\ \infty>k>1$ (2) $\Omega_s>0,\ \infty>n>1$ (3)

(4) $T_1=-\frac{1}{a+b}$ $K=\frac{ab}{a+b}$

(5) $\omega_{s1}=\frac{\omega_0(1+\gamma_0^2)\sin\phi_c}{\cos\phi_c+\gamma_0\sin\phi_c-\frac{1}{g_c}}$, $\omega_{s2}=\frac{\omega_0(1+\gamma_0^2)\sin\phi_c}{g_c-\cos\phi_c+\gamma_0\sin\phi_c}$

Index